Calculus Test and Exam Prep:

A Collection of Problems and Worked Solutions

James Stewart

McMaster University
and University of Toronto

NELSON / EDUCATION

NELSON E D U C A T I O N

ISBN-13: 978-0-17-667036-8
ISBN-10: 0-17-667036-X

Cover Credit:

Sukharevskyy Dmytro (nevodka)/ shutterstock

CONTENTS

1 | FUNCTIONS, LIMITS, AND MODELS

1–4 ■ Determine whether the curve is the graph of a function of x. If it is, state the domain and range of the function.

1.

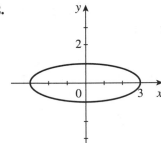

2.

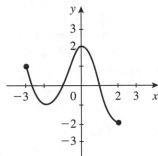

3.

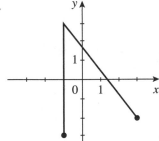

4.

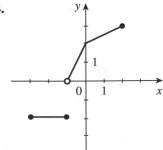

5–10 ■ Find the domain of the function.

5. $f(x) = \dfrac{x+2}{x^2-1}$

6. $f(x) = \dfrac{x^4}{x^2+x-6}$

7. $g(x) = \sqrt[4]{x^2-6x}$

8. $h(x) = \sqrt[4]{7-3x}$

9. $f(t) = \sqrt[3]{t-1}$

10. $g(x) = \sqrt{x^2-2x-8}$

11–25 ■ Find the domain and sketch the graph of the function.

11. $f(x) = 3 - 2x$

12. $f(x) = x^2 + 2x - 1$

13. $g(x) = \sqrt{-x}$

14. $g(x) = \sqrt{6-2x}$

15. $h(x) = \sqrt{x^2-4}$

16. $F(x) = \dfrac{1}{x}$

17. $G(x) = |x| + x$

18. $G(x) = |x| - x$

19. $H(x) = |2x|$

20. $f(x) = x/|x|$

21. $H(x) = |2x-3|$

22. $f(x) = \dfrac{x^2-1}{x-1}$

23. $f(x) = \dfrac{x^2+5x+6}{x+2}$

24. $f(x) = \begin{cases} 0 & \text{if } x < 2 \\ 1 & \text{if } x \geq 2 \end{cases}$

25. $f(x) = \begin{cases} -1 & \text{if } x < -1 \\ 1 & \text{if } -1 \leq x \leq 1 \\ -1 & \text{if } x > 1 \end{cases}$

26–28 ■ Find the limit.

26. $\displaystyle\lim_{x \to 3} \dfrac{1}{(x-3)^8}$

27. $\displaystyle\lim_{x \to \pi^-} \csc x$

28. $\displaystyle\lim_{x \to 2^+} \dfrac{x-1}{x^2(x+2)}$

29–43 ■ Evaluate the limit, if it exists.

29. $\displaystyle\lim_{x \to -3} \dfrac{x^2-x+12}{x+3}$

30. $\displaystyle\lim_{x \to -3} \dfrac{x^2-x-12}{x+3}$

31. $\displaystyle\lim_{x \to -2} \dfrac{x+2}{x^2-x-6}$

32. $\displaystyle\lim_{x \to 1} \dfrac{x^2+x-2}{x^2-3x+2}$

33. $\lim\limits_{h \to 0} \dfrac{(h-5)^2 - 25}{h}$

34. $\lim\limits_{x \to -1} \dfrac{x^2 - x - 2}{x + 1}$

35. $\lim\limits_{x \to 1} \dfrac{x^2 - x - 2}{x + 1}$

36. $\lim\limits_{t \to 1} \dfrac{t^3 - t}{t^2 - 1}$

37. $\lim\limits_{x \to -1} \dfrac{x^2 - x - 3}{x + 1}$

38. $\lim\limits_{t \to 2} \dfrac{t^2 + t - 6}{t^2 - 4}$

39. $\lim\limits_{t \to 0} \dfrac{\sqrt{2 - t} - \sqrt{2}}{t}$

40. $\lim\limits_{x \to 1} \left[\dfrac{1}{x - 1} - \dfrac{2}{x^2 - 1} \right]$

41. $\lim\limits_{x \to 2} \dfrac{\frac{1}{x} - \frac{1}{2}}{x - 2}$

42. $\lim\limits_{x \to 0} \dfrac{x}{\sqrt{1 + 3x} - 1}$

43. $\lim\limits_{x \to 2} \dfrac{x - \sqrt{3x - 2}}{x^2 - 4}$

44. Prove that $\lim\limits_{x \to 0^+} \sqrt{x} \cos^4 x = 0$.

45. Evaluate $\lim\limits_{x \to 1} \dfrac{\sqrt[3]{x} - 1}{\sqrt{x} - 1}$.

46. (a) If we start from 0° latitude and proceed in a westerly direction, we can let $T(x)$ denote the temperature at the point x at any given time. Assuming that T is a continuous function of x, show that at any fixed time there are at least two diametrically opposite points on the equator that have exactly the same temperature.

(b) Does the result in part (a) hold for points lying on any circle on Earth's surface?

(c) Does the result in part (a) hold for barometric pressure and for altitude above sea level?

1 | ANSWERS TO SELECTED EXERCISES

1. Yes, $[-3, 2]$, $[-2, 2]$

2. No

3. No

4. Yes, $[-3, 2]$, $\{-2\} \cup (0, 3]$

5. $\{x \mid x \neq \pm 1\} = (-\infty, -1) \cup (-1, 1) \cup (1, \infty)$

6. $\{x \mid x \neq -3, 2\} = (-\infty, -3] \cup [-3, 2] \cup [2, \infty)$

7. $\{x \mid x \leq 0 \text{ or } x \geq 6\} = (-\infty, 0] \cup [6, \infty)$

8. $\left(-\infty, \dfrac{7}{3}\right]$

9. $(-\infty, \infty)$

10. $(-\infty, -2] \cup [4, \infty)$

11. $(-\infty, \infty)$

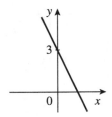

12. $(-\infty, \infty)$

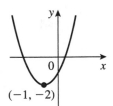

13. $(-\infty, 0]$

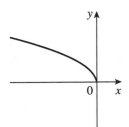

14. $(-\infty, 3]$

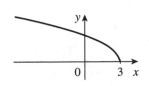

15. $(-\infty, -2] \cup [2, \infty)$

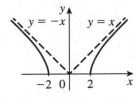

16. $\{x \mid x \neq 0\}$

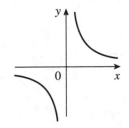

17. $(-\infty, \infty)$

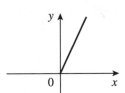

18. $(-\infty, \infty)$

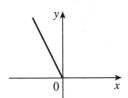

19. $(-\infty, \infty)$

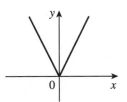

20. $(-\infty, 0) \cup (0, \infty)$

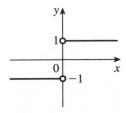

21. $(-\infty, \infty)$

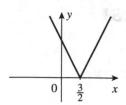

22. $(-\infty, 1) \cup (1, \infty)$

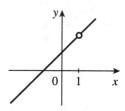

23. $(-\infty, -2) \cup (-2, \infty)$

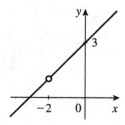

24. $(-\infty, \infty)$

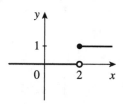

25. $(-\infty, \infty)$

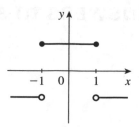

26. ∞

27. ∞

28. $-\infty$

29. Does not exist

30. -7

31. $-\dfrac{1}{3}$

32. -3

33. -10

34. -3

35. -1

36. 1

37. Does not exist

38. $\dfrac{5}{4}$

39. $-\sqrt{2}/4$

40. $\dfrac{1}{2}$

41. $-\dfrac{1}{4}$

42. $\dfrac{2}{3}$

43. $\dfrac{1}{16}$

44. 0

45. $\dfrac{2}{3}$

46. (b) yes

1 | SOLUTIONS TO SELECTED EXERCISES

1. Yes, the curve is the graph of a function because it passes the Vertical Line Test. The domain is $[-3, 2]$ and the range is $[-2, 2]$.

2. No, the curve is not the graph of a function because a vertical line intersects the curve more than once and hence, the curve fails the Vertical Line Test.

3. No, the curve is not the graph of a function since for $x = -1$ there are infinitely many points on the curve.

4. Yes, the curve is the graph of a function with domain $[-3, 2]$ and range $\{-2\} \cup (0, 3]$.

5. $f(x) = \dfrac{x+2}{x^2 - 1}$ is defined for all x except when $x^2 - 1 = 0 \Leftrightarrow x = 1$ or $x = -1$, so the domain is $\{x \mid x \neq \pm 1\}$.

6. $f(x) = x^4/(x^2 + x - 6)$ is defined for all x except when $0 = x^2 + x - 6 = (x + 3)(x - 2) \Leftrightarrow x = -3$ or 2, so the domain is $\{x \mid x \neq -3, 2\}$.

7. $g(x) = \sqrt[4]{x^2 - 6x}$ is defined when $0 \leq x^2 - 6x = x\,(x - 6) \Leftrightarrow x \geq 6$ or $x \leq 0$, so the domain is $(-\infty, 0] \cup [6, \infty)$.

8. $h(x) = \sqrt[4]{7 - 3x}$ is defined when $7 - 3x \geq 0$ or $x \leq \dfrac{7}{3}$, so the domain is $\left(-\infty, \dfrac{7}{3}\right]$.

9. $f(t) = \sqrt[3]{t - 1}$ is defined for every t, since every real number has a cube root. The domain is the set of all real numbers, $\mathbb{R}$.

10. $g(x) = \sqrt{x^2 - 2x - 8}$ is defined when $0 \leq x^2 - 2x - 8 = (x - 4)(x + 2) \Leftrightarrow x \geq 4$ or $x \leq -2$, so the domain is $(-\infty, -2] \cup [4, \infty)$.

11. $f(x) = 3 - 2x$. Domain is $\mathbb{R}$.

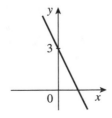

12. $f(x) = x^2 + 2x - 1 = (x^2 + 2x + 1) - 2 = (x + 1)^2 - 2$ so the graph is a parabola with vertex at $(-1, -2)$. The domain is $\mathbb{R}$.

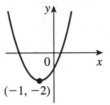

13. $g(x) = \sqrt{-x}$. The domain is $\{x \mid -x \geq 0\} = (-\infty, 0]$.

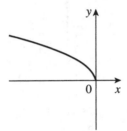

14. $g(x) = \sqrt{6 - 2x}$. The domain is $\{x \mid 6 - 2x \geq 0\} = (-\infty, 3]$.

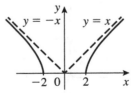

15. $h(x) = \sqrt{x^2 - 4}$. Now $y = \sqrt{x^2 - 4} \Rightarrow y^2 = x^2 - 4 \Leftrightarrow x^2 - y^2 = 4$, so the graph is the top half of a hyperbola. The domain is $\{x \mid x^2 - 4 \geq 0\} = (-\infty, -2] \cup [2, \infty)$.

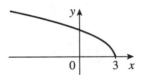

16. $F(x) = \dfrac{1}{x}$. The domain is $\{x \mid x \neq 0\}$.

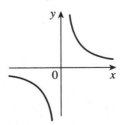

17. $G(x) = |x| + x$. Since $|x| = \begin{cases} x & \text{if } x \geq 0 \\ -x & \text{if } x < 0 \end{cases}$ we have

$$G(x) = \begin{cases} x + x & \text{if } x \geq 0 \\ -x + x & \text{if } x < 0 \end{cases} = \begin{cases} 2x & \text{if } x \geq 0 \\ 0 & \text{if } x < 0 \end{cases}$$

Domain is $\mathbb{R}$. Note that the negative x-axis is part of the graph of G.

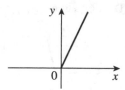

18. $G(x) = |x| - x = \begin{cases} 0 & \text{if } x \geq 0 \\ -2x & \text{if } x < 0 \end{cases}$ Domain is $\mathbb{R}$.

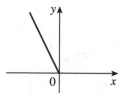

19. $H(x) = |2x| = \begin{cases} 2x & \text{if } 2x \geq 0 \\ -2x & \text{if } 2x < 0 \end{cases} = \begin{cases} 2x & \text{if } x \geq 0 \\ -2x & \text{if } x < 0 \end{cases}$

Domain is $\mathbb{R}$.

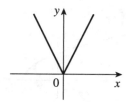

20. $f(x) = \dfrac{x}{|x|} = \begin{cases} x/x & \text{if } x > 0 \\ x/(-x) & \text{if } x < 0 \end{cases} = \begin{cases} 1 & \text{if } x > 0 \\ -1 & \text{if } x < 0 \end{cases}$

Note that we did not use $x \geq 0$, because $x \neq 0$. Hence, the domain of f is $\{x | x \neq 0\}$.

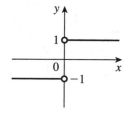

21. $H(x) = |2x - 3| = \begin{cases} 2x - 3 & \text{if } x \geq \dfrac{3}{2} \\ 3 - 2x & \text{if } x < \dfrac{3}{2} \end{cases}$ Domain is $\mathbb{R}$.

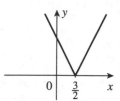

22. $f(x) = \dfrac{x^2 - 1}{x - 1} = \dfrac{(x + 1)(x - 1)}{x - 1}$, so for $x \neq 1$, $f(x) = x + 1$. Domain is $\{x | x \neq 1\}$.

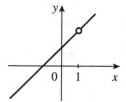

23. $f(x) = \dfrac{x^2 + 5x + 6}{x + 2} = \dfrac{(x + 3)(x + 2)}{x + 2}$, so for $x \neq -2$, $f(x) = x + 3$. Domain is $\{x | x \neq -2\}$. The hole in the graph can be found using the simplified function, $h(x) = x + 3$. $h(-2) = 1$ indicates that the hole has coordinates $(-2, 1)$.

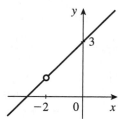

24. $f(x) = \begin{cases} 0 & \text{if } x < 2 \\ 1 & \text{if } x \geq 2 \end{cases}$ Domain is $\mathbb{R}$.

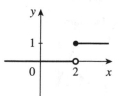

25. $f(x) = \begin{cases} 1 & \text{if } -1 \le x \le 1 \\ -1 & \text{if } x > 1 \text{ or } x < -1 \end{cases}$ Domain is $\mathbb{R}$.

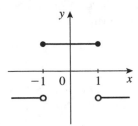

26. $\lim\limits_{x \to 3} \dfrac{1}{(x-3)^8} = \infty$ because $(x-3)^8 \to 0$ as $x \to 3$ and

$\dfrac{1}{(x-3)^8} > 0$ whenever $x \ne 3$.

27. As $x \to \pi^-$, $\sin x \to 0^+$, so $\lim\limits_{x \to \pi^-} \csc x = \infty$.

28. $\lim\limits_{x \to -2^+} \dfrac{x-1}{x^2(x+2)} = -\infty$ since the numerator is

negative and the denominator approaches 0 from the positive side as $x \to -2^+$.

29. $\lim\limits_{x \to -3} \dfrac{x^2 - x + 12}{x+3}$ does not exist since $x + 3 \to 0$ but

$x^2 - x + 12 \to 24$ as $x \to -3$.

30. $\lim\limits_{x \to -3} \dfrac{x^2 - x - 12}{x+3} = \lim\limits_{x \to -3} \dfrac{(x+3)(x-4)}{x+3}$

$= \lim\limits_{x \to -3} (x-4) = -3 - 4 = -7$

31. $\lim\limits_{x \to -2} \dfrac{x+2}{x^2 - x - 6} = \lim\limits_{x \to -2} \dfrac{x+2}{(x-3)(x+2)}$

$= \lim\limits_{x \to -2} \dfrac{1}{x-3} = -\dfrac{1}{5}$

32. $\lim\limits_{x \to 1} \dfrac{x^2 + x - 2}{x^2 - 3x + 2} = \lim\limits_{x \to 1} \dfrac{(x+2)(x-1)}{(x-2)(x-1)}$

$= \lim\limits_{x \to 1} \dfrac{x+2}{x-2} = \dfrac{1+2}{1-2} = -3$

33. $\lim\limits_{h \to 0} \dfrac{(h-5)^2 - 25}{h} = \lim\limits_{h \to 0} \dfrac{(h^2 - 10h + 25) - 25}{h}$

$= \lim\limits_{h \to 0} \dfrac{h^2 - 10h}{h} = \lim\limits_{h \to 0}(h - 10)$

$= -10$

34. $\lim\limits_{x \to -1} \dfrac{x^2 - x - 2}{x+1} = \lim\limits_{x \to -1} \dfrac{(x+1)(x-2)}{x+1}$

$= \lim\limits_{x \to -1}(x - 2) = -3$

35. $\lim\limits_{x \to 1} \dfrac{x^2 - x - 2}{x+1} = \dfrac{1^2 - 1 - 2}{1+1} = -1$

36. $\lim\limits_{t \to 1} \dfrac{t^3 - t}{t^2 - 1} = \lim\limits_{t \to 1} \dfrac{t(t^2 - 1)}{t^2 - 1} = \lim\limits_{t \to 1} t = 1$

37. $\lim\limits_{x \to -1} \dfrac{x^2 - x - 3}{x+1}$ does not exist since as $x \to -1$,

numerator $\to -1$ and denominator $\to 0$.

38. $\lim\limits_{t \to 2} \dfrac{t^2 + t - 6}{t^2 - 4} = \lim\limits_{t \to 2} \dfrac{(t+3)(t-2)}{(t+2)(t-2)} = \lim\limits_{t \to 2} \dfrac{t+3}{t+2} = \dfrac{5}{4}$

39. $\lim\limits_{t \to 0} \dfrac{\sqrt{2-t} - \sqrt{2}}{t}$

$= \lim\limits_{t \to 0} \dfrac{\sqrt{2-t} - \sqrt{2}}{t} \cdot \dfrac{\sqrt{2-t} + \sqrt{2}}{\sqrt{2-t} + \sqrt{2}}$

$= \lim\limits_{t \to 0} \dfrac{-t}{t\left(\sqrt{2-t} + \sqrt{2}\right)}$

$= \lim\limits_{t \to 0} \dfrac{-1}{\sqrt{2-t} + \sqrt{2}} = -\dfrac{1}{2\sqrt{2}}$

$= -\dfrac{\sqrt{2}}{4}$

40. $\lim\limits_{x \to 1}\left(\dfrac{1}{x-1} - \dfrac{2}{x^2 - 1}\right) = \lim\limits_{x \to 1} \dfrac{(x+1) - 2}{(x-1)(x+1)}$

$= \lim\limits_{x \to 1} \dfrac{x-1}{(x-1)(x+1)}$

$= \lim\limits_{x \to 1} \dfrac{1}{x+1} = \dfrac{1}{2}$

41. $\lim\limits_{x \to 2} \dfrac{1/x - \frac{1}{2}}{x - 2} = \lim\limits_{x \to 2} \dfrac{2-x}{2x(x-2)} = \lim\limits_{x \to 2} \dfrac{-1}{2x} = -\dfrac{1}{4}$

42. $\lim\limits_{x \to 0} \dfrac{x}{\sqrt{1 + 3x} - 1}$

$= \lim\limits_{x \to 0} \dfrac{x\left(\sqrt{1+3x} + 1\right)}{\left(\sqrt{1+3x} - 1\right)\left(\sqrt{1+3x} + 1\right)}$

$= \lim\limits_{x \to 0} \dfrac{x\left(\sqrt{1+3x} + 1\right)}{3x}$

$= \lim\limits_{x \to 0} \dfrac{\sqrt{1+3x} + 1}{3}$

$= \dfrac{\sqrt{1} + 1}{3} = \dfrac{2}{3}$

43. $\displaystyle\lim_{x\to 2}\frac{x-\sqrt{3x-2}}{x^2-4}$

$$=\lim_{x\to 2}\frac{\left(x-\sqrt{3x-2}\right)\left(x-\sqrt{3x-2}\right)}{(x^2-4)\left(x-\sqrt{3x-2}\right)}$$

$$=\lim_{x\to 2}\frac{x^2-3x+2}{(x^2-4)\left(x+\sqrt{3x-2}\right)}$$

$$=\lim_{x\to 2}\frac{(x-2)(x-1)}{(x-2)(x+2)\left(x+\sqrt{3x-2}\right)}$$

$$=\lim_{x\to 2}\frac{(x-1)}{(x+2)\left(x+\sqrt{3x-2}\right)}$$

$$=\frac{1}{4\left(2+\sqrt{4}\right)}=\frac{1}{16}$$

44. $1\le \cos x\le 1 \Rightarrow 0\le\cos^4 x\le 1 \Rightarrow$
$0\le \sqrt{x}\cos^4 x\le \sqrt{x}$. But $\displaystyle\lim_{x\to 0^+}0=\lim_{x\to 0^+}\sqrt{x}=0$.
So by the Squeeze Theorem, $\displaystyle\lim_{x\to 0^+}\sqrt{x}\cos^4 x=0$.

45. Let $t=\sqrt[6]{x}$, so $x=t^6$. Then $t\to 1$ as $x\to 1$, so

$$\lim_{x\to 1}\frac{\sqrt[3]{x}-1}{\sqrt{x}-1}=\lim_{t\to 1}\frac{t^2-1}{t^3-1}=\lim_{t\to 1}\frac{(t-1)(t+1)}{(t-1)(t^2+t+1)}$$

$$=\lim_{t\to 1}\frac{t+1}{t^2+t+1}=\frac{1+1}{1^2+1+1}=\frac{2}{3}$$

Another method: Multiply both the numerator and
the denominator by $\left(\sqrt{x}+1\right)\left(\sqrt[3]{x^2}+\sqrt[3]{x}+1\right)$.

46. (a) Consider $G(x)=T(x+180°)-T(x)$. Fix any
number a. If $G(a)=0$, we are done:

Temperature at a = Temperature at $a+180°$.
If $G(a)>0$, then

$$G(a+180°)=T(a+360°)-T(a+180°)$$
$$=T(a)-T(a+180°)=-G(a)<0$$

Also, G is continuous since temperature
varies continuously. So, by the Intermediate
Value Theorem, G has a zero on the interval $[a, a+180°]$. If $G(a)<0$, then a similar
argument applies.

(b) Yes. The same argument applies.

(c) The same argument applies for quantities that
vary continuously, such as barometric pressure.
But one could argue that altitude above sea level
is sometimes discontinuous, so the result might
not always hold for that quantity.

2 | INVERSE FUNCTIONS

1–6 ■ Find a formula for the inverse of the function.

1. $f(x) = 4x + 7$

2. $f(x) = \dfrac{x-2}{x+2}$

3. $f(x) = \dfrac{1+3x}{5-2x}$

4. $f(x) = 5 - 4x^3$

5. $f(x) = \sqrt{2+5x}$

6. $f(x) = x^2 + x, \quad x \geq -\dfrac{1}{2}$

7. Suppose the curve $y = f(x)$ passes through the origin and the point $(1, 1)$. Find the value of the integral $\int_0^1 f'(x)\, dx$.

8–13 ■ Make a rough sketch of the graph of each function.

8. $y = 2^x + 1$

9. $y = 2^{x+1}$

10. $y = 3^{-x}$

11. $y = -3^x$

12. $y = -3^{-x}$

13. $y = 10^x - 1$

14–19 ■ Find the exact value of the expression.

14. $\log_2 64$

15. $\log_6 \dfrac{1}{36}$

16. $\log_8 4$

17. $\log_3 \dfrac{1}{27}$

18. $e^{\ln 6}$

19. $\log_3 3^{\sqrt{5}}$

20. Show that

$$\frac{d^n}{dx^n}(e^{ax}\sin bx) = r^n e^{ax}\sin(bx + n\theta)$$

where a and b are positive numbers, $r^2 = a^2 + b^2$, and $\theta = \tan^{-1}(b/a)$.

21. A peach pie is taken out of the oven at 5:00 P.M. At that time it is piping hot: 100°C.

At 5:10 P.M. its temperature is 80°C; at 5:20 P.M. it is 65°C. What is the temperature of the room?

2 | ANSWERS TO SELECTED EXERCISES

1. $f^{-1}(x) = \dfrac{1}{4}(x - 7)$

2. $f^{-1}(x) = \dfrac{2(1 + x)}{1 - x}$

3. $f^{-1}(x) = \dfrac{5x - 1}{2x + 3}$

4. $f^{-1}(x) = \left(\dfrac{5 - x}{4}\right)^{1/3}$

5. $f^{-1}(x) = \dfrac{x^2 - 2}{5}, x \geq 0$

6. $f^{-1}(x) = \dfrac{1}{2}\left(-1 + \sqrt{1 + 4x}\right).$

8.

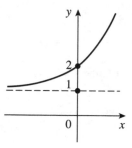

9.

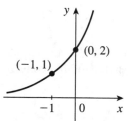

10.

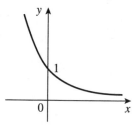

11.

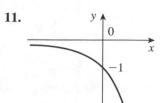

12.

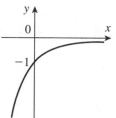

13.

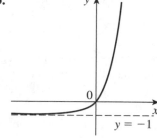

14. 6

15. -2

16. $\dfrac{2}{3}$

17. -3

18. 6

19. $\sqrt{5}$

2 | SOLUTIONS TO SELECTED EXERCISES

1. $y = f(x) = 4x + 7 \Rightarrow 4x = y - 7 \Rightarrow x = (y - 7)/4$.
Interchange x and y: $y = (x - 7)/4$. So
$f^{-1}(x) = (x - 7)/4$.

2. $y = f(x) = \dfrac{x - 2}{x + 2} \Rightarrow xy + 2y = x - 2 \Rightarrow$

$x(1 - y) = 2(y + 1) \Rightarrow x = \dfrac{2(1 + y)}{1 - y}$. Interchange

x and y: $y = \dfrac{2(1 + x)}{1 - x}$. So $f^{-1}(x) = \dfrac{2(1 + x)}{1 - x}$.

3. $y = f(x) = \dfrac{1 + 3x}{5 - 2x} \Rightarrow 5y - 2xy = 1 + 3x \Rightarrow$

$5y - 1 = 3x + 2xy \Rightarrow x(3 + 2y) = 5y - 1 \Rightarrow$

$x = \dfrac{5y - 1}{2y + 3}$. Interchange x and y: $y = \dfrac{5x - 1}{2x + 3}$. So

$f^{-1}(x) = \dfrac{5x - 1}{2x + 3}$.

4. $y = f(x) = 5 - 4x^3 \Rightarrow 4x^3 = 5 - y \Rightarrow$

$x^3 = (5 - y)/4 \Rightarrow x = \left(\dfrac{5 - y}{4}\right)^{1/3}$. Interchange x and

y: $y = \left(\dfrac{5 - x}{4}\right)^{1/3}$. So $f^{-1}(x) = \left(\dfrac{5 - x}{4}\right)^{1/3}$.

5. $y = f(x) = \sqrt{2 + 5x} \Rightarrow y^2 = 2 + 5x$ and $y \geq 0 \Rightarrow$

$5x = y^2 - 2 \Rightarrow x = \dfrac{y^2 - 2}{5}$, $y \geq 0$. Interchange x and

y: $y = \dfrac{x^2 - 2}{5}$, $x \geq 0$. So $f^{-1}(x) = \dfrac{x^2 - 2}{5}$, $x \geq 0$.

6. $y = f(x) = x^2 + x \Rightarrow x^2 + x - y = 0 \Rightarrow$

$x = \dfrac{1}{2}(-1 \pm \sqrt{1 + 4y})$ by the quadratic formula.

But $x \geq -\dfrac{1}{2} \Rightarrow x = \dfrac{1}{2}(-1 + \sqrt{1 + 4y})$.

Interchange x and y: $y = \dfrac{1}{2}(-1 + \sqrt{1 + 4x})$. So

$f^{-1}(x) = \dfrac{1}{2}(-1 + \sqrt{1 + 4x})$.

7. By FTC2, $\int_0^1 f'(x)\,dx = f(1) - f(0) = 1 - 0 = 1$.

8.

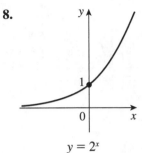

$y = 2^x$

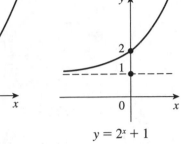

$y = 2^x + 1$

9.

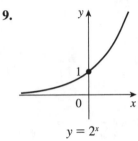

$y = 2^x$

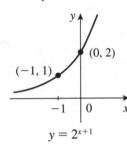

$y = 2^{x+1}$

10.

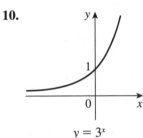

$y = 3^x$

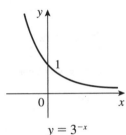

$y = 3^{-x}$

11.

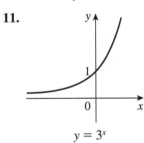

$y = 3^x$

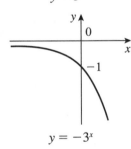

$y = -3^x$

12.

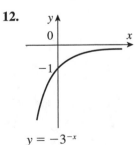

$y = -3^{-x}$

13. We start with the graph of $y = 10^x$ and shift it 1 unit downward.

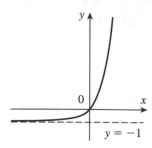

14. $\log_2 64 = 6$ since $2^6 = 64$.

15. $\log_6 \dfrac{1}{36} = -2$ since $6^{-2} = \dfrac{1}{36}$.

16. $\log_8 4 = \dfrac{2}{3}$ since $8^{2/3} = 4$.

17. $\log_3 \dfrac{1}{27} = -3$ since $3^{-3} = \dfrac{1}{27}$.

18. $e^{\ln 6} = 6$

19. $\log_3 3^{\sqrt{5}} = \sqrt{5}$

20. Consider the statement that $\dfrac{d^n}{dx^n}(e^{ax} \sin bx)$

$= r^n e^{ax} \sin(bx + n\theta)$. For $n = 1$, $\dfrac{d}{dx}(e^{ax} \sin bx)$

$= ae^{ax} \sin bx + be^{ax} \cos bx$, and

$re^{ax} \sin(bx + \theta) = re^{ax}[\sin bx \cos \theta + \cos bx \sin \theta]$

$= re^{ax}\left(\dfrac{a}{r} \sin bx + \dfrac{b}{r} \cos bx\right)$

$= ae^{ax} \sin bx + be^{ax} \cos bx$

since $\tan \theta = \dfrac{b}{a} \Rightarrow \sin \theta = \dfrac{b}{r}$ and $\cos \theta = \dfrac{a}{r}$.

So the statement is true for $n = 1$. Assume it is true for $n = k$. Then

$\dfrac{d^{k+1}}{dx^{k+1}}(e^{ax} \sin bx) = \dfrac{d}{dx}[r^k e^{ax} \sin(bx + k\theta)]$

$= r^k ae^{ax} \sin(bx + k\theta) + r^k e^{ax} b \cos(bx + k\theta)$

$= r^k e^{ax}[a \sin(bx + k\theta) + b \cos(bx + k\theta)]$

But

$\sin[bx + (k+1)\theta] = \sin[(bx + k\theta) + \theta]$

$= \sin(bx + k\theta) \cos \theta + \sin \theta \cos(bx + k\theta)$

$= \dfrac{a}{r} \sin(bx + k\theta) + \dfrac{b}{r} \cos(bx + k\theta)$

Hence, $a \sin(bx + k\theta) + b \cos(bx + k\theta) = r \sin[bx + (k+1)\theta]$. So

$\dfrac{d^{k+1}}{dx^{k+1}}(e^{ax} \sin bx)$

$= r^k e^{ax}[a \sin(bx + k\theta) + b \cos(bx + k\theta)]$

$= r^k e^{ax}[r \sin(bx + (k+1)\theta)]$

$= r^{k+1} e^{ax}[\sin(bx + (k+1)\theta)]$

Therefore, the statement is true for all n by mathematical induction.

3 | DERIVATIVES

1–5 ■ Differentiate the function.

1. $y = x^{4/3} - x^{2/3}$

2. $y = 3x + 2e^x$

3. $y = A + \dfrac{B}{x} + \dfrac{C}{x^2}$

4. $y = x + \sqrt[5]{x^2}$

5. $v = x\sqrt{x} + \dfrac{1}{x^2\sqrt{x}}$

6–18 ■ Differentiate.

6. $h(x) = \dfrac{x + 2}{x - 1}$

7. $f(u) = \dfrac{1 - u^2}{1 + u^2}$

8. $G(s) = (s^2 + s + 1)(s^2 + 2)$

9. $g(x) = (1 + \sqrt{x})(x - x^3)$

10. $H(x) = (x^3 - x + 1)(x^{-2} + 2x^{-3})$

11. $H(t) = e^t(1 + 3t^2 + 5t^4)$

12. $y = \dfrac{3t - 7}{t^2 + 5t - 4}$

13. $y = \dfrac{4t + 5}{2 - 3t}$

14. $y = \dfrac{x^2 + 4x + 3}{\sqrt{x}}$

15. $y = \dfrac{u^2 - u - 2}{u + 1}$

16. $y = \dfrac{e^x}{x + e^x}$

17. $f(x) = \dfrac{x^5}{x^3 - 2}$

18. $s = \sqrt{t}(t^3 - \sqrt{t} + 1)$

19–26 ■ Differentiate.

19. $y = \sin x + \cos x$

20. $y = \cos x - 2\tan x$

21. $y = e^x \sin x$

22. $y = \dfrac{\tan x}{x}$

23. $y = \dfrac{\sin x}{1 + \cos x}$

24. $y = \dfrac{x}{\sin x + \cos x}$

25. $y = \tan\theta(\sin\theta + \cos\theta)$

26. $y = \csc x \cot x$

27–42 ■ Find the derivative of the function.

27. $F(x) = (x^3 - 5x)^4$

28. $f(t) = (2t^2 + 6t + 1)^{-8}$

29. $g(x) = \sqrt{x^2 - 7x}$

30. $f(t) = \dfrac{1}{(t^2 - 2t - 5)^4}$

31. $h(t) = \left(t - \dfrac{1}{t}\right)^{3/2}$

32. $F(y) = \left(\dfrac{y - 6}{y + 7}\right)^3$

33. $s(t) = \sqrt[4]{\dfrac{t^3 + 1}{t^3 - 1}}$

34. $f(z) = \dfrac{1}{\sqrt[5]{2z - 1}}$

35. $f(x) = \dfrac{x}{\sqrt{7 - 3x}}$

36. $y = 5^{-1/x}$

37. $y = \sqrt{1 + 2\tan x}$

38. $y = \cos^2(\cos x) + \sin^2(\cos x)$

39. $f(x) = [x^3 + (2x - 1)^3]^3$ **40.** $g(t) = \sqrt[4]{(1 - 3t)^4 + t^4}$

41. $y = \cos^2\left(\dfrac{1 - \sqrt{x}}{1 + \sqrt{x}}\right)$

42. $y = \sqrt{1 + \tan(x + (1/x))}$

43–46 ■ Find f' and state the domains of f and f'.

43. $f(x) = x^2 \sec^2 3x$

44. $f(x) = \sin\sqrt{2x + 1}$

45. $f(x) = \sqrt{\cos\sqrt{x}}$

46. $f(x) = \cos\sqrt{x} + \sqrt{\cos x}$

CHALLENGE

47. (a) Find the domain of the function
$$f(x) = \sqrt{1 - \sqrt{2 - \sqrt{3 - x}}}.$$
(b) Find $f'(x)$.

⊞ (c) Check your work in parts (a) and (b) by graphing f and f' on the same screen.

48–52 ■ Find dy/dx by implicit differentiation.

48. $y^5 + 3x^2y^2 + 5x^4 = 12$ **49.** $x^4 + y^4 = 16$

50. $\dfrac{y}{x - y} = x^2 + 1$

51. $x\sqrt{1 + y} + y\sqrt{1 + 2x} = 2x$

52. $2xy = (x^2 + y^2)^{3/2}$

53–56 ■ Differentiate the function.

53. $f(x) = \ln(2 - x)$

54. $f(x) = \log_3(x^2 - 4)$

55. $f(x) = \log_{10}\left(\dfrac{x}{x-1}\right)$ **56.** $F(x) = \ln\sqrt{x}$

57. $y = \sqrt{\dfrac{x^2+1}{x+1}}$ **58.** $y = \dfrac{e^x\sqrt{x^5+2}}{(x+1)^4(x^2+3)^2}$

59. $y = \dfrac{(x^3+1)^4\sin^2 x}{\sqrt[3]{x}}$

60. The figure shows the graph of a population of Cyprian honeybees raised in an apiary.

  (a) Use a linear approximation to predict the bee population after 18 weeks and after 20 weeks.

  (b) Are your predictions underestimates or overestimates? Why?

  (c) Which of your predictions do you think is the more accurate? Why?

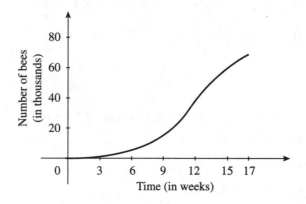

61. Verify the linear approximation $\sqrt{1+x} \approx 1 + \dfrac{1}{2}x$ at $a = 0$.

Then determine the values of x for which the linear approximation is accurate to within 0.1.

 CHALLENGE

62. Find points P and Q on the parabola $y = 1 - x^2$ so that the triangle ABC formed by the x-axis and the tangent lines at P and Q is an equilateral triangle.

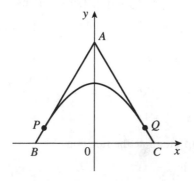

 CHALLENGE

63. Find the point where the curves $y = x^3 - 3x + 4$ and $y = 3(x^2 - x)$ are tangent to each other, that is, have a common tangent line. Illustrate by sketching both curves and the common tangent.

 CHALLENGE

64. Suppose f is a function that satisfies the equation
$$f(x+y) = f(x) + f(y) + x^2 y + xy^2$$
for all real numbers x and y. Suppose also that
$$\lim_{x\to 0}\frac{f(x)}{x} = 1$$

  (a) Find $f(0)$. (b) Find $f'(0)$. (c) Find $f'(x)$.

 CHALLENGE

65. A car is traveling at night along a highway shaped like a parabola with its vertex at the origin (see the figure). The car starts at a point 100 m west and 100 m north of the origin and travels in an easterly direction. There is a statue located 100 m east and 50 m north of the origin. At what point on the highway will the car's headlights illuminate the statue?

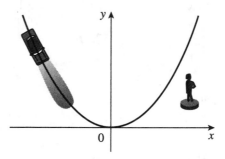

66. A container in the shape of an inverted cone has height 16 cm and radius 5 cm at the top. It is partially filled with a liquid that oozes through the sides at a rate proportional to the area of the container that is in contact with the liquid. (The surface area of a cone is $\pi r l$, where r is the radius and l is the slant height.) If we pour the liquid into the container at a rate of 2 cm³/min, then the height of the liquid decreases at a rate of 0.3 cm/min when the height is 10 cm. If our goal is to keep the liquid at a constant height of 10 cm, at what rate should we pour the liquid into the container?

67. (a) The cubic function $f(x) = x(x - 2)(x - 6)$ has three distinct zeros: 0, 2, and 6, Graph f and its tangent lines at the *average* of each pair of zeros. What do you notice?

    (b) Suppose the cubic function $f(x) = (x - a)(x - b)(x - c)$ has three distinct zeros: a, b, and c. Prove, with the help of a computer algebra system, that a tangent line drawn at the average of the zeros a and b intersects the graph of f at the third zero.

CAS

3 | ANSWERS TO SELECTED EXERCISES

1. $y' = \dfrac{4}{3}x^{1/3} - \dfrac{2}{3}x^{-1/3}$

2. $y' = 3 + 2e^x$

3. $y' = -\dfrac{B}{x^2} - 2\dfrac{C}{x^3}$

4. $y' = 1 + \dfrac{2}{5\sqrt[5]{x^3}}$

5. $v' = \dfrac{3}{2}\sqrt{x} - \dfrac{5}{2x^3\sqrt{x}}$

6. $h'(x) = -\dfrac{3}{(x-1)^2}$

7. $f'(u) = -\dfrac{4u}{(1+u^2)^2}$

8. $G'(s) = (2s+1)(s^2+2) + (s^2+s+1)(2s)$
$\left[\,= 4s^3 + 3s^2 + 6s + 2\,\right]$

9. $g'(x) = 1 - 3x^2 + \dfrac{3}{2}x^{1/2} - \dfrac{7}{2}x^{5/2}$

10. $H'(x) = 1 + x^{-2} + 2x^{-3} - 6x^{-4}$

11. $H'(t) = e^t(5t^4 + 20t^3 + 3t^2 + 6t + 1)$

12. $y' = \dfrac{-3t^2 + 14t + 23}{(t^2 + 5t - 4)^2}$

13. $y' = \dfrac{23}{(2-3t)^2}$

14. $y' = \dfrac{3}{2}\sqrt{x} + \dfrac{2}{\sqrt{x}} - \dfrac{3}{2x\sqrt{x}}$

15. $y' = 1$

16. $y' = \dfrac{e^x(x-1)}{(x+e^x)^2}$

17. $f'(x) = \dfrac{2x^4(x^3 - 5)}{(x^3 - 2)^2}$

18. $s' = \dfrac{7}{2}t^{5/2} - 1 + \dfrac{1}{2\sqrt{t}}$

19. $dy/dx = \cos x - \sin x$

20. $dy/dx = -\sin x - 2\sec^2 x$

21. $dy/dx = e^x(\cos x + \sin x)$

22. $\dfrac{dy}{dx} = \dfrac{x\sec^2 x - \tan x}{x^2}$

23. $\dfrac{dy}{dx} = \dfrac{1}{1 + \cos x}$

24. $\dfrac{dy}{dx} = \dfrac{(1+x)\sin x + (1-x)\cos x}{1 + \sin 2x}$

25. $y' = \sin\theta - \sin\theta\tan\theta + \sin\theta\sec^2\theta + \sec\theta$

26. $dy/dx = -\csc x\,(\cot^2 x + \csc^2 x)$

27. $F'(x) = 4(x^3 - 5x)^3(3x^2 - 5)$

28. $f'(t) = -16(2t^2 - 6t + 1)^{-9}(2t - 3)$

29. $g'(x) = \dfrac{2x - 7}{2\sqrt{x^2 - 7x}}$

30. $f'(t) = \dfrac{8(1 - t)}{(t^2 - 2t - 5)^5}$

31. $h'(t) = \dfrac{3}{2}(t - 1/t)^{1/2}(1 + 1/t^2)$

32. $F'(y) = \dfrac{39(y - 6)^2}{(y + 7)^4}$

33. $s'(t) = \dfrac{1}{2}\left(\dfrac{t^3 + 1}{t^3 + 1}\right)^{-3/4} \dfrac{-3t^2}{(t^3 - 1)^2}$

34. $f'(z) = -\dfrac{2}{5}(2z - 1)^{-6/5}$ **35.** $f'(x) = \dfrac{14 - 3x}{2(7 - 3x)^{3/2}}$

36. $y' = 5^{-1/x}(\ln 5)/x^2$ **37.** $y' = \dfrac{\sec^2 x}{\sqrt{1 + 2\tan x}}$

38. $y' = 0$

39. $f'(x) = 9\left[x^3 + (2x - 1)^3\right]^2(9x^2 - 8x + 2)$

40. $g'(t) = \left[(1 - 3t)^4 + t^4\right]^{-3/4}\left[t^3 - 3(1 - 3t^3)\right]$

41. $y' = \dfrac{2}{\sqrt{x}(1 + \sqrt{x})^2}\sin\left(\dfrac{1 - \sqrt{x}}{1 + \sqrt{x}}\right)\cos\left(\dfrac{1 - \sqrt{x}}{1 + \sqrt{x}}\right)$

42. $y' = \dfrac{(x^2 - 1)\sec^2\left(x + \dfrac{1}{x}\right)}{2x^2\sqrt{1 + \tan\left(x + \dfrac{1}{x}\right)}}$

43. $f'(x) = 2x\sec^2 3x\,(1 + 3x\tan 3x)$,
$\left\{x \mid x \neq (2n - 2)\dfrac{\pi}{6}, n \text{ an integer}\right\}$(both f and f')

44. $f'(x) = \dfrac{\cos\sqrt{2x + 1}}{\sqrt{2x + 1}}$,
$\mathrm{dom}(f) = \left[-\dfrac{1}{2}, \infty\right), \mathrm{dom}(f') = \left(-\dfrac{1}{2}, \infty\right)$

45. $f'(x) = -\dfrac{\sin\sqrt{x}}{4\sqrt{x}\sqrt{\cos\sqrt{x}}}$,
$\mathrm{dom}(f) = \{x \mid 0 \leq x \leq \pi^2/4 \text{ or}$
$[(4n - 1)\pi/2]^2 \leq x \leq [(4n + 1)\pi/2]^2$
for some $n \in \{1, 2, 3, \ldots\}\}$,
$\mathrm{dom}(f') = \{x \mid 0 < x < \pi^2/4 \text{ or}$
$[(4n - 1)\pi/2]^2 < x < [(4n + 1)\pi/2]^2$
for some $n \in \{1, 2, 3, \ldots\}\}$

46. $f'(x) = -\dfrac{\sin\sqrt{x}}{2\sqrt{x}} - \dfrac{\sin x}{2\sqrt{\cos x}}$,

$\text{dom}(f) = \{x \mid 0 \le x \le \pi/2 \text{ or}$

$\qquad (4n-1)\pi/2 \le x \le (4n+1)\pi/2$

$\qquad \text{for some } n = 1, 2, 3, \ldots\},$

$\text{dom}(f') = \{x \mid 0 < x < \pi/2 \text{ or}$

$\qquad (4n-1)\pi/2 < x < (4n+1)\pi/2$

$\qquad \text{for some } n = 1, 2, 3, \ldots\}$

47. (a) $[-1, 2]$

(b) $-\dfrac{1}{8\sqrt{1-\sqrt{2-\sqrt{3-x}}}\sqrt{2-\sqrt{3-x}}\sqrt{3-x}}$

48. $-\dfrac{20x^3 + 6xy^2}{5y^4 + 6x^2y}$ **49.** $\dfrac{x^3}{y^3}$

50. $\dfrac{y}{x} + 2(x-y)^2$ or $\dfrac{3x^2 + 1 - 2xy}{x^2 + 2}$

51. $\dfrac{2 - \sqrt{1+y} - y/\sqrt{1+2x}}{\sqrt{1+2x} + x/(2\sqrt{1+y})}$

52. $\dfrac{3x(x^2+y^2)^{1/2} - 2y}{2x - 3y(x^2+y^2)^{1/2}}$ **53.** $f'(x) = \dfrac{1}{x-2}$

54. $f'(x) = \dfrac{2x}{(x^2-4)\ln 3}$

55. $f'(x) = -\dfrac{1}{x(x-1)\ln 10}$

56. $F'(x) = \dfrac{1}{2x}$

57. $y' = \sqrt{\dfrac{x^2+1}{x+1}}\left[\dfrac{x}{x^2+1} - \dfrac{1}{2(x+1)}\right]$

58. $y' = \dfrac{e^x\sqrt{x^5+2}}{(x+1)^4(x^2+3)^2}\left[1 + \dfrac{5x^4}{2(x^5+2)} - \dfrac{4}{x+1} - \dfrac{4x}{x^2+3}\right]$

59. $y' = \dfrac{(x^3+1)^4 \sin^2 x}{x^{1/3}}\left(\dfrac{12x^2}{x^3+1} + 2\cot x - \dfrac{1}{3x}\right)$

60. (a) 72,500; 77,500

(b) Overestimates; tangent above graph

(c) 18 weeks; closer to given data

61. $-0.69 < x < 1.09$

62. $\left(\pm\sqrt{3}/2, \dfrac{1}{4}\right)$

64. (a) 0

(b) 1

(c) $f'(x) = x^2 + 1$

66. $2 + \dfrac{375}{128}\pi \approx 11.204\,\text{cm}^3/\text{min}$

3 | SOLUTIONS TO SELECTED EXERCISES

1. $y = x^{4/3} - x^{2/3} \Rightarrow y' = \dfrac{4}{3}x^{1/3} - \dfrac{2}{3}x^{-1/3}$

2. $y = 3x + 2e^x \Rightarrow y' = 3 + 2e^x$

3. $y = A + \dfrac{B}{x} + \dfrac{C}{x^2} = A + Bx^{-1} + Cx^{-2} \Rightarrow$

$y' = -Bx^{-2} - 2Cx^{-3} = -\dfrac{B}{x^2} - 2\dfrac{C}{x^3}$

4. $y = x + \sqrt[5]{x^2} = x + x^{2/5} \Rightarrow$

$y' = 1 + \dfrac{2}{5}x^{-3/5} = 1 + \dfrac{2}{5\sqrt[5]{x^3}}$

5. $v = x\sqrt{x} + \dfrac{1}{x^2\sqrt{x}} = x^{3/2} + x^{-5/2} \Rightarrow$

$v' = \dfrac{3}{2}x^{1/2} - \dfrac{5}{2}x^{-7/2} = \dfrac{3}{2}\sqrt{x} - \dfrac{5}{2x^3\sqrt{x}}$

6. $h(x) = \dfrac{x+2}{x-1} \Rightarrow$

$h'(x) = \dfrac{(x-1)(1) - (x+2)(1)}{(x-1)^2}$

$= \dfrac{x - 1 - x - 2}{(x-1)^2} = -\dfrac{3}{(x-1)^2}$

7. $f(u) = \dfrac{1 - u^2}{1 + u^2} \Rightarrow$

$f'(u) = \dfrac{(1 + u^2)(-2u) - (1 - u^2)(2u)}{(1 + u^2)^2}$

$= \dfrac{-2u - 2u^3 - 2u + 2u^3}{(1 + u^2)^2} = -\dfrac{4u}{(1 + u^2)^2}$

8. $G(s) = (s^2 + s + 1)(s^2 + 2) \Rightarrow$

$G'(s) = (s^2 + s + 1)(2s) + (s^2 + 2)(2s + 1)$

$= 2s^3 + 2s^2 + 2s + 2s^3 + s^2 + 4s + 2$

$= 4s^3 + 3s^2 + 6s + 2$

9. $g(x) = (1 + \sqrt{x})(x - x^3) = x - x^3 + x^{3/2} - x^{7/2} \Rightarrow$

$g'(x) = 1 - 3x^2 + \dfrac{3}{2}x^{1/2} - \dfrac{7}{2}x^{5/2}$

Another Method: Use the Product Rule.

10. $H(x) = (x^3 - x + 1)(x^{-2} + 2x^{-3})$

$= (x^3 - x + 1)(x^{-2}) + (x^3 - x + 1)(2x^{-3})$

$= x - x^{-1} + x^{-2} + 2 - 2x^{-2} + 2x^{-3}$

$= 2 + x - x^{-1} - x^{-2} + 2x^{-3}$

$\Rightarrow H'(x) = 1 + x^{-2} + 2x^{-3} - 6x^{-4}$

Another Method: Use the Product Rule.

11. $H(t) = e^t(1 + 3t^2 + 5t^4) \Rightarrow$

$H'(t) = e^t(6t + 20t^3) + (1 + 3t^2 + 5t^4)e^t$

$= e^t(5t^4 + 20t^3 + 3t^2 + 6t + 1)$

12. $y = \dfrac{3t - 7}{t^2 + 5t - 4} \Rightarrow$

$y' = \dfrac{(t^2 + 5t - 4)(3) - (3t - 7)(2t + 5)}{(t^2 + 5t - 4)^2}$

$= \dfrac{-3t^2 + 14t + 23}{(t^2 + 5t - 4)^2}$

13. $y = \dfrac{4t + 5}{2 - 3t} \Rightarrow$

$y' = \dfrac{(2 - 3t)(4) - (4t + 5)(-3)}{(2 - 3t)^2} = \dfrac{23}{(2 - 3t)^2}$

14. $y = \dfrac{x^2 + 4x + 3}{\sqrt{x}} = x^{3/2} + 4x^{1/2} + 3x^{-1/2} \Rightarrow$

$y' = \dfrac{3}{2}x^{1/2} + 4\left(\dfrac{1}{2}\right)x^{-1/2} + 3\left(-\dfrac{1}{2}\right)x^{-3/2}$

$= \dfrac{3}{2}\sqrt{x} + \dfrac{2}{\sqrt{x}} - \dfrac{3}{2x\sqrt{x}}$

Another Method: Use the Quotient Rule.

15. $y = \dfrac{u^2 - u - 2}{u + 1} = \dfrac{(u - 2)(u + 1)}{u + 1} = u - 2 \text{ for } u \neq -1.$

$y' = \dfrac{d}{du}(u - 2) = 1$

16. $y = \dfrac{e^x}{x + e^x} \Rightarrow$

$y' = \dfrac{(x + e^x)(e^x) - e^x(1 + e^x)}{(x + e^x)^2}$

$= \dfrac{e^x(x + e^x - 1 - e^x)}{(x + e^x)^2} = \dfrac{e^x(x - 1)}{(x + e^x)^2}$

17. $f(x) = \dfrac{x^5}{x^3 - 2} \Rightarrow$

$f'(x) = \dfrac{(x^3 - 2)(5x^4) - x^5(3x^2)}{(x^3 - 2)^2} = \dfrac{2x^4(x^3 - 5)}{(x^3 - 2)^2}$

18. $s = \sqrt{t}(t^3 - \sqrt{t} + 1) = t^{7/2} - t + t^{1/2} \Rightarrow$

$s' = \dfrac{7}{2}t^{5/2} - 1 + \dfrac{1}{2\sqrt{t}}.$

Another Method: Use the Product Rule.

19. $y = \sin x + \cos x \Rightarrow dy/dx = \cos x - \sin x$

20. $y = \cos x - 2\tan x \Rightarrow dy/dx = -\sin x - 2\sec^2 x$

21. $y = e^x \sin x \Rightarrow$

$dy/dx = e^x(\cos x) + (\sin x)e^x = e^x(\cos x + \sin x)$

22. $y = \dfrac{\tan x}{x} \Rightarrow \dfrac{dy}{dx} = \dfrac{x\sec^2 x - \tan x}{x^2}$

23. $y = \dfrac{\sin x}{1 + \cos x} \Rightarrow$

$\dfrac{dy}{dx} = \dfrac{(1 + \cos x)\cos x - \sin x(-\sin x)}{(1 + \cos x)^2}$

$= \dfrac{\cos x + \cos^2 x + \sin^2 x}{(1 + \cos x)^2}$

$= \dfrac{\cos x + 1}{(1 + \cos x)^2} = \dfrac{1}{1 + \cos x}$

24. $y = \dfrac{x}{\sin x + \cos x} \Rightarrow$

$\dfrac{dy}{dx} = \dfrac{(\sin x + \cos x) - x(\cos x - \sin x)}{(\sin x + \cos x)^2}$

$= \dfrac{(1 + x)\sin x + (1 - x)\cos x}{\sin^2 x + \cos^2 x + 2\sin x\cos x}$

$= \dfrac{(1 + x)\sin x + (1 - x)\cos x}{1 + \sin 2x}$

25. $y = \tan\theta(\sin\theta + \cos\theta) \Rightarrow$

$y' = \tan\theta(\cos\theta - \sin\theta) + (\sin\theta + \cos\theta)\sec^2\theta$

$= \sin\theta - \sin\theta\tan\theta + \sin\theta\sec^2\theta + \sec\theta$

26. $y = \csc x\cot x \Rightarrow$

$dy/dx = (-\csc x\cot x)\cot x + \csc x(-\csc^2 x)$

$= -\csc x(\cot^2 x + \csc^2 x)$

27. $F(x) = (x^3 - 5x)^4 \Rightarrow$

$F'(x) = 4(x^3 - 5x)^3\dfrac{d}{dx}(x^3 - 5x)$

$= 4(x^3 - 5x)^3(3x^2 - 5)$

28. $f(t) = (2t^2 - 6t + 1)^{-8} \Rightarrow$

$f'(t) = -8(2t^2 - 6t + 1)^{-9}(4t - 6)$

$= -16(2t^2 - 6t + 1)^{-9}(2t - 3)$

29. $g(x) = \sqrt{x^2 - 7x} = (x^2 - 7x)^{1/2} \Rightarrow$

$g'(x) = \dfrac{1}{2}(x^2 - 7x)^{-1/2}(2x - 7) = \dfrac{2x - 7}{2\sqrt{x^2 - 7x}}$

30. $f(t) = \dfrac{1}{(t^2 - 2t - 5)^4} = (t^2 - 2t - 5)^{-4} \Rightarrow$

$f'(t) = -4(t^2 - 2t - 5)^{-5}(2t - 2) = \dfrac{8(1 - t)}{(t^2 - 2t - 5)^5}$

31. $h(t) = (t - 1/t)^{3/2} \Rightarrow$

$h'(t) = \dfrac{3}{2}(t - 1/t)^{1/2}(1 + 1/t^2)$

32. $F(y) = \left(\dfrac{y - 6}{y + 7}\right)^3 \Rightarrow$

$F'(y) = 3\left(\dfrac{y - 6}{y + 7}\right)^2\dfrac{(y + 7)(1) - (y - 6)(1)}{(y + 7)^2}$

$= 3\left(\dfrac{y - 6}{y + 7}\right)^2\dfrac{13}{(y + 7)^2} = \dfrac{39(y - 6)^2}{(y + 7)^4}$

33. $s(t) = \left(\dfrac{t^3 + 1}{t^3 - 1}\right)^{1/4} \Rightarrow$

$s'(t) = \dfrac{1}{4}\left(\dfrac{t^3 + 1}{t^3 - 1}\right)^{-3/4}\dfrac{3t^2(t^3 - 1) - (t^3 + 1)(3t^2)}{(t^3 - 1)^2}$

$= \dfrac{1}{2}\left(\dfrac{t^3 + 1}{t^3 - 1}\right)^{-3/4}\dfrac{-3t^2}{(t^3 - 1)^2}$

34. $f(z) = (2z - 1)^{-1/5} \Rightarrow$

$f'(z) = -\dfrac{1}{5}(2z - 1)^{-6/5}(2) = -\dfrac{2}{5}(2z - 1)^{-6/5}$

35. $f(x) = \dfrac{x}{\sqrt{7 - 3x}} \Rightarrow$

$f'(x) = \dfrac{\sqrt{7 - 3x} - x\left(\dfrac{1}{2}\right)(7 - 3x)^{-1/2}(-3)}{7 - 3x}$

$= \dfrac{1}{\sqrt{7 - 3x}} + \dfrac{3x}{2(7 - 3x)^{3/2}}$ or $\dfrac{14 - 3x}{2(7 - 3x)^{3/2}}$

36. Using Formula 5 and the Chain Rule, $y = 5^{-1/x} \Rightarrow$

$y' = 5^{-1/x}(\ln 5)\left[-1\cdot(-x^{-2})\right] = 5^{-1/x}(\ln 5)/x^2$

37. $y = \sqrt{1 + 2\tan x} \Rightarrow$

$y' = \dfrac{1}{2}(1 + 2\tan x)^{-1/2}2\sec^2 x = \dfrac{\sec^2 x}{\sqrt{1 + 2\tan x}}$

38. $y = \cos^2(\cos x) + \sin^2(\cos x) = 1 \Rightarrow y' = 0$

39. $f(x) = [x^3 + (2x - 1)^3]^3 \Rightarrow$

$f'(x) = 3[x^3 + (2x - 1)^3]^2[3x^2 + 3(2x - 1)^2(2)]$

$= 9[x^3 + (2x - 1)^3]^2[9x^2 - 8x + 2]$

40. $g(t) = \sqrt[4]{(1 - 3t)^4 + t^4} \Rightarrow$

$g'(t) = \dfrac{1}{4}[(1 - 3t)^4 + t^4]^{-3/4}[4(1 - 3t)^3(-3) + 4t^3]$

$= [(1 - 3t)^4 + t^4]^{-3/4}[t^3 - 3(1 - 3t^3)]$

41. $y = \cos^2\left(\dfrac{1 - \sqrt{x}}{1 + \sqrt{x}}\right) \Rightarrow$

$$y' = 2\cos\left(\dfrac{1 - \sqrt{x}}{1 + \sqrt{x}}\right)(-1)\sin\left(\dfrac{1 - \sqrt{x}}{1 + \sqrt{x}}\right)$$

$$\dfrac{(1 + \sqrt{x})\left(-\dfrac{1}{2\sqrt{x}}\right) - (1 - \sqrt{x})\dfrac{1}{2\sqrt{x}}}{(1 + \sqrt{x})^2}$$

$$= \dfrac{2}{\sqrt{x}(1 + \sqrt{x})^2}\sin\left(\dfrac{1 - \sqrt{x}}{1 + \sqrt{x}}\right)\cos\left(\dfrac{1 - \sqrt{x}}{1 + \sqrt{x}}\right)$$

42. $y = \sqrt{1 + \tan\left(x + \dfrac{1}{x}\right)} \Rightarrow$

$$y' = \dfrac{1}{2\sqrt{1 + \tan\left(x + \dfrac{1}{x}\right)}}\left[\sec^2\left(x + \dfrac{1}{x}\right)\right]\left(1 - \dfrac{1}{x^2}\right)$$

$$= \dfrac{(x^2 - 1)\sec^2\left(x + \dfrac{1}{x}\right)}{2x^2\sqrt{1 + \tan\left(x + \dfrac{1}{x}\right)}}$$

43. $f(x) = x^2\sec^2 3x \Rightarrow$

$f'(x) = 2x\sec^2 3x + x^2(2\sec 3x)(\sec 3x\tan 3x)(3)$

$\quad = 2x\sec^2 3x(1 + 3x\tan 3x)$

Domain of f = domain of $f' = \{x\,|\,\cos 3x \neq 0\}$

$$= \left\{x\,\Big|\,x \neq (2n - 1)\dfrac{\pi}{6}, n \text{ an integer}\right\}$$

44. $f(x) = \sin\sqrt{2x + 1} \Rightarrow$

$$f'(x) = \cos\sqrt{2x + 1}\left(\dfrac{1}{2\sqrt{2x + 1}}\right)(2) = \dfrac{\cos\sqrt{2x + 1}}{\sqrt{2x + 1}}.$$

$$\text{Dom}(f) = \{x\,|\,2x + 1 \geq 0\} = \left[-\dfrac{1}{2}, \infty\right).$$

$$\text{Dom}(f') = \{x\,|\,2x + 1 > 0\} = \left(-\dfrac{1}{2}, \infty\right).$$

45. $f(x) = \sqrt{\cos\sqrt{x}} \Rightarrow$

$$f'(x) = \dfrac{1}{2}(\cos\sqrt{x})^{-1/2}(-\sin\sqrt{x})\left(\dfrac{1}{2}\right)x^{-1/2}$$

$$= -\dfrac{\sin\sqrt{x}}{4\sqrt{x}\sqrt{\cos\sqrt{x}}}$$

Domain of $f = \{x\,|\,x \geq 0 \text{ and } \cos\sqrt{x} \geq 0\}$

$$= \left\{x\,\Big|\,0 \leq x \leq \dfrac{\pi^2}{4} \text{ or } \left[(4n - 1)\dfrac{\pi}{2}\right]^2 \leq x\right.$$

$$\left. \leq \left[(4n + 1)\dfrac{\pi}{2}\right]^2 \text{ for some } n \in \{1, 2, 3, ...\}\right\}$$

Domain of $f' = \{x\,|\,x > 0 \text{ and } \cos\sqrt{x} > 0\}$

$$= \left\{x\,\Big|\,0 < x < \dfrac{\pi^2}{4} \text{ or } \left[(4n - 1)\dfrac{\pi}{2}\right]^2 < x\right.$$

$$\left. < \left[(4n + 1)\dfrac{\pi}{2}\right]^2 \text{ for some } n \in \{1, 2, 3, ...\}\right\}$$

46. $\cos\sqrt{x} + \sqrt{\cos x} \Rightarrow$

$$f'(x) = -\sin\sqrt{x}\dfrac{1}{2}x^{-1/2} + \dfrac{1}{2}(\cos x)^{-1/2}(-\sin x)$$

$$= -\dfrac{\sin\sqrt{x}}{2\sqrt{x}} - \dfrac{\sin x}{2\sqrt{\cos x}}$$

Domain of $f = \{x\,|\,x \geq 0 \text{ and } \cos x \geq 0\}$

$$= \left\{x\,\Big|\,0 \leq x \leq \dfrac{\pi}{2} \text{ or } (4n - 1)\dfrac{\pi}{2} \leq x\right.$$

$$\left. \leq (4n + 1)\dfrac{\pi}{2} \text{ for some } n \in \{1, 2, 3, ...\}\right\}$$

Domain of $f' = \{x\,|\,x > 0 \text{ and } \cos x > 0\}$

$$= \left\{x\,\Big|\,0 < x < \dfrac{\pi}{2} \text{ or } (4n - 1)\dfrac{\pi}{2} < x\right.$$

$$\left. < (4n + 1)\dfrac{\pi}{2} \text{ for some } n \in \{1, 2, 3, ...\}\right\}$$

47. (a) $f(x) = \sqrt{1 - \sqrt{2 - \sqrt{3 - x}}} \Rightarrow$

$D = \{x\,|\,3 - x \geq 0, 2 - \sqrt{3 - x} \geq 0,$

$\quad\quad 1 - \sqrt{2 - \sqrt{3 - x}} \geq 0\}$

$\quad = \{x\,|\,3 \geq x, 2 \geq \sqrt{3 - x}, 1 \geq \sqrt{2 - \sqrt{3 - x}}\}$

$\quad = \{x\,|\,3 \geq x, 4 \geq 3 - x, 1 \geq 2 - \sqrt{3 - x}\}$

$\quad = \{x\,|\,x \leq 3, x \geq -1, 1 \leq \sqrt{3 - x}\}$

$\quad = \{x\,|\,x \leq 3, x \geq -1, 1 \leq 3 - x\}$

$\quad = \{x\,|\,x \leq 3, x \geq -1, x \leq 2\}$

$\quad = \{x\,|-1 \leq x \leq 2\} = [-1, 2]$

(b) $f(x) = \sqrt{1 - \sqrt{2 - \sqrt{3 - x}}} \Rightarrow$

$$f'(x) = \dfrac{1}{\sqrt{1 - \sqrt{2 - \sqrt{3 - x}}}}$$

$$\dfrac{d}{dx}(1 - \sqrt{2 - \sqrt{3 - x}})$$

$$= \dfrac{1}{2\sqrt{1 - \sqrt{2 - \sqrt{3 - x}}}} \cdot \dfrac{-1}{2\sqrt{2 - \sqrt{3 - x}}}$$

$$\dfrac{d}{dx}(2 - \sqrt{3 - x})$$

$$= -\dfrac{1}{8\sqrt{1 - \sqrt{2 - \sqrt{3 - x}}}\sqrt{2 - \sqrt{3 - x}}\sqrt{3 - x}}$$

(c)

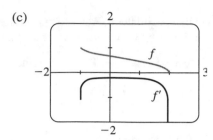

Note that f is always decreasing and f' is always negative.

48. $y^5 + 3x^2y^2 + 5x^4 = 12 \Rightarrow$

$5y^4y' + 6xy^2 + 6x^2yy' + 20x^3 = 0 \Rightarrow$

$y' = -\dfrac{20x^3 + 6xy^2}{5y^4 + 6x^2y}$

49. $x^4 + y^4 = 16 \Rightarrow 4x^3 + 4y^3y' = 0 \Rightarrow y' = -\dfrac{x^3}{y^3}$

50. $\dfrac{y}{x-y} = x^2 + 1 \Rightarrow$

$2x = \dfrac{(x-y)y' - y(1-y')}{(x-y)^2} = \dfrac{xy' - y}{(x-y)^2} \Rightarrow$

$y' = \dfrac{y}{x} + 2(x-y)^2.$

Another Method: Write the equation as
$y = (x-y)(x^2+1) = x^3 + x - yx^2 - y$. Then
$y' = \dfrac{3x^2 + 1 - 2xy}{x^2 + 2}.$

51. $x\sqrt{1+y} + y\sqrt{1+2x} = 2x \Rightarrow$

$\sqrt{1+y} + x\dfrac{1}{2\sqrt{1+y}}y' + y'\sqrt{1+2x}$

$+ y\dfrac{2}{2\sqrt{1+2x}} = 2 \Rightarrow y' = \dfrac{2 - \sqrt{1+y} - \dfrac{y}{\sqrt{1+2x}}}{\sqrt{1+2x} + \dfrac{x}{2\sqrt{1+y}}}$

52. $2xy = (x^2+y^2)^{3/2} \Rightarrow$

$2y + 2xy' = \dfrac{3}{2}(x^2+y^2)^{1/2}(2x+2yy') \Rightarrow$

$y' = \dfrac{3x(x^2+y^2)^{1/2} - 2y}{2x - 3y(x^2+y^2)^{1/2}}$

53. $f(x) = \ln(2-x) \Rightarrow$

$f'(x) = \dfrac{1}{2-x}\dfrac{d}{dx}(2-x) = \dfrac{-1}{2-x} = \dfrac{1}{x-2}$

54. $f(x) = \log_3(x^2-4) \Rightarrow$

$f'(x) = \dfrac{1}{(x^2-4)\ln 3}(2x) = \dfrac{2x}{(x^2-4)\ln 3}$

55. $f(x) = \log_{10}\left(\dfrac{x}{x-1}\right) = \log_{10}x - \log_{10}(x-1) \Rightarrow$

$f'(x) = \dfrac{1}{x\ln 10} - \dfrac{1}{(x-1)\ln 10}$ or $-\dfrac{1}{x(x-1)\ln 10}$

56. $F(x) = \ln\sqrt{x} = \ln x^{1/2} = \dfrac{1}{2}\ln x \Rightarrow$

$F'(x) = \dfrac{1}{2}\left(\dfrac{1}{x}\right) = \dfrac{1}{2x}$

57. $y = \sqrt{\dfrac{x^2+1}{x+1}} \Rightarrow \ln y = \dfrac{1}{2}\left[\ln(x^2+1) - \ln(x+1)\right]$

$\Rightarrow \dfrac{y'}{y} = \dfrac{1}{2}\left(\dfrac{2x}{x^2+1} - \dfrac{1}{x+1}\right) \Rightarrow$

$y' = \sqrt{\dfrac{x^2+1}{x+1}}\left[\dfrac{x}{x^2+1} - \dfrac{1}{2(x+1)}\right]$

58. $y = \dfrac{e^x\sqrt{x^5+2}}{(x+1)^4(x^2+3)^2} \Rightarrow$

$\ln y = x + \dfrac{1}{2}\ln(x^5+2) - 4\ln|x+1| - 2\ln(x^2+3)$

$\Rightarrow \dfrac{y'}{y} = 1 + \dfrac{5x^4}{2(x^5+2)} - \dfrac{4}{x+1} - \dfrac{4x}{x^2+3}.$ So

$y' = \dfrac{e^x\sqrt{x^5+2}}{(x+1)^4(x^2+3)^2}\left[1 + \dfrac{5x^4}{2(x^5+2)} - \right.$

$\left.\dfrac{4}{x+1} - \dfrac{4x}{x^2+3}\right]$

59. $y = \dfrac{(x^3+1)^4\sin^2 x}{x^{1/3}} \Rightarrow$

$\ln|y| = 4\ln|x^3+1| + 2\ln|\sin x| - \dfrac{1}{3}\ln|x|.$ So

$\dfrac{y'}{y} = 4\dfrac{3x^2}{x^3+1} + 2\dfrac{\cos x}{\sin x} - \dfrac{1}{3x} \Rightarrow$

$y' = \dfrac{(x^3+1)^4\sin^2 x}{x^{1/3}}\left(\dfrac{12x^2}{x^3+1} + 2\cot x - \dfrac{1}{3x}\right).$

60. (a)

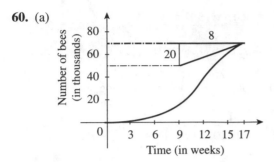

From the figure,

$$P'(17) \approx \frac{20}{8} = 2.5 \text{ thousand bees/week.}$$

$$P(18) \approx P(17) + P'(17)(18 - 17)$$
$$\approx 70 + 2.5(1)$$
$$= 72.5 \text{ or } 72,500 \text{ bees}$$
$$P(20) \approx P(17) + P'(17)(20 - 17)$$
$$\approx 70 + 2.5(3)$$
$$= 77.5 \text{ or } 77,500 \text{ bees}$$

(b) Since the tangent line at $t = 17$ is above the graph, our predictions are overestimates.

(c) $P(18)$ is more accurate than $P(20)$ since it is closer to the given data.

61. $f(x) = \sqrt{1 + x} \Rightarrow f'(x) = \dfrac{1}{2\sqrt{1 + x}}$ so

$f(0) = 1$ and $f'(0) = \dfrac{1}{2}$. Thus,

$$f(x) \approx f(0) + f'(0)(x - 0) = 1 + \frac{1}{2}(x - 0)$$

$$= 1 + \frac{1}{2}x$$

We need $\sqrt{1 + x} - 0.1 < 1 + \dfrac{1}{2}x < \sqrt{1 + x} + 0.1$.

By zooming in or using an intersect feature, we see that this is true when $-0.69 < x < 1.09$.

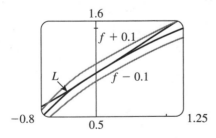

62. Let a be the x-coordinate of Q. Since the derivative of $y = 1 - x^2$ is $y' = -2x$, the slope at Q is $-2a$. But

since the triangle is equilateral, $\overline{AO}/\overline{OC} = \sqrt{3}/1$, so the slope at Q is $-\sqrt{3}$. Therefore, we must have that $-2a = -\sqrt{3} \Rightarrow a = \dfrac{\sqrt{3}}{2}$. Thus, the point Q

has coordinates $\left(\dfrac{\sqrt{3}}{2}, 1 - \left(\dfrac{\sqrt{3}}{2}\right)^2\right) = \left(\dfrac{\sqrt{3}}{2}, \dfrac{1}{4}\right)$ and

by symmetry, P has coordinates $\left(-\dfrac{\sqrt{3}}{2}, \dfrac{1}{4}\right)$.

64. (a) Put $x = 0$ and $y = 0$ in the equation: $f(0 + 0) = f(0) + f(0) + 0^2 \cdot 0 + 0 \cdot 0^2 \Rightarrow f(0) = 2f(0)$. Subtracting $f(0)$ from each side of this equation gives $f(0) = 0$.

(b) $f'(0) = \lim\limits_{h \to 0} \dfrac{f(0 + h) - f(0)}{h}$

$$= \lim_{h \to 0} \frac{\left[f(0) + f(h) + 0^2 h + 0 h^2\right] - f(0)}{h}$$

$$= \lim_{h \to 0} \frac{f(h)}{h} = \lim_{x \to 0} \frac{f(x)}{x} = 1$$

(c) $f'(x) = \lim\limits_{h \to 0} \dfrac{f(x + h) - f(x)}{h}$

$$= \lim_{h \to 0} \frac{\left[f(x) + f(h) + x^2 h + x h^2\right] - f(x)}{h}$$

$$= \lim_{h \to 0} \frac{f(h) + x^2 h + x h^2}{h}$$

$$= \lim_{h \to 0} \left[\frac{f(h)}{h} + x^2 + x h\right] = 1 + x^2$$

66.

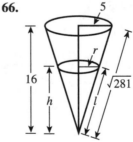

By similar triangles, $\dfrac{r}{5} = \dfrac{h}{16} \Rightarrow r = \dfrac{5h}{16}$.

The volume of the cone is $V = \dfrac{1}{3}\pi r^2 h = \dfrac{1}{3}\pi\left(\dfrac{5h}{16}\right)^2$

$h = \dfrac{25\pi}{768}h^3$, so $\dfrac{dV}{dt} = \dfrac{25\pi}{256}h^2\dfrac{dh}{dt}$. Now the rate of

change of the volume is also equal to the difference of what is being added (2 cm³/min) and what is oozing out ($k\pi rl$, where πrl is the area of the cone and k is a proportionality constant). Thus, $\dfrac{dV}{dt} = 2 - k\pi rl$.

Equating the two expressions for $\dfrac{dV}{dt}$ and

substituting $h = 0$, $\dfrac{dh}{dt} = -0.3$, $r = \dfrac{5(10)}{16} = \dfrac{25}{8}$,

and $\dfrac{l}{\sqrt{281}} = \dfrac{10}{16} \Leftrightarrow l = \dfrac{5}{8}\sqrt{281}$, we get

$\dfrac{25\pi}{256}(10)^2(-0.3) = 2 - k\pi\,\dfrac{25}{8}\cdot\dfrac{5}{8}\sqrt{281} \Leftrightarrow$

$\dfrac{125k\pi\sqrt{281}}{64} = 2 + \dfrac{750\pi}{256}$. Solving for k gives

us $k = \dfrac{256 + 375\pi}{250\pi\sqrt{281}}$. To maintain a certain height,

the rate of oozing, $k\pi rl$, must equal the rate of the

liquid being poured in; that is, $\dfrac{dV}{dt} = 0$.

$k\pi rl = \dfrac{256 + 375\pi}{250\pi\sqrt{281}}\cdot\pi\cdot\dfrac{25}{8}\cdot\dfrac{5\sqrt{281}}{8} =$

$\dfrac{256 + 375\pi}{128} \approx 11.204 \ \text{cm}^3/\text{min}.$

4 | APPLICATIONS OF DIFFERENTIATION

1–11 ■ Find the absolute maximum and absolute minimum values of f on the given interval.

1. $f(x) = x^2 - 2x + 2$, $\quad [0, 3]$

2. $f(x) = 1 - 2x - x^2$, $\quad [-4, 1]$

3. $f(x) = x^3 - 12x + 1$, $\quad [-3, 5]$

4. $f(x) = 4x^3 - 15x^2 + 12x + 7$, $\quad [0, 3]$

5. $f(x) = 2x^3 + 3x^2 + 4$, $\quad [-2, 1]$

6. $f(x) = 18x + 15x^2 - 4x^3$, $\quad [-3, 4]$

7. $f(x) = x^4 - 4x^2 + 2$, $\quad [-3, 2]$

8. $f(x) = 3x^5 - 5x^3 - 1$, $\quad [-2, 2]$

9. $f(x) = x^2 + 2/x$, $\quad [\frac{1}{2}, 2]$

10. $f(x) = \sqrt{9 - x^2}$, $\quad [-1, 2]$

11. $f(x) = \dfrac{x}{x + 1}$, $\quad [1, 2]$

12–15 ■ Verify that the function satisfies the three hypotheses of Rolle's Theorem on the given interval. Then find all numbers c that satisfy the conclusion of Rolle's Theorem.

12. $f(x) = x^3 - x$, $\quad [-1, 1]$

13. $f(x) = x^3 + x^2 - 2x + 1$, $\quad [-2, 0]$

14. $f(x) = \cos 2x$, $\quad [0, \pi]$

15. $f(x) = \sin x + \cos x$, $\quad [0, 2\pi]$

16. Show that the equation $x^5 + 10x + 3 = 0$ has exactly one real root.

17–19

(a) Find the intervals on which f is increasing or decreasing.

(b) Find the local maximum and minimum values of f.

(c) Find the intervals of concavity and the inflection points.

17. $f(x) = x^6 + 192x + 17$

18. $f(x) = \dfrac{x}{(1 + x)^2}$

19. $f(x) = 2 \sin x + \sin^2 x$, $\quad 0 \le x \le 2\pi$

20–24

(a) Find the intervals of increase or decrease.

(b) Find the local maximum and minimum values.

(c) Find the intervals of concavity and the inflection points.

(d) Use the information from parts (a), (b), and (c) to sketch the graph. Check your work with a graphing device if you have one.

20. $P(x) = x\sqrt{x^2 + 1}$ **21.** $Q(x) = x - 3x^{1/3}$

22. $Q(x) = x^{1/3}(x + 3)^{2/3}$ **23.** $f(x) = \ln(1 + x^2)$

24. $f(\theta) = \sin^2 \theta$, $\quad 0 \le \theta \le 2\pi$

25–34 ■ Find the limit. Use l'Hospital's Rule where appropriate. If there is a more elementary method, use it. If l'Hospital's Rule doesn't apply, explain why.

25. $\displaystyle \lim_{x \to 2} \frac{x - 2}{x^2 - 4}$ **26.** $\displaystyle \lim_{x \to 1} \frac{x^2 + 3x - 4}{x - 1}$

27. $\displaystyle \lim_{x \to -1} \frac{x^6 - 1}{x^4 - 1}$ **28.** $\displaystyle \lim_{x \to 0} \frac{\tan x}{x + \sin x}$

29. $\displaystyle \lim_{x \to 0} \frac{e^x - 1}{\sin x}$ **30.** $\displaystyle \lim_{x \to 0} \frac{x + \tan x}{\sin x}$

31. $\displaystyle \lim_{x \to 0} \frac{\sin x}{x^3}$ **32.** $\displaystyle \lim_{x \to \pi} \frac{\tan x}{x}$

33. $\displaystyle \lim_{x \to 3\pi/2} \frac{\cos x}{x - (3\pi/2)}$ **34.** $\displaystyle \lim_{t \to 16} \frac{\sqrt[4]{t} - 2}{t - 16}$

35–40 ■ Use the guidelines of this section to sketch the curve.

35. $y = 1 - 3x + 5x^2 - x^3$ **36.** $y = 2x^3 - 6x^2 - 18x + 7$

37. $y = 4x^3 - x^4$ **38.** $y = 2 - x - x^9$

39. $y = \dfrac{1}{(x - 1)(x + 2)}$ **40.** $y = \dfrac{1}{x^2(x + 3)}$

41–48 ■ Find the most general antiderivative of the function. (Check your answer by differentiation.)

41. $g(t) = \dfrac{t^3 + 2t^2}{\sqrt{t}}$

42. $f(t) = 3 \cos t - 4 \sin t$ **43.** $f(\theta) = e^\theta + \sec \theta \tan \theta$

44. $h(x) = \sin x - 2 \cos x$ **45.** $f(t) = \sin t - 2\sqrt{t}$

46. $f(t) = \sec^2 t + t^2$

47. $f'(x) = x^4 - 2x^2 + x - 1$

48. $f'(x) = \sin x - \sqrt[5]{x^2}$

49–54 ■ Find $f(x)$.

49. $f'(x) = 3 \cos x + 5 \sin x, \quad f(0) = 4$

50. $f'(x) = \sin x - 2\sqrt{x} \quad f(0) = 0$

51. $f'(x) = 2 + \sqrt[5]{x^3}, \quad f(1) = 3$

52. $f'(x) = 4 - 3(1 + x^2)^{-1}, \quad f(1) = 0$

53. $f''(x) = -8, \quad f(0) = 6, \quad f'(0) = 5$

54. $f''(x) = x, \quad f(0) = -3, \quad f'(0) = 2$

55–58 ■ A particle is moving with the given data. Find the position of the particle.

55. $v(t) = 3 - 2t, \quad s(0) = 4$

56. $v(t) = 3\sqrt{t}, \quad s(1) = 5$

57. $a(t) = 3t + 8, \quad s(0) = 1, \quad v(0) = -2$

58. $a(t) = t^2 - t, \quad s(0) = 0, \quad s(6) = 12$

 CHALLENGE

59. Find points P and Q on the parabola $y = 1 - x^2$ so that the triangle ABC formed by the x-axis and the tangent lines at P and Q is an equilateral triangle.

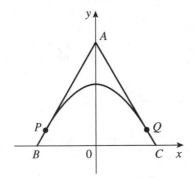

 CHALLENGE

60. The figure shows a rotating wheel with radius 40 cm and a connecting rod AP with length 1.2 m. The pin P slides back and forth along the x-axis as the wheel rotates counterclockwise at a rate of 360 revolutions per minute.

(a) Find the angular velocity of the connecting rod, $d\alpha/dt$, in radians per second, when $\theta = \pi/3$.

(b) Express the distance $x = |OP|$ in terms of θ.

(c) Find an expression for the velocity of the pin P in terms of θ.

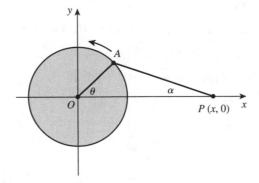

 CHALLENGE

61. The line $y = mx + b$ intersects the parabola $y = x^2$ in points A and B (see the figure). Find the point P on the arc AOB of the parabola that maximizes the area of the triangle PAB.

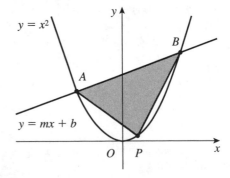

 CHALLENGE

62. Find the absolute maximum value of the function

$$f(x) = \frac{1}{1 + |x|} + \frac{1}{1 + |x - 2|}$$

4 | ANSWERS TO SELECTED EXERCISES

1. Abs. max. $f(3) = 5$; abs. min. $f(1) = 1$

2. Abs. max. $f(-1) = 2$; abs. min. $f(-4) = -7$

3. Abs. max. $f(5) = 66$; abs. min. $f(2) = -15$

4. Abs. max. $f(3) = 16$; abs. min. $f(2) = 3$

5. Abs. max. $f(1) = 9$; abs. min. $f(-2) = 0$

6. Abs. max. $f(-3) = 189$; abs. min. $f\left(-\dfrac{1}{2}\right) = -\dfrac{19}{4}$

7. Abs. max. $f(-3) = 47$; abs. min. $f\left(\pm\sqrt{2}\right) = -2$

8. Abs. max. $f(2) = 55$; abs. min. $f(-2) = -57$

9. Abs. max. $f(2) = 5$; abs. min. $f(1) = 3$

10. Abs. max. $f(0) = 3$; abs. min. $f(2) = \sqrt{5}$

11. Abs. max. $f(2) = \dfrac{2}{3}$; abs. min. $f(1) = \dfrac{1}{2}$

12. $\pm\dfrac{1}{\sqrt{3}}$

13. $\dfrac{-1 - \sqrt{7}}{3}$

14. $\dfrac{\pi}{2}$

15. $\dfrac{\pi}{4}, \dfrac{5\pi}{4}$

17. (a) Inc. on $(-2, \infty)$, dec. on $(-\infty, -2)$

   (b) Loc. min. $f(-2) = -303$

   (c) CU on $\mathbb{R}$

18. (a) Inc. on $(-1, 1)$; dec. on $(-\infty, -1)$, $(1, \infty)$

   (b) Loc. max. $f(1) = \dfrac{1}{4}$

   (c) CU on $(2, \infty)$; CD on $(-\infty, -1)$, $(-1, 2)$; IP $\left(2, \dfrac{2}{9}\right)$

19. (a) Inc. on $\left(0, \dfrac{\pi}{2}\right)$, $\left(\dfrac{3\pi}{2}, 2\pi\right)$; dec. on $\left(\dfrac{\pi}{2}, \dfrac{3\pi}{2}\right)$

   (b) Loc. max. $f\left(\dfrac{\pi}{2}\right) = 3$; loc. min. $f\left(\dfrac{3\pi}{2}\right) = -1$

   (c) CU on $\left(0, \dfrac{\pi}{6}\right)$, $\left(\dfrac{5\pi}{6}, 2\pi\right)$; CD on $\left(\dfrac{\pi}{6}, \dfrac{5\pi}{6}\right)$; IP $\left(\dfrac{\pi}{6}, \dfrac{5}{4}\right)$, $\left(\dfrac{5\pi}{6}, \dfrac{5}{4}\right)$

20. (a) Inc. on $\mathbb{R}$

   (b) None

   (c) CU on $(0, \infty)$, CD on $(-\infty, 0)$, IP $(0, 0)$

   (d)
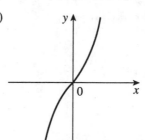

21. (a) Inc. on $(-\infty, -1)$, $(1, \infty)$; dec. on $(-1, 1)$

   (b) Loc. max. $Q(-1) = 2$, loc. min. $Q(1) = -2$

   (c) CU on $(0, \infty)$, CD on $(-\infty, 0)$, IP $(0, 0)$

   (d)
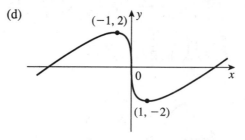

22. (a) Inc. on $(-\infty, -3)$, $(-1, \infty)$; dec. on $(-3, -1)$

   (b) Loc. max. $Q(-3) = 0$, loc. min. $Q(-1) = -4^{1/3} \approx -1.6$

   (c) CU on $(-\infty, -3)$, $(-3, 0)$; CD on $(0, \infty)$; IP $(0, 0)$

   (d)
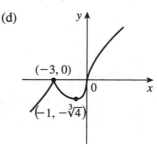

23. (a) Inc. on $(0, \infty)$, dec. on $(-\infty, 0)$

(b) Loc. min. $f(0) = 0$

(c) CU on $(-1, 1)$; CD on $(-\infty, -1)$, $(1, \infty)$; IP $(\pm 1, \ln 2)$

(d)
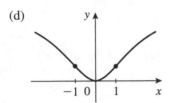

24. (a) Inc. on $\left(0, \dfrac{\pi}{2}\right)$, $\left(\pi, \dfrac{3\pi}{2}\right)$; dec. on $\left(\dfrac{\pi}{2}, \pi\right)$, $\left(\dfrac{3\pi}{2}, 2\pi\right)$

(b) Loc. max. $f\left(\dfrac{\pi}{2}\right) = f\left(\dfrac{3\pi}{2}\right) = 1$, loc. min. $f(\pi) = 0$

(c) CU on $\left(0, \dfrac{\pi}{4}\right)$, $\left(\dfrac{3\pi}{4}, \dfrac{5\pi}{4}\right)$, $\left(\dfrac{7\pi}{4}, 2\pi\right)$; CD on $\left(\dfrac{\pi}{4}, \dfrac{3\pi}{4}\right)$, $\left(\dfrac{5\pi}{4}, \dfrac{7\pi}{4}\right)$; IP$\left(\dfrac{\pi}{4}, \dfrac{1}{2}\right)$, $\left(\dfrac{3\pi}{4}, \dfrac{1}{2}\right)$, $\left(\dfrac{5\pi}{4}, \dfrac{1}{2}\right)$, $\left(\dfrac{7\pi}{4}, \dfrac{1}{2}\right)$

(d)
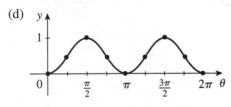

25. $\dfrac{1}{4}$ **26.** 5   **27.** $\dfrac{3}{2}$ **28.** $\dfrac{1}{2}$ **29.** 1

30. 2   **31.** ∞ **32.** 0   **33.** 1   **34.** $\dfrac{1}{32}$

35. A. $\mathbb{R}$ B. y-int. 1   C. None   D. None

E. Inc. on $\left(\dfrac{1}{3}, 3\right)$; dec. on $\left(-\infty, \dfrac{1}{3}\right)$, $(3, \infty)$

F. Loc. min. $f\left(\dfrac{1}{3}\right) = \dfrac{14}{27}$, loc. max $f(3) = 10$

G. CU on $\left(-\infty, \dfrac{5}{3}\right)$, CD on $\left(\dfrac{5}{3}, \infty\right)$, IP$\left(\dfrac{5}{3}, \dfrac{142}{27}\right)$

H.
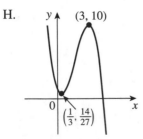

36. A. $\mathbb{R}$ B. y-int. 7   C. None   D. None

E. Inc. on $(-\infty, -1)$, $(3, \infty)$; dec. on $(-1, 3)$

F. Loc. max. $f(-1) = 17$, loc. min. $f(3) = -47$

G. CU on $(1, \infty)$, CD on $(-\infty, 1)$. IP $(1, -15)$

H.
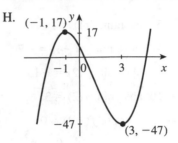

37. A. $\mathbb{R}$ B. y-int. 0; x-int 0, 4   C. None   D. None

E. Inc. on $(-\infty, 3)$, dec. on $(3, \infty)$ F. Loc. max. $f(3) = 27$ G. CU on $(0, 2)$; CD on $(-\infty, 0)$, $(2, \infty)$. IP $(0, 0)$, $(2, 16)$

H.
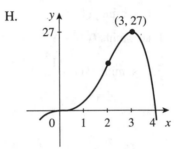

38. A. $\mathbb{R}$ B. y-int. 2, x-int. 1   C. None   D. None

E. Dec. on $\mathbb{R}$ F. None   G. CU on $(-\infty, 0)$, CD on $(0, \infty)$. IP $(0, 2)$

H.
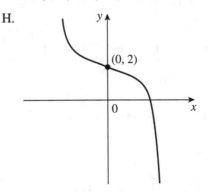

39. A. $\{x \mid x \neq -2, 1\}$ B. y-int. $f(0) = -\dfrac{1}{2}$ C. None

D. HA $y = 0$; VA $x = -2$, $x = 1$ E. Inc. on $(-\infty, -2)$, $\left(-2, -\dfrac{1}{2}\right)$; dec. on $\left(-\dfrac{1}{2}, 1\right)$, $(1, \infty)$

F. Loc. max. $f\left(-\dfrac{1}{2}\right) = -\dfrac{4}{9}$ G. CD on $(-2, 1)$; CU on $(-\infty, -2)$, $(1, \infty)$

H.

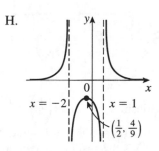

$x = -2$ $x = 1$

$\left(\frac{1}{2}, \frac{4}{9}\right)$

40. A. $\{x \mid x \neq 0, -3\}$ B. None C. None D. HA
$y = 0$; VA $x = 0, x = -3$ E. Inc. on $(-2, 0)$; dec.
on $(-\infty, -3), (-3, -2), (0, \infty)$ F. Loc. min.
$f(-2) = \dfrac{1}{4}$ G. CU on $(-3, 0), (0, \infty)$; CD on
$(-\infty, -3)$

H.

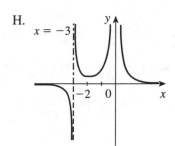

$x = -3$

-2 0

41. $\dfrac{2}{7}t^{7/2} + \dfrac{4}{5}t^{5/2} + C$

42. $3 \sin t + 4 \cos t + C$

43. $e^{\theta} + \sec\theta + C_n$ on the interval $\left(n\pi - \dfrac{\pi}{2}, n\pi + \dfrac{\pi}{2}\right)$

44. $-\cos x - 2\sin x + C$

45. $-\cos t - \dfrac{4}{3}t^{3/2} + C$

46. $\tan t + \dfrac{1}{3}t^3 + C_n$ on the interval $\left(n\pi - \dfrac{\pi}{2}, n\pi + \dfrac{\pi}{2}\right)$

47. $\dfrac{1}{5}x^5 - \dfrac{2}{3}x^3 + \dfrac{1}{2}x^2 - x + C$

48. $-\cos x - \dfrac{5}{7}x^{7/5} + C$

49. $3\sin x - 5\cos x + 9$

50. $-\cos x - \dfrac{4}{3}x^{3/2} + 1$

51. $2x + \dfrac{5}{8}x^{8/5} + \dfrac{3}{8}$

52. $4x - 3\arctan x + \dfrac{3\pi}{4} - 4$

53. $-4x^2 + 5x + 6$

54. $\dfrac{1}{6}x^3 + 2x - 3$

55. $s(t) = 3t - t^2 + 4$

56. $s(t) = 2t^{3/2} + 3$

57. $s(t) = \dfrac{1}{2}t^3 + 4t^2 - 2t + 1$

58. $s(t) = \dfrac{1}{12}t^4 - \dfrac{1}{6}t^3 - 10t$

59. $\left(\pm\sqrt{3}/2, \dfrac{1}{4}\right)$

60. (a) $4\pi\sqrt{3}/\sqrt{11} \ rad/s$
(b) $40(\cos\theta + \sqrt{8 + \cos^2\theta})$ cm
(c) $-480\pi\sin\theta(1 + \cos\theta/\sqrt{8 + \cos^2\theta})$ cm/s

61. $(m/2, m^2/4)$

62. $\dfrac{4}{3}$

4 | SOLUTIONS TO SELECTED EXERCISES

1. $f(x) = x^2 - 2x + 2$, $[0, 3]$. $f'(x) = 2x - 2 = 0 \Leftrightarrow$ $x = 1$. $f(0) = 2$, $f(1) = 1$, $f(3) = 5$. So $f(3) = 5$ is the absolute maximum and $f(1) = 1$ is the absolute minimum.

2. $f(x) = 1 - 2x - x^2$, $[-4, 1]$. $f'(x) = -2 - 2x = 0$ $\Leftrightarrow x = -1$. $f(-4) = -7$, $f(-1) = 2$, $f(1) = -2$. So $f(-4) = -7$ is the absolute minimum, $f(-1) = 2$ is the absolute maximum.

3. $f(x) = x^3 - 12x + 1$, $[-3, 5]$.
$f'(x) = 3x^2 - 12 = 3(x^2 - 4) = 3(x + 2)(x - 2) = 0$ $\Leftrightarrow x = \pm 2$. $f(-3) = 10$, $f(-2) = 17$, $f(2) = -15$, $f(5) = 66$. So $f(2) = -15$ is the absolute minimum and $f(5) = 66$ is the absolute maximum.

4. $f(x) = 4x^3 - 15x^2 + 12x + 7$, $[0, 3]$.
$f'(x) = 12x^2 - 30x + 12 = 6(2x - 1)(x - 2) = 0 \Leftrightarrow$ $x = \dfrac{1}{2}, 2$. $f(0) = 7$, $f\left(\dfrac{1}{2}\right) = \dfrac{39}{4}$, $f(2) = 3$, $f(3) = 16$.
So $f(3) = 16$ is the absolute maximum and $f(2) = 3$ the absolute minimum.

5. $f(x) = 2x^3 + 3x^2 + 4$, $[-2, 1]$.
$f'(x) = 6x^2 + 6x = 6x(x + 1) = 0 \Leftrightarrow x = -1, 0$.
$f(-2) = 0$, $f(-1) = 5$, $f(0) = 4$, $f(1) = 9$. So $f(1) = 9$ is the absolute maximum and $f(-2) = 0$ is the absolute minimum.

6. $f(x) = 18x + 15x^2 - 4x^3$, $[-3, 4]$.
$f'(x) = 18 + 30x - 12x^2 = 6(3 - x)(1 + 2x) = 0 \Leftrightarrow$ $x = 3, -\dfrac{1}{2}$. $f(-3) = 189$, $f\left(-\dfrac{1}{2}\right) = -\dfrac{19}{4}$, $f(3) = 81$,
$f(4) = 56$. So $f(-3) = 189$ is the absolute maximum and $f\left(-\dfrac{1}{2}\right) = -\dfrac{19}{4}$ is the absolute minimum.

7. $f(x) = x^4 - 4x^2 + 2$, $[-3, 2]$.
$f'(x) = 4x^3 - 8x = 4x(x^2 - 2) = 0 \Leftrightarrow x = 0, \pm\sqrt{2}$.
$f(-3) = 47$, $f\left(-\sqrt{2}\right) = -2$, $f(0) = 2$, $f\left(\sqrt{2}\right) = -2$,
$f(2) = 2$, so $f\left(\pm\sqrt{2}\right) = -2$ is the absolute minimum and $f(-3) = 47$ is the absolute maximum.

8. $f(x) = 3x^5 - 5x^3 - 1$, $[-2, 2]$.
$f'(x) = 15x^4 - 15x^2 = 15x^2(x + 1)(x - 1) = 0 \Leftrightarrow$ $x = -1, 0, 1$. $f(-2) = -57$, $f(-1) = 1$, $f(0) = -1$, $f(1) = -3$, $f(2) = 55$. So $f(-2) = -57$ is the absolute minimum and $f(2) = 55$ is the absolute maximum.

9. $f(x) = x^2 + \dfrac{2}{x}$, $\left[\dfrac{1}{2}, 2\right]$. $f'(x) = 2x - \dfrac{2}{x^2} = 2\dfrac{x^3 - 1}{x^2} = 0$ $\Leftrightarrow x^3 - 1 = 0 \Leftrightarrow (x - 1)(x^2 + x + 1) = 0$, but $x^2 + x + 1 \neq 0$, so $x = 1$. The denominator is 0 at

$x = 0$, but not in the desired interval. $f\left(\dfrac{1}{2}\right) = \dfrac{17}{4}$, $f(1) = 3$, $f(2) = 5$. So $f(1) = 3$ is the absolute minimum and $f(2) = 5$ is the absolute maximum.

10. $f(x) = \sqrt{9 - x^2}$, $[-1, 2]$. $f'(x) = -x/\sqrt{9 - x^2} = 0$ $\Leftrightarrow x = 0$. $f(-1) = 2\sqrt{2}$, $f(0) = 3$, $f(2) = \sqrt{5}$. So $f(2) = \sqrt{5}$ is the absolute minimum and $f(0) = 3$ is the absolute maximum.

11. $f(x) = \dfrac{x}{x + 1}$, $[1, 2]$.
$f'(x) = \dfrac{(x + 1) - x}{(x + 1)^2} = \dfrac{1}{(x + 1)^2} \neq 0 \Rightarrow$ no critical number. $f(1) = \dfrac{1}{2}$ and $f(2) = \dfrac{2}{3}$, so $f(1) = \dfrac{1}{2}$ is the absolute minimum and $f(2) = \dfrac{2}{3}$ is the absolute maximum.

12. $f(x) = x^3 - x$, $[-1, 1]$. f, being a polynomial, is continuous on $[-1, 1]$ and differentiable on $(-1, 1)$. Also $f(-1) = 0 = f(1)$.
$f'(c) = 3c^2 - 1 = 0 \Rightarrow c = \pm\dfrac{1}{\sqrt{3}}$.

13. $f(x) = x^3 + x^2 - 2x + 1$, $[-2, 0]$. f, being a polynomial, is continuous on $[-2, 0]$ and differentiable on $(-2, 0)$. Also $f(-2) = 1 = f(0)$.
$f'(c) = 3c^2 + 2c - 2 = 0 \Rightarrow c = \dfrac{-1 + \sqrt{7}}{3}$, but only $\dfrac{-1 - \sqrt{7}}{3}$ lies in the interval $(-2, 0)$.

14. $f(x) = \cos 2x$, $[0, \pi]$. f is continuous on $[0, \pi]$ and differentiable on $(0, \pi)$. Also $f(0) = 1 = f(\pi)$. $f'(c) = -2\sin 2c = 0 \Rightarrow \sin 2c = 0 \Rightarrow 2c = \pi$ $\Rightarrow c = \dfrac{\pi}{2}$ [since $c \in (0, \pi)$].

15. $f(x) = \sin x + \cos x$, $[0, 2\pi]$. Since $\sin x$ and $\cos x$ are continuous on $[0, 2\pi]$ and differentiable on $(0, 2\pi)$ so is their sum $f(x)$. $f(0) = 1 = f(2\pi)$. $f'(c) = \cos c - \sin c = 0 \Leftrightarrow \cos c = \sin c$ $\Leftrightarrow c = \dfrac{\pi}{4}$ or $\dfrac{5\pi}{4}$.

16. $f(x) = x^5 + 10x + 3$. Since f is continuous and $f(-1) = -8$ and $f(0) = 3$, the equation $f(x) = 0$ has at least one root in $(-1, 0)$ by the Intermediate Value Theorem. Suppose that the equation has more than one root; say a and b are both roots with $a < b$. Then $f(a) = 0 = f(b)$ so by Rolle's Theorem $f'(x) = 5x^4 + 10 = 0$ has a root in (a, b). But this is impossible since clearly $f'(x) \geq 10 > 0$ for all real x.

17. (a) $f(x) = x^6 + 192x + 17 \Rightarrow$
$f'(x) = 6x^5 + 192 = 6(x^5 + 32)$. So $f'(x) > 0$
$\Leftrightarrow x^5 > -32 \Leftrightarrow x > -2$ and $f'(x) < 0 \Leftrightarrow$
$x < -2$. So f is increasing on $(-2, \infty)$ and decreasing on $(-\infty, -2)$.

(b) f changes from decreasing to increasing at its only critical number, $x = -2$. Thus, $f(-2) = -303$ is a local minimum.

(c) $f''(x) = 30x^4 \geq 0$ for all x, so the concavity of f doesn't change and there is no inflection point. f is concave upward on $(-\infty, \infty)$.

18. (a) $f(x) = x/(1 + x)^2 \Rightarrow$

$$f'(x) = \frac{(1 + x)^2(1) - (x)2(1 + x)}{[(1 + x)^2]^2}$$

$$= \frac{(1 + x)[(1 + x) - 2x]}{(1 + x)^4}$$

$$= \frac{(1 + x)(1 - x)}{(1 + x)^4} = \frac{1 - x}{(1 + x)^3}$$

So $f'(x) > 0 \Leftrightarrow -1 < x < 1$ and $f'(x) < 0 \Leftrightarrow$
$x < -1$ or $x > 1$. So f is increasing on $(-1, 1)$ and f is decreasing on $(-\infty, -1)$ and $(1, \infty)$.

(b) f changes from increasing to decreasing at $x = 1$. $x = -1$ is not in the domain of f. Thus, $f(1) = \dfrac{1}{4}$ is a local maximum.

(c) $f''(x) = \dfrac{(1 + x)^3(-1) - (1 - x)3(1 + x)^2}{[(1 + x)^3]^2}$

$$= \frac{(1 + x)^2[-1(1 + x) - 3(1 - x)]}{(1 + x)^6}$$

$$= \frac{2x - 4}{(1 + x)^4}$$

$f''(x) > 0 \Leftrightarrow x > 2$ and $f''(x) < 0 \Leftrightarrow x < 2$
$(x \neq -1)$. Thus, f is concave upward on $(2, \infty)$ and f is concave downward on $(-\infty, -1)$ and $(-1, 2)$. There is an inflection point at $\left(2, \dfrac{2}{9}\right)$.

19. (a) $f(x) = 2 \sin x + \sin^2 x$ on $[0, 2\pi] \Rightarrow$
$f'(x) = 2 \cos x + 2 \sin x \cos x = 2 \cos x (1 + \sin x)$.
$f'(x) > 0 \Leftrightarrow \cos x > 0$ (since $1 + \sin x \geq 0$
with equality when $x = \dfrac{3\pi}{2}$, a value where

$\cos x = 0) \Leftrightarrow 0 \leq x < \dfrac{\pi}{2}$ or $\dfrac{3\pi}{2} < x \leq 2\pi$. So f is increasing on $\left(0, \dfrac{\pi}{2}\right)$ and $\left(\dfrac{3\pi}{2}, 2\pi\right)$, and f is decreasing on $\left(\dfrac{\pi}{2}, \dfrac{3\pi}{2}\right)$.

(b) Since f changes from increasing to decreasing at $x = \dfrac{\pi}{2}$, $f\left(\dfrac{\pi}{2}\right) = 3$ is a local maximum. Since f changes from decreasing to increasing at $x = \dfrac{3\pi}{2}$, $f\left(\dfrac{3\pi}{2}\right) = -1$ is a local minimum.

(c) $f''(x) = 2 \cos x (\cos x) + (1 + \sin x)(-2 \sin x)$

$$= 2 \cos^2 x - 2 \sin x - 2 \sin^2 x$$

$$= 2(1 - \sin^2 x) - 2 \sin x - 2 \sin^2 x$$

$$= 2 - 2 \sin x - 4 \sin^2 x$$

$$= 2(1 + \sin x)(1 - 2 \sin x)$$

$f''(x) > 0 \Leftrightarrow 1 - 2 \sin x > 0 \Leftrightarrow \sin x < \dfrac{1}{2} \Leftrightarrow$
$0 \leq x < \dfrac{\pi}{6}$ or $\dfrac{5\pi}{6} < x \leq 2\pi$, so f is concave upward on $\left(0, \dfrac{\pi}{6}\right)$ and $\left(\dfrac{5\pi}{6}, 2\pi\right)$, and concave downward on $\left(\dfrac{\pi}{6}, \dfrac{5\pi}{6}\right)$. There are inflection points at $\left(\dfrac{\pi}{6}, \dfrac{5}{4}\right)$ and $\left(\dfrac{5\pi}{6}, \dfrac{5}{4}\right)$.

20. (a) $P(x) = x\sqrt{x^2 + 1} \Rightarrow$
$$P'(x) = \sqrt{x^2 + 1} + \frac{x^2}{\sqrt{x^2 + 1}} = \frac{2x^2 + 1}{\sqrt{x^2 + 1}} > 0,$$
so P is increasing on $\mathbb{R}$.

(b) No maximum or minimum

(c) $P''(x) = \dfrac{4x\sqrt{x^2 + 1} - (2x^2 + 1)\dfrac{x}{\sqrt{x^2 + 1}}}{x^2 + 1}$

$$= \frac{x(2x^2 + 3)}{(x^2 + 1)^{3/2}} > 0 \Leftrightarrow$$

$x > 0$, so P is CU on $(0, \infty)$ and CD on $(-\infty, 0)$.
IP at $(0, 0)$

(d)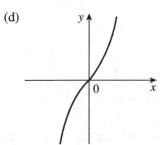

21. (a) $Q(x) = x - 3x^{1/3} \Rightarrow Q'(x) = 1 - \dfrac{1}{x^{2/3}} > 0 \Leftrightarrow$

$x^{2/3} > 1 \Leftrightarrow x^2 > 1 \Leftrightarrow x < -1$ or $x > 1$, so Q is increasing on $(-\infty, -1)$, and $(1, \infty)$, and decreasing on $(-1, 1)$.

(b) $Q'(x) = 0 \Leftrightarrow x = \pm 1$; $Q(1) = -2$ is a local minimum, and $Q(-1) = 2$ is a local maximum.

(c) $Q''(x) = \dfrac{2}{3}x^{-5/3} > 0 \Leftrightarrow x > 0$, so Q is CU on $(0, \infty)$ and CD on $(-\infty, 0)$. Inflection point at $(0, 0)$

(d)

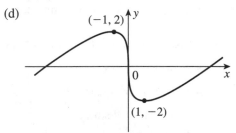

22. (a) $Q(x) = x^{1/3}(x + 3)^{2/3} \Rightarrow$

$Q'(x) = \dfrac{1}{3}x^{-2/3}(x + 3)^{2/3} + x^{1/3}\left(\dfrac{2}{3}\right)(x + 3)^{-1/3}$

$= \dfrac{x + 1}{x^{2/3}(x + 3)^{1/3}}$

The critical numbers are -3, -1, and 0. Note that $x^{2/3} \geq 0$ for all x. So $Q'(x) > 0$ when $x < -3$ or $x > -1$ and $Q'(x) < 0$ when $-3 < x < -1 \Rightarrow Q$ is increasing on $(-\infty, -3)$ and $(-1, \infty)$ and decreasing on $(-3, -1)$.

(b) $Q(-3) = 0$ is a local maximum and $Q(-1) = -4^{1/3} \approx -1.6$ is a local minimum.

(c) $Q''(x) = -\dfrac{2}{x^{5/3}(x + 3)^{4/3}} \Rightarrow Q''(x) > 0$ when $x > 0$, so Q is CU on $(-\infty, -3)$ and $(-3, 0)$ and CD on $(0, \infty)$. IP at $(0, 0)$

(d)

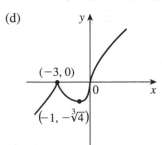

23. (a) $f(x) = \ln(1 + x^2) \Rightarrow f'(x) = \dfrac{2x}{1 + x^2} > 0 \Leftrightarrow$

$x > 0$, so f is increasing on $(0, \infty)$ and decreasing on $(-\infty, 0)$.

(b) $f(0) = 0$ is a local minimum.

(c) $f''(x) = \dfrac{2(1 + x^2) - 2x(2x)}{(1 + x^2)^2} = \dfrac{2(1 - x^2)}{(1 + x^2)^2} > 0 \Leftrightarrow$

$|x| < 1$, so f is CU on $(-1, 1)$, CD on $(-\infty, -1)$ and $(1, \infty)$. There are IP at $(1, \ln 2)$ and $(-1, \ln 2)$.

(d)

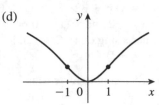

24. (a) $f(\theta) = \sin^2 \theta \Rightarrow$

$f'(\theta) = 2 \sin \theta \cos \theta = \sin 2\theta > 0 \Leftrightarrow$
$2\theta \in (0, \pi) \cup (2\pi, 3\pi) \Leftrightarrow \theta \in$

$\left(0, \dfrac{\pi}{2}\right) \cup \left(\pi, \dfrac{3\pi}{2}\right)$. So f is increasing on

$\left(0, \dfrac{\pi}{2}\right)$ and $\left(\pi, \dfrac{3\pi}{2}\right)$, and decreasing on

$\left(\dfrac{\pi}{2}, \pi\right)$ and $\left(\dfrac{3\pi}{2}, 2\pi\right)$.

(b) Local minimum $f(\pi) = 0$, local maxima

$f\left(\dfrac{\pi}{2}\right) = f\left(\dfrac{3\pi}{2}\right) = 1$

(c) $f''(\theta) = 2 \cos 2\theta > 0 \Leftrightarrow$

$2\theta \in \left(0, \dfrac{\pi}{2}\right) \cup \left(\dfrac{3\pi}{2}, \dfrac{5\pi}{2}\right) \cup \left(\dfrac{7\pi}{2}, 4\pi\right) \Leftrightarrow$

$\theta \in \left(0, \dfrac{\pi}{4}\right) \cup \left(\dfrac{3\pi}{4}, \dfrac{5\pi}{4}\right) \cup \left(\dfrac{7\pi}{4}, 2\pi\right)$, so f is

CU on these intervals and CD on $\left(\dfrac{\pi}{4}, \dfrac{3\pi}{4}\right)$ and

$\left(\dfrac{5\pi}{4}, \dfrac{7\pi}{4}\right)$. IP at $\left(\dfrac{n\pi}{4}, \dfrac{1}{2}\right)$, $n = 1, 3, 5, 7$

The use of l'Hospital's Rule is indicated by an H above the equal sign: $\overset{H}{=}$.

25. $\lim\limits_{x \to 2} \dfrac{x - 2}{x^2 - 4} = \lim\limits_{x \to 2} \dfrac{x - 2}{(x - 2)(x + 2)} = \lim\limits_{x \to 2} \dfrac{1}{x + 2} = \dfrac{1}{4}$

26. $\lim\limits_{x \to 1} \dfrac{x^2 + 3x - 4}{x - 1} = \lim\limits_{x \to 1} \dfrac{(x - 1)(x + 4)}{x - 1}$

$= \lim\limits_{x \to 1} (x + 4) = 5$

27. $\lim\limits_{x \to -1} \dfrac{x^6 - 1}{x^4 - 1} \overset{H}{=} \lim\limits_{x \to -1} \dfrac{6x^5}{4x^3} = \dfrac{-6}{-4} = \dfrac{3}{2}$

28. $\displaystyle\lim_{x\to0}\frac{\tan x}{x+\sin x}\overset{\text{H}}{=}\lim_{x\to0}\frac{\sec^2 x}{1+\cos x}=\frac{1}{1+1}=\frac{1}{2}$

29. $\displaystyle\lim_{x\to0}\frac{e^x-1}{\sin x}\overset{\text{H}}{=}\lim_{x\to0}\frac{e^x}{\cos x}=\frac{1}{1}=1$

30. $\displaystyle\lim_{x\to0}\frac{x+\tan x}{\sin x}\overset{\text{H}}{=}\lim_{x\to0}\frac{1+\sec^2 x}{\cos x}=\frac{1+1^2}{1}=2$

31. $\displaystyle\lim_{x\to0}\frac{\sin x}{x^3}\overset{\text{H}}{=}\lim_{x\to0}\frac{\cos x}{3x^2}=\infty$

32. $\displaystyle\lim_{x\to\pi}\frac{\tan x}{x}=\frac{\tan\pi}{\pi}=\frac{0}{\pi}=0$. L'Hospital's Rule does not apply because the denominator doesn't approach 0.

33. $\displaystyle\lim_{x\to3\pi/2}\frac{\cos x}{x-3\pi/2}\overset{\text{H}}{=}\lim_{x\to3\pi/2}\frac{-\sin x}{1}=-\sin\frac{3\pi}{2}=1$

34. $\displaystyle\lim_{t\to16}\frac{\sqrt[4]{t}-2}{t-16}=\lim_{t\to16}\frac{\sqrt[4]{t}-2}{\left(\sqrt{t}+4\right)\left(\sqrt{t}-4\right)}$

$\displaystyle=\lim_{t\to16}\frac{\sqrt[4]{t}-2}{\left(\sqrt{t}+4\right)\left(\sqrt[4]{t}+2\right)\left(\sqrt[4]{t}-2\right)}$

$\displaystyle=\lim_{t\to16}\frac{1}{\left(\sqrt{t}+4\right)\left(\sqrt[4]{t}+2\right)}$

$\displaystyle=\frac{1}{(4+4)(2+2)}=\frac{1}{32}$

35. $y=f(x)=1-3x+5x^2-x^3$

  A. $D=\mathbb{R}$ **B.** y-intercept $=f(0)=1$

  C. No symmetry   **D.** No asymptote

  E. $f'(x)=-3+10x-3x^2=-(3x-1)(x-3)>0$

  $\Leftrightarrow(3x-1)(x-3)<0\Leftrightarrow\frac{1}{3}<x<3$. $f'(x)<0$

  $\Leftrightarrow x<\frac{1}{3}$ or $x<3$. So f is increasing on $\left(\frac{1}{3},3\right)$ and

  decreasing on $\left(-\infty,\frac{1}{3}\right)$ and $(3,\infty)$.   **F.** The critical

  numbers occur when $f'(x)=-(3x-1)(x-3)=0$

  $\Leftrightarrow x=\frac{1}{3},3$. The local minimum is $f\left(\frac{1}{3}\right)=\frac{14}{27}$

  and the local maximum is $f(3)=10$.

  G. $f''(x)=10-6x>0\Leftrightarrow x<\frac{5}{3}$, so f

  is CU on $\left(-\infty,\frac{5}{3}\right)$ and CD on $\left(\frac{5}{3},\infty\right)$. IP $\left(\frac{5}{3},\frac{142}{27}\right)$

  H.

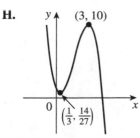

36. $y=f(x)=2x^3-6x^2-18x+7$

  A. $D=\mathbb{R}$ **B.** y-intercept $=f(0)=7$

  C. No symmetry   **D.** No asymptote

  E. $f'(x)=6x^2-12x-18=6(x+1)(x-3)>0$

  $\Leftrightarrow(x+1)(x-3)>0\Leftrightarrow x<-1$ or $x>3$.

  $f'(x)<0\Leftrightarrow-1<x<3$. So f is increasing on

  $(-\infty,-1)$ and $(3,\infty)$ and decreasing on $(-1,3)$.

  F. The critical numbers are $x=-1,3$. The local

  maximum is $f(-1)=17$ and the local minimum is

  $f(3)=-47$.   **G.** $y''=12x-12>0\Leftrightarrow x>1$, so f

  is CU on $(1,\infty)$ and CD on $(-\infty,1)$. IP $(1,-15)$

  H.

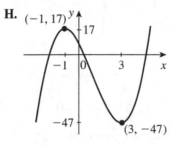

37. $y=f(x)=4x^3-x^4$ **A.** $D=\mathbb{R}$

  B. y-intercept $=f(0)=0$, x-intercept

  $\Rightarrow y=0\Leftrightarrow x^3(4-x)=0\Leftrightarrow x=0,4$

  C. No symmetry   **D.** No asymptote

  E. $y'=12x^2-4x^3=4x^2(3-x)>0\Leftrightarrow x<3$,

  so f is increasing on $(-\infty,3)$ and decreasing on

  $(3,\infty)$.   **F.** Local maximum is $f(3)=27$, no local

  minimum.   **G.** $y''=12x(2-x)>0\Leftrightarrow0<x<2$,

  so f is CU on $(0,2)$ and CD on $(-\infty,0)$ and $(2,\infty)$.

  IP $(0,0)$ and $(2,16)$

  H.

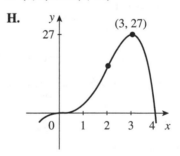

38. $y=f(x)=2-x-x^9$

  $=-(x-1)(x^8+x^7+x^6+x^5+x^4+x^3+x^2+x+2)$

  A. $D=\mathbb{R}$ **B.** y-intercept: $f(0)=2$; x-intercept:

  $f(x)=0\Leftrightarrow x=1$ (By part E below, f is decreasing

  on its domain, so it has only one x-intercept.)

  C. No symmetry   **D.** No asymptote

  E. $f'(x)=-1-9x^8=-1(9x^8+1)<0$ for all x, so

  f is decreasing on $\mathbb{R}$.   **F.** No maximum or minimum

G. $f''(x) = -72x^7 > 0 \Leftrightarrow x < 0$, so f is CU on $(-\infty, 0)$ and CD on $(0, \infty)$. IP at $(0, 2)$

H.

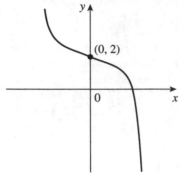

(0, 2)

39. $y = f(x) = \dfrac{1}{(x-1)(x+2)} = \dfrac{1}{x^2+x-2}$

A. $D = \{x \mid x \neq -2, 1\} = (-\infty, -2) \cup (-2, 1) \cup (1, \infty)$

B. y-intercept: $f(0) = -\dfrac{1}{2}$; no x-intercept

C. No symmetry

D. $\displaystyle\lim_{x \to \pm\infty} \dfrac{1}{x^2+2x-2} = \lim_{x \to \pm\infty} \dfrac{1/x^2}{1 + 1/x - 2/x^2}$

$= \dfrac{0}{1} = 0$

so $y = 0$ is a HA. $x = -2$ and $x = 1$ are VA.

E. $f'(x) = \dfrac{(x^2+x-2) \cdot 0 - 1(2x+1)}{(x-1)^2(x+2)^2}$

$= -\dfrac{2x+1}{(x-1)^2(x+2)^2} > 0 \Leftrightarrow$

$x < -\dfrac{1}{2}(x \neq -2)$; $f'(x) < 0 \Leftrightarrow x > -\dfrac{1}{2}(x \neq 1)$. So f is increasing on $(-\infty, -2)$ and $\left(-2, -\dfrac{1}{2}\right)$, and f is decreasing on $\left(-\dfrac{1}{2}, 1\right)$ and $(1, \infty)$.

F. $f\left(-\dfrac{1}{2}\right) = -\dfrac{4}{9}$ is a local maximum.

G. $f''(x)$

$= \dfrac{(x^2+x-2)^2(-2) - [-(2x+1)](2)(x^2+x-2)(2x+1)}{[(x-1)^2(x+2)^2]^2}$

$= \dfrac{2(x^2+x-2)[-1(x^2+x-2) + (2x+1)^2]}{(x-1)^4(x+2)^4}$

$= \dfrac{2(-x^2-x+2+4x^2+4x+1)}{(x-1)^3(x+2)^3}$

$= \dfrac{2(3x^2+3x+3)}{(x-1)^3(x+2)^3} = \dfrac{6(x^2+x+1)}{(x-1)^3(x+2)^3}$

The numerator is always positive, so the sign of f'' is determined by the denominator, which is negative only for $-2 < x < 1$. Thus, f is CD on $(-2, 1)$ and CU on $(-\infty, -2)$ and $(1, \infty)$. No IP.

H.

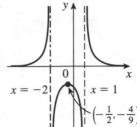

$x = -2$ | $x = 1$

$\left(-\dfrac{1}{2}, -\dfrac{4}{9}\right)$

40. $y = f(x) = \dfrac{1}{x^2(x+3)}$

A. $D = \{x \mid x \neq 0, -3\} = (-\infty, -3) \cup (-3, 0) \cup (0, \infty)$

B. No intercept   **C.** No symmetry

D. $\displaystyle\lim_{x \to \pm\infty} \dfrac{1}{x^2(x+3)} = 0$, so $y = 0$ is a HA.

$\displaystyle\lim_{x \to 0} \dfrac{1}{x^2(x+3)} = \infty$ and $\displaystyle\lim_{x \to -3^+} \dfrac{1}{x^2(x+3)} = \infty$,

$\displaystyle\lim_{x \to -3^-} \dfrac{1}{x^2(x+3)} = -\infty$, so $x = 0$ and $x = -3$ are VA.

E. $f'(x) = -\dfrac{3(x+2)}{x^3(x+3)^2} > 0 \Leftrightarrow -2 < x < 0$;

$f'(x) < 0 \Leftrightarrow x < -2$ or $x > 0$. So f is increasing on $(-2, 0)$ and decreasing on $(-\infty, -3)$, $(-3, -2)$, and $(0, \infty)$.   **F.** $f(-2) = \dfrac{1}{4}$ is a local minimum.

G. $f''(x)$

$= -3 \dfrac{x^3(x+3)^2 - (x+2)[3x^2(x+3)^2 + x^3 2(x+3)]}{x^6(x+3)^4}$

$= \dfrac{6(2x^2+8x+9)}{x^4(x+3)^3}$

Since $2x^2 + 8x + 9 > 0$ for all x, $f''(x) > 0 \Leftrightarrow x > -3(x \neq 0)$, so f is CU on $(-3, 0)$ and $(0, \infty)$, and CD on $(-\infty, -3)$. No IP

H.

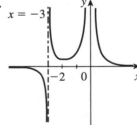

$x = -3$

-2 0

41. $g(t) = \dfrac{t^3 + 2t^2}{\sqrt{t}} = t^{5/2} + 2t^{3/2} \Rightarrow$

$G(t) = \dfrac{t^{7/2}}{7/2} + \dfrac{2t^{5/2}}{5/2} + C = \dfrac{2}{7}t^{7/2} + \dfrac{4}{5}t^{5/2} + C.$ Note that g has domain $(0, \infty)$.

42. $f(t) = 3\cos t - 4\sin t \Rightarrow$
$F(t) = 3(\sin t) - 4(-\cos t) + C = 3\sin t + 4\cos t + C$

43. $f(\theta) = e^{\theta} + \sec\theta\tan\theta \Rightarrow F(\theta) = e^{\theta} + \sec\theta + C_n$ on the interval $\left(n\pi - \dfrac{\pi}{2}, n\pi + \dfrac{\pi}{2}\right)$.

44. $h(x) = \sin x - 2\cos x \Rightarrow$
$H(x) = -\cos x - 2\sin x + C$

45. $f(t) = \sin t - 2\sqrt{t} \Rightarrow$
$F(t) = -\cos t - 2\left(\dfrac{1}{3/2}\right)t^{3/2} + C = -\cos t - \dfrac{4}{3}t^{3/2} + C$

46. $f(t) = \sec^2 t + t^2 \Rightarrow F(t) = \tan t + \dfrac{1}{3}t^3 + C_n$ on the interval $\left(n\pi - \dfrac{\pi}{2}, n\pi + \dfrac{\pi}{2}\right)$.

47. $f'(x) = x^4 - 2x^2 + x - 1 \Rightarrow$
$f(x) = \dfrac{1}{5}x^5 - \dfrac{2}{3}x^3 + \dfrac{1}{2}x^2 - x + C$

48. $f'(x) = \sin x - x^{2/5} \Rightarrow f(x) = -\cos x - \dfrac{5}{7}x^{7/5} + C$

49. $f'(x) = 3\cos x + 5\sin x \Rightarrow$
$f(x) = 3\sin x - 5\cos x + C \Rightarrow 4 = f(0) = -5 + C$
$\Rightarrow C = 9 \Rightarrow f(x) = 3\sin x - 5\cos x + 9$

50. $f'(x) = \sin x - 2x^{1/2} \Rightarrow f(x) = -\cos x = \dfrac{4}{3}x^{3/2} + C$
$\Rightarrow f(0) = -1 - 0 + C = 0 \Rightarrow C = 1,$ so
$f(x) = -\cos x - \dfrac{4}{3}x^{3/2} + 1.$

51. $f'(x) = 2 + x^{3/5} \Rightarrow f(x) = 2x + \dfrac{5}{8}x^{8/5} + C \Rightarrow$
$3 = f(1) = 2 + \dfrac{5}{8} + C \Rightarrow C = \dfrac{3}{8} \Rightarrow$
$f(x) = 2x + \dfrac{5}{8}x^{8/5} + \dfrac{3}{8}$

52. $f'(x) = 4 - \dfrac{3}{1 + x^2} \Rightarrow f(x) = 4x - 3\arctan x + C.$
Now $f(1) = 4\cdot 1 - 3\arctan 1 + C = 0 \Rightarrow$
$C = 3\cdot\dfrac{\pi}{4} - 4.$ Therefore
$f(x) = 4x - 3\arctan x + \dfrac{3\pi}{4} - 4.$

53. $f''(x) = -8 \Rightarrow f'(x) = -8x + C \Rightarrow$
$5 = f'(0) = C \Rightarrow f'(x) = -8x + 5 \Rightarrow$
$f(x) = -4x^2 + 5x + D \Rightarrow 6 = f(0) = D \Rightarrow$
$f(x) = -4x^2 + 5x + 6$

54. $f''(x) = x \Rightarrow f'(x) = \dfrac{1}{2}x^2 + C \Rightarrow$
$2 = f'(0) = C \Rightarrow f'(x) = \dfrac{1}{2}x^2 + 2 \Rightarrow$
$f(x) = \dfrac{1}{6}x^3 + 2x + D \Rightarrow -3 = f(0) = D \Rightarrow$
$f(x) = \dfrac{1}{6}x^3 + 2x - 3$

55. $v(t) = s'(t) = 3 - 2t \Rightarrow s(t) = 3t - t^2 + C \Rightarrow$
$4 = s(0) = C \Rightarrow s(t) = 3t - t^2 + 4$

56. $v(t) = s'(t) = 3\sqrt{t} \Rightarrow s(t) = 2t^{3/2} + C \Rightarrow$
$5 = s(1) = 2 + C \Rightarrow C = 3,$ so $s(t) = 2t^{3/2} + 3$

57. $a(t) = v'(t) = 3t + 8 \Rightarrow v(t) = \dfrac{3}{2}t^2 + 8t + C \Rightarrow$
$-2 = v(0) = C \Rightarrow v(t) = \dfrac{3}{2}t^2 + 8t - 2 \Rightarrow$
$s(t) = \dfrac{1}{2}t^3 + 4t^2 - 2t + D \Rightarrow 1 = s(0) = D \Rightarrow$
$s(t) = \dfrac{1}{2}t^3 + 4t^2 - 2t + 1$

58. $a(t) = v'(t) = t^2 - t \Rightarrow v(t) = \dfrac{1}{3}t^3 - \dfrac{1}{2}t^2 + C \Rightarrow$
$s(t) = \dfrac{1}{12}t^4 - \dfrac{1}{6}t^3 + Ct + D \Rightarrow 0 = s(0) = D$ and
$12 = s(6) = 108 - 36 + 6C + 0 \Rightarrow C = -10 \Rightarrow$
$s(t) = \dfrac{1}{12}t^4 - \dfrac{1}{6}t^3 - 10t$

59. Let a be the x-coordinate of Q. Since the derivative of $y = 1 - x^2$ is $y' = -2x$, the slope at Q is $-2a$. But since the triangle is equilateral, $\overline{AO}/\overline{OC} = \sqrt{3}/1$, so the slope at Q is $-\sqrt{3}$. Therefore, we must have that $-2a = -\sqrt{3} \Rightarrow$ $a = \dfrac{\sqrt{3}}{2}.$ Thus, the point Q has coordinates $\left(\dfrac{\sqrt{3}}{2}, 1 - \left(\dfrac{\sqrt{3}}{2}\right)^2\right) = \left(\dfrac{\sqrt{3}}{2}, \dfrac{1}{4}\right)$ and by symmetry, P has coordinates $\left(-\dfrac{\sqrt{3}}{2}, \dfrac{1}{4}\right)$.

60. We can assume without loss of generality that $\theta = 0$ at time $t = 0$, so that $\theta = 12\pi t$ rad. [The angular velocity of the wheel is 360 rpm $= 360\cdot(2\pi\,\text{rad})/(60\,\text{s}) = 12\pi\,\text{rad/s.}$] Then the position of A as a function of time is

$A = (40 \cos \theta, 40 \sin \theta) = (40 \cos 12\pi t, 40 \sin 12\pi t)$,

so $\sin \alpha = \dfrac{y}{1.2\,\text{m}} = \dfrac{40 \sin \theta}{120} = \dfrac{\sin \theta}{3} = \dfrac{1}{3} \sin 12\pi t$.

(a) Differentiating the expression for $\sin \alpha$, we get

$\cos \alpha \cdot \dfrac{d\alpha}{dt} = \dfrac{1}{3} \cdot 12\pi \cdot \cos 12\pi t = 4\pi \cos \theta$.

When $\theta = \dfrac{\pi}{3}$, we have $\sin \alpha = \dfrac{1}{3} \sin \theta = \dfrac{\sqrt{3}}{6}$,

so $\cos \alpha = \sqrt{1 - \left(\dfrac{\sqrt{3}}{6}\right)^2} = \sqrt{\dfrac{11}{12}}$ and

$\dfrac{d\alpha}{dt} = \dfrac{4\pi \cos \frac{\pi}{3}}{\cos \alpha} = \dfrac{2\pi}{\sqrt{11/12}} = \dfrac{4\pi\sqrt{3}}{\sqrt{11}}$

≈ 6.56 rad/s.

(b) By the Law of Cosines, $|AP|^2 =$

$|OA|^2 + |OP|^2 - 2|OA||OP| \cos \theta \Rightarrow$

$120^2 = 40^2 + |OP|^2 - 2 \cdot 40|OP| \cos \theta \Rightarrow$

$|OP|^2 - (80 \cos \theta)|OP| - 12{,}800 = 0 \Rightarrow$

$|OP| = \dfrac{1}{2}\left(80 \cos \theta \pm \sqrt{6400 \cos^2 \theta + 51{,}200}\right)$

$= 40 \cos \theta \pm 40\sqrt{\cos^2 \theta + 8}$

$= 40\left(\cos \theta + \sqrt{8 + \cos^2 \theta}\right)$ cm

$[\text{since}\,|OP| > 0]$

As a check note that $|OP| = 160$ cm when

$\theta = 0$ and $|OP| = 80\sqrt{2}$ cm when $\theta = \dfrac{\pi}{2}$.

(c) By part (b), the x-coordinate of P is given by

$x = 40\left(\cos \theta + \sqrt{8 + \cos^2 \theta}\right)$, so $\dfrac{dx}{dt}$

$= \dfrac{dx}{d\theta}\dfrac{d\theta}{dt} = 40\left(-\sin \theta - \dfrac{2 \cos \theta \sin \theta}{2\sqrt{8 + \cos^2 \theta}}\right) \cdot$

$12\pi = -480\pi \sin \theta\left(1 + \dfrac{\cos \theta}{\sqrt{8 + \cos^2 \theta}}\right)$ cm/s.

In particular, $dx/dt = 0$ cm/s when $\theta = 0$ and

$dx/dt = -480\pi$ cm/s when $\theta = \dfrac{\pi}{2}$.

61. $A = (x_1, x_1^2)$ and $B = (x_2, x_2^2)$, where x_1 and x_2 are the solutions of the quadratic equation $x^2 = mx + b$. Let $P = (x, x^2)$ and set $A_1 = (x_1, 0)$, $B_1 = (x_2, 0)$, and $P_1 = (x, 0)$. Let $f(x)$ denote the area of triangle PAB.

Then $f(x)$ can be expressed in terms of the areas of three trapezoids as follows:

$f(x) = \text{area}\,(A_1ABB_1) - \text{area}\,(A_1APP_1)$

$\qquad - \text{area}\,(B_1BPP_1)$

$= \dfrac{1}{2}(x_1^2 + x_2^2)(x_2 - x_1) - \dfrac{1}{2}(x_1^2 + x^2)(x - x_1)$

$\qquad - \dfrac{1}{2}(x^2 + x_2^2)(x_2 - x)$

After expanding and canceling terms, we get

$f(x) = \dfrac{1}{2}(x_2 x_1^2 - x_1 x_2^2 - x x_1^2 + x_1 x^2 - x_2 x^2 - x x_2^2)$

$= \dfrac{1}{2}\left[x_1^2(x_2 - x) + x_2^2(x - x_1) + x^2(x_1 - x_2)\right]$

$f'(x) = \dfrac{1}{2}\left[-x_1^2 + x_2^2 + 2x(x_1 - x_2)\right]$.

$f''(x) = \dfrac{1}{2}\left[2(x_1 - x_2)\right] = x_1 - x_2 < 0$ since $x_2 > x_1$.

$f'(x) = 0 \Rightarrow 2x(x_1 - x_2) = x_1^2 - x_2^2 \Rightarrow x_P = \dfrac{1}{2}(x_1 + x_2)$.

$f(x_P) = \dfrac{1}{2}\left(x_1^2\left[\dfrac{1}{2}(x_2 - x_1)\right] + x_2^2\left[\dfrac{1}{2}(x_2 - x_1)\right]\right.$

$\qquad \left. + \dfrac{1}{4}(x_1 - x_2)^2(x_1 - x_2)\right)$

$= \dfrac{1}{2}\left[\dfrac{1}{2}(x_2 - x_1)(x_1^2 - x_2^2) - \dfrac{1}{4}(x_2 - x_1)(x_1 - x_2)^2\right]$

$= \dfrac{1}{8}(x_2 - x_1)\left[2(x_1^2 + x_2^2) - (x_1^2 + 2x_1 x_2 + x_2^2)\right]$

$= \dfrac{1}{8}(x_2 - x_1)(x_1^2 - 2x_1 x_2 + x_2^2)$

$= \dfrac{1}{8}(x_2 - x_1)(x_1 - x_2)^2 = \dfrac{1}{8}(x_2 - x_1)(x_2 - x_1)^2$

$= \dfrac{1}{8}(x_2 - x_1)^3$

To put this in terms of m and b, we solve the system $y = x_1^2$ and $y = mx_1 + b$, giving us

$x_1^2 - mx_1 - b = 0 \Rightarrow x_1 = \dfrac{1}{2}\left(m - \sqrt{m^2 + 4b}\right)$.

Similarly, $x_2 = \dfrac{1}{2}\left(m + \sqrt{m^2 + 4b}\right)$ The area is then

$\dfrac{1}{8}(x_2 - x_1)^3 = \dfrac{1}{8}\left(\sqrt{m^2 + 4b}\right)^3$, and is attained at the

point $P(x_P, x_P^2) = P\left(\dfrac{1}{2}m, \dfrac{1}{4}m^2\right)$.

Note: Another way to get an expression for $f(x)$ is to use the formula for an area of a triangle in terms of the coordinates of the vertices:

$$f(x) = \frac{1}{2}\left[(x_2 x_1^2 - x_1 x_2^2) + (x_1 x^2 - x x_1^2) + (x x_2^2 - x_2 x^2)\right].$$

62. $f(x) = \dfrac{1}{1 + |x|} + \dfrac{1}{1 + |x - 2|}$

$$= \begin{cases} \dfrac{1}{1 - x} + \dfrac{1}{1 - (x - 2)} & \text{if } x < 0 \\[2mm] \dfrac{1}{1 + x} + \dfrac{1}{1 - (x - 2)} & \text{if } 0 \le x < 2 \Rightarrow \\[2mm] \dfrac{1}{1 + x} + \dfrac{1}{1 + (x - 2)} & \text{if } x \ge 2 \end{cases}$$

$$f'(x) = \begin{cases} \dfrac{1}{(1 - x)^2} + \dfrac{1}{(3 - x)^2} & \text{if } x < 0 \\[2mm] \dfrac{-1}{(1 + x)^2} + \dfrac{1}{(3 - x)^2} & \text{if } 0 < x < 2 \\[2mm] \dfrac{1}{(1 + x)^2} - \dfrac{1}{(x - 1)^2} & \text{if } x > 2 \end{cases}$$

We see that $f'(x) > 0$ for $x < 0$ and $f'(x) < 0$ for $x > 2$. For $0 < x < 2$, we have

$$f'(x) = \frac{1}{(3 - x)^2} - \frac{1}{(x + 1)^2}$$

$$= \frac{(x^2 + 2x + 1) - (x^2 - 6x + 9)}{(3 - x)^2 (x + 1)^2}$$

$$= \frac{8(x - 1)}{(3 - x)^2 (x + 1)^2}, \text{ so } f'(x) < 0 \text{ for}$$

$0 < x < 1$, $f'(1) = 0$ and $f'(x) > 0$ for $1 < x < 2$. We have shown that $f'(x) > 0$ for $x < 0$; $f'(x) < 0$ for $0 < x < 1$; $f'(x) > 0$ for $1 < x < 2$; and $f'(x) < 0$ for $x > 2$. Therefore, by the First Derivative Test, the local maxima of f are at $x = 0$ and $x = 2$, where f takes the value $\dfrac{4}{3}$. Therefore, $\dfrac{4}{3}$ is the absolute maximum value of f.

5 | INTEGRALS

1. (a) Estimate the area under the graph of $f(x) = x^3 + 2$ from $x = -1$ to $x = 2$ using three rectangles and right endpoints. Then improve your estimate by using six rectangles. Sketch the curve and the approximating rectangles.

   (b) Repeat part (a) using left endpoints.

   (c) Repeat part (a) using midpoints.

   (d) From your sketches in parts (a), (b), and (c), which appears to be the best estimate?

2–15 ■ Evaluate the integral.

2. $\displaystyle\int_0^1 (1 - 2x - 3x^2)\, dx$

3. $\displaystyle\int_1^2 (5x^2 - 4x + 3)\, dx$

4. $\displaystyle\int_0^1 (y^9 - 2y^5 + 3y)\, dy$

5. $\displaystyle\int_1^3 \left(\frac{1}{t^2} - \frac{1}{t^4}\right) dt$

6. $\displaystyle\int_{-2}^4 (3x - 5)\, dx$

7. $\displaystyle\int_1^2 x^{-2}\, dx$

8. $\displaystyle\int_0^2 (x^3 - 1)^2\, dx$

9. $\displaystyle\int_0^1 u(\sqrt{u} + \sqrt[3]{u})\, du$

10. $\displaystyle\int_{-1}^2 |x - x^2|\, dx$

11. $\displaystyle\int_{-2}^3 |x^2 - 1|\, dx$

12. $\displaystyle\int_1^{-1} (x - 1)(3x + 2)\, dx$

13. $\displaystyle\int_1^4 \left(\sqrt{t} - \frac{2}{\sqrt{t}}\right) dt$

14. $\displaystyle\int_1^8 \left(\sqrt[3]{r} + \frac{1}{\sqrt[3]{r}}\right) dr$

15. $\displaystyle\int_{-1}^0 (x + 1)^3\, dx$

CHALLENGE

16. Suppose the curve $y = f(x)$ passes through the origin and the point $(1, 1)$. Find the value of the integral $\int_0^1 f'(x)\, dx$.

CHALLENGE

17. Show that $\dfrac{1}{17} \leq \displaystyle\int_1^2 \frac{1}{1 + x^4}\, dx \leq \dfrac{7}{24}$.

CHALLENGE

18. If $f(x) = \displaystyle\int_0^{g(x)} \frac{1}{\sqrt{1 + t^3}}\, dt$, where

   $g(x) = \displaystyle\int_0^{\cos x} \left[1 + \sin(t^2)\right] dt$, find $f'(\pi/2)$.

19–28 ■ Evaluate the indefinite integral.

19. $\displaystyle\int \sec x \tan x \sqrt{1 + \sec x}\, dx$

20. $\displaystyle\int t^2 \cos(1 - t^3)\, dt$

21. $\displaystyle\int e^x \sin(e^x)\, dx$

22. $\displaystyle\int \cos^4 x \sin x\, dx$

23. $\displaystyle\int \frac{x + 1}{x^2 + 2x}\, dx$

24. $\displaystyle\int \frac{e^x}{e^{2x} + 1}\, dx$

25. $\displaystyle\int x^3(1 - x^2)^{3/2}\, dx$

26. $\displaystyle\int \frac{\cos \sqrt{x}}{\sqrt{x}}\, dx$

27. $\displaystyle\int \sin(2x + 3)\, dx$

28. $\displaystyle\int \cos(7 - 3x)\, dx$

29–36 ■ Evaluate the definite integral, if it exists.

29. $\displaystyle\int_0^1 \cos \pi t\, dt$

30. $\displaystyle\int_0^{\pi/4} \sin 4t\, dt$

31. $\displaystyle\int_1^4 \frac{1}{x^2} \sqrt{1 + \frac{1}{x}}\, dx$

32. $\displaystyle\int_0^3 \frac{dx}{2x + 3}$

33. $\displaystyle\int_0^1 (2x - 1)^{100}\, dx$

34. $\displaystyle\int_0^4 \sqrt{1 - 2x}\, dx$

35. $\displaystyle\int_0^1 (x^4 + x)^5(4x^3 + 1)\, dx$

36. $\displaystyle\int_2^3 \frac{3x^2 - 1}{(x^3 - x)^2}\, dx$

5 | ANSWERS TO SELECTED EXERCISES

1. (a) 15, 12.1875

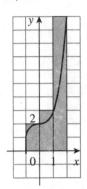 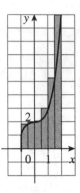

(b) 6, 7.6875

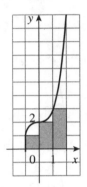 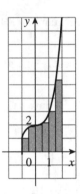

(c) 9.375, 9.65625

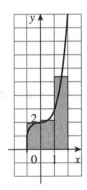 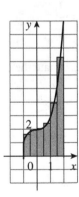

(d) M_6

2. -1

3. $\dfrac{26}{3}$

4. $\dfrac{19}{15}$

5. $\dfrac{28}{81}$

6. -12

7. $\dfrac{1}{2}$

8. $\dfrac{86}{7}$

9. $\dfrac{29}{35}$

10. $\dfrac{11}{6}$

11. $\dfrac{28}{3}$

12. 2

13. $\dfrac{2}{3}$

14. $\dfrac{63}{4}$

15. $\dfrac{1}{4}$

18. -1

19. $\dfrac{2}{3}(1 + \sec x)^{3/2} + C$

20. $-\dfrac{1}{3}\sin(1 - t^3) + C$

21. $-\cos(e^x) + C$

22. $-\dfrac{1}{5}\cos^5 x + C$

23. $\dfrac{1}{2}\ln|x^2 + 2x| + C$

24. $\tan^{-1}(e^x) + C$

25. $\dfrac{1}{7}(1 - x^2)^{7/2} - \dfrac{1}{5}(1 - x^2)^{5/2} + C$

26. $2\sin\sqrt{x} + C$

27. $-\dfrac{1}{2}\cos(2x + 3) + C$

28. $-\dfrac{1}{3}\sin(7 - 3x) + C$

29. 0

30. $\dfrac{1}{2}$

31. $\dfrac{4\sqrt{2}}{3} - \dfrac{5\sqrt{5}}{12}$

32. $\dfrac{1}{2}\ln 3$

33. $\dfrac{1}{101}$

34. $-\dfrac{26}{3}$

35. $\dfrac{32}{3}$

36. $\dfrac{1}{8}$

5 | SOLUTIONS TO SELECTED EXERCISES

1. (a) $f(x) = x^3 + 2$ and $\Delta x = \dfrac{2-(-1)}{3} = 1 \Rightarrow$

$R_3 = 1 \cdot f(0) + 1 \cdot f(1) + 1 \cdot f(2)$
$= 1 \cdot 2 + 1 \cdot 3 + 1 \cdot 10 = 15$

$\Delta x = \dfrac{2-(-1)}{6} = 0.5 \Rightarrow$

$R_6 = 0.5 \big[f(-0.5) + f(0) + f(0.5)$
$\quad + f(1) + f(1.5) + f(2) \big]$
$= 0.5\,(1.875 + 2 + 2.125 + 3 + 5.375 + 10)$
$= 0.5\,(24.375) = 12.1875$

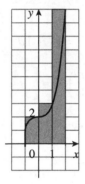 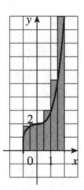

(b) $L_3 = 1 \cdot f(-1) + 1 \cdot f(0) + 1 \cdot f(1)$
$= 1 \cdot 1 + 1 \cdot 2 + 1 \cdot 3 = 6$

$L_6 = 0.5 \big[f(-1) + f(-0.5) + f(0)$
$\quad + f(0.5) + f(1) + f(1.5) \big]$
$= 0.5\,(1 + 1.875 + 2 + 2.125 + 3 + 5.375)$
$= 0.5\,(15.375) = 7.6875$

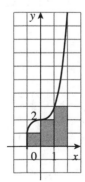 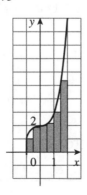

(c) $M_3 = 1 \cdot f(-0.5) + 1 \cdot f(0.5) + 1 \cdot f(1.5)$
$= 1 \cdot 1.875 + 1 \cdot 2.125 + 1 \cdot 5.375 = 9.375$

$M_6 = 0.5 \big[f(-0.75) + f(-0.25) + f(0.25)$
$\quad + f(0.75) + f(1.25) + f(1.75) \big]$
$= 0.5\,(1.578125 + 1.984375 + 2.015625$
$\quad + 2.421875 + 3.953125 + 7.359375)$
$= 0.5\,(19.3125) = 9.65625$

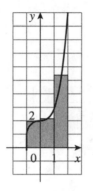 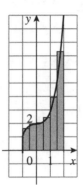

(d) M_6 appears to be the best estimate.

2. $\displaystyle\int_0^1 (1 - 2x - 3x^2)\, dx = \left[x - 2 \cdot \frac{1}{2}x^2 - 3 \cdot \frac{1}{3}x^3 \right]_0^1$

$= [x - x^2 - x^3]_0^1 = (1 - 1 - 1) - 0 = -1$

3. $\displaystyle\int_1^2 (5x^2 - 4x + 3)\, dx = \left[5 \cdot \frac{1}{3}x^3 - 4 \cdot \frac{1}{2}x^2 + 3x \right]_1^2$

$= 5 \cdot \dfrac{8}{3} - 4 \cdot 2 + 6 - \left(\dfrac{5}{3} - 2 + 3 \right) = \dfrac{26}{3}$

4. $\displaystyle\int_0^1 (y^9 - 2y^5 + 3y)\, dy = \left[\frac{1}{10}y^{10} - 2\left(\frac{1}{6}y^6 \right) \right.$

$\left. + \, 3\left(\frac{1}{2}y^2 \right) \right]_0^1$

$= \left(\dfrac{1}{10} - \dfrac{1}{3} + \dfrac{3}{2} \right) - 0 = \dfrac{19}{15}$

5. $\displaystyle\int_1^3 \left(\frac{1}{t^2} - \frac{1}{t^4} \right) dt = \int_1^3 (t^{-2} - t^{-4})\, dt$

$= \left[\dfrac{t^{-1}}{-1} - \dfrac{t^{-3}}{-3} \right]_1^3 = \left[\dfrac{1}{3t^3} - \dfrac{1}{t} \right]_1^3$

$= \left(\dfrac{1}{81} - \dfrac{1}{3} \right) - \left(\dfrac{1}{3} - 1 \right) = \dfrac{28}{81}$

6. $\displaystyle\int_{-2}^{4} (3x - 5)\,dx = \left(3 \cdot \frac{1}{2}x^2 - 5x\right)\Big|_{-2}^{4}$

$\qquad = (3 \cdot 8 - 5 \cdot 4) - [3 \cdot 2 - (-10)] = -12$

7. $\displaystyle\int_{1}^{2} x^{-2}\,dx = [-x^{-1}]_1^2 = [-1/x]_1^2 = -\frac{1}{2} + 1 = \frac{1}{2}$

8. $\displaystyle\int_{0}^{2} (x^3 - 1)^2\,dx = \int_{0}^{2} (x^6 - 2x^3 + 1)\,dx$

$\qquad = \left[\frac{1}{7}x^7 - 2\left(\frac{1}{4}x^4\right) + x\right]_0^2 = \left(\frac{128}{7} - 2 \cdot 4 + 2\right) - 0$

$\qquad = \frac{86}{7}$

9. $\displaystyle\int_{0}^{1} u\left(\sqrt{u} + \sqrt[3]{u}\right)\,du$

$\qquad = \int_{0}^{1} (u^{3/2} + u^{4/3})\,du = \left[\frac{u^{5/2}}{5/2} + \frac{u^{7/3}}{7/3}\right]_0^1$

$\qquad = \left[\frac{2}{5}u^{5/2} + \frac{3}{7}u^{7/3}\right]_0^1 = \frac{2}{5} + \frac{3}{7} = \frac{29}{35}$

10. $\displaystyle\int_{-1}^{2} |x - x^2|\,dx$

$\qquad = \int_{-1}^{0} (x^2 - x)\,dx + \int_{0}^{1} (x - x^2)\,dx + \int_{1}^{2} (x^2 - x)\,dx$

$\qquad = \left[\frac{x^3}{3} - \frac{x^2}{2}\right]_{-1}^{0} + \left[\frac{x^2}{2} - \frac{x^3}{3}\right]_0^1 + \left[\frac{x^3}{3} - \frac{x^2}{2}\right]_1^2$

$\qquad = 0 - \left(-\frac{1}{3} - \frac{1}{2}\right) + \left(\frac{1}{2} - \frac{1}{3}\right) - 0 + \left(\frac{8}{3} - 2\right)$

$\qquad\quad - \left(\frac{1}{3} - \frac{1}{2}\right)$

$\qquad = \frac{11}{6}$

11. $\displaystyle\int_{-2}^{3} |x^2 - 1|\,dx$

$\qquad = \int_{-2}^{-1} (x^2 - 1)\,dx + \int_{-1}^{1} (1 - x^2)\,dx + \int_{1}^{3} (x^2 - 1)\,dx$

$\qquad = \left[\frac{x^3}{3} - x\right]_{-2}^{-1} + \left[x - \frac{x^3}{3}\right]_{-1}^{1} + \left[\frac{x^3}{3} - x\right]_{1}^{3}$

$\qquad = \left(-\frac{1}{3} + 1\right) - \left(-\frac{8}{3} + 2\right) + \left(1 - \frac{1}{3}\right)$

$\qquad\quad - \left(-1 + \frac{1}{3}\right) + (9 - 3) - \left(\frac{1}{3} - 1\right)$

$\qquad = \frac{28}{3}$

12. $\displaystyle\int_{1}^{-1} (x - 1)(3x + 2)\,dx = -\int_{-1}^{1} (3x^2 - x - 2)\,dx$

$\qquad = -\left[3\frac{x^3}{3} - \frac{x^2}{2} - 2x\right]_{-1}^{1}$

$\qquad = \left[-x^3 + \frac{x^2}{2} + 2x\right]_{-1}^{1}$

$\qquad = \left(-1 + \frac{1}{2} + 2\right) - \left(1 + \frac{1}{2} - 2\right) = 2$

13. $\displaystyle\int_{1}^{4}\left(\sqrt{t} - \frac{2}{\sqrt{t}}\right)\,dt = \int_{1}^{4} (t^{1/2} - 2t^{-1/2})\,dt$

$\qquad = \left[\frac{t^{3/2}}{3/2} - 2\frac{t^{1/2}}{1/2}\right]_1^4 = \left[\frac{2}{3}t^{3/2} - 4t^{1/2}\right]_1^4$

$\qquad = \left(\frac{2}{3} \cdot 8 - 4 \cdot 2\right) - \left(\frac{2}{3} - 4\right) = \frac{2}{3}$

14. $\displaystyle\int_{1}^{8}\left(\sqrt[3]{r} + \frac{1}{\sqrt[3]{r}}\right)\,dr = \int_{1}^{8} (r^{1/3} + r^{-1/3})\,dr$

$\qquad = \left[\frac{r^{4/3}}{4/3} + \frac{r^{2/3}}{2/3}\right]_1^8 = \left[\frac{3}{4}r^{4/3} + \frac{3}{2}r^{2/3}\right]_1^8$

$\qquad = \left(\frac{3}{4} \cdot 16 + \frac{3}{2} \cdot 4\right) - \left(\frac{3}{4} + \frac{3}{2}\right) = \frac{63}{4}$

15. $\displaystyle\int_{-1}^{0} (x + 1)^3\,dx = \int_{-1}^{0} (x^3 + 3x^2 + 3x + 1)\,dx$

$\qquad = \left[\frac{x^4}{4} + 3\frac{x^3}{3} + 3\frac{x^2}{2} + x\right]_{-1}^{0}$

$\qquad = 0 - \left[\frac{1}{4} - 1 + \frac{3}{2} - 1\right] = 2 - \frac{7}{4} = \frac{1}{4}$

16. By FTC2, $\displaystyle\int_{0}^{1} f'(x)\,dx = f(1) - f(0) = 1 - 0 = 1.$

17. For $1 \le x \le 2$, we have $x^4 \le 2^4 = 16$, so $1 + x^4 \le 17$

$\qquad$ and $\dfrac{1}{1 + x^4} \ge \dfrac{1}{17}$. Thus, $\displaystyle\int_{1}^{2} \frac{1}{1 + x^4}\,dx \ge$

$\qquad \displaystyle\int_{1}^{2} \frac{1}{17}\,dx = \frac{1}{17}$. Also $1 + x^4 > x^4$ for $1 \le x \le 2$, so

$$\frac{1}{1+x^4} < \frac{1}{x^4} \text{ and } \int_1^2 \frac{1}{1+x^4}\, dx < \int_1^2 x^{-4}\, dx$$

$$= \left[\frac{x^{-3}}{-3}\right]_1^2 = -\frac{1}{24} + \frac{1}{3} = \frac{7}{24}. \text{ Thus, we}$$

have the estimate $\dfrac{1}{17} \le \displaystyle\int_1^2 \dfrac{1}{1+x^4}\, dx \le \dfrac{7}{24}$.

18. $f(x) = \displaystyle\int_0^{g(x)} \frac{1}{\sqrt{1+t^3}}\, dt$, where $g(x) =$

$\displaystyle\int_0^{\cos x} [1 + \sin(t^2)]\, dt$. Using FTC1 and the Chain

Rule (twice) we have $f'(x) = \dfrac{1}{\sqrt{1+[g(x)]^3}}\, g'(x)$

$$= \frac{1}{\sqrt{1+[g(x)]^3}}[1 + \sin(\cos^2 x)](-\sin x).$$

Now $g\left(\dfrac{\pi}{2}\right) = \displaystyle\int_0^0 [1 + \sin(t^2)]\, dt = 0$, so $f'\left(\dfrac{\pi}{2}\right)$

$$= \frac{1}{\sqrt{1+0}}(1 + \sin 0)(-1) = 1 \cdot 1 \cdot (-1) = -1.$$

19. Let $u = 1 + \sec x$. Then $du = \sec x \tan x\, dx$, so

$$\int \sec x \tan x \sqrt{1 + \sec x}\, dx = \int u^{1/2}\, du$$

$$= \frac{2}{3}u^{3/2} + C$$

$$= \frac{2}{3}(1 + \sec x)^{3/2} + C$$

20. Let $u = 1 - t^3$. Then $du = -3t^2\, dt$, so

$$\int t^2 \cos(1 - t^3)\, dt = \int \cos u \left(-\frac{1}{3}du\right)$$

$$= -\frac{1}{3}\sin u + C$$

$$= -\frac{1}{3}\sin(1 - t^3) + C$$

21. Let $u = e^x$. Then $du = e^x\, dx$, so

$$\int e^x \sin(e^x)\, dx = \int \sin u\, du$$

$$= -\cos u + C = -\cos(e^x) + C$$

22. Let $u = \cos x$. Then $du = -\sin x\, dx$, so

$$\int \cos^4 x \sin x\, dx = \int u^4(-du)$$

$$= -\frac{1}{5}u^5 + C = -\frac{1}{5}\cos^5 x + C$$

23. Let $u = x^2 + 2x$. Then $du = 2(x+1)dx$, so

$$\int \frac{x+1}{x^2 + 2x}\, dx = \int \frac{\frac{1}{2}du}{u}$$

$$= \frac{1}{2}\ln|u| + C = \frac{1}{2}\ln|x^2 + 2x| + C$$

24. Let $u = e^x$. Then $du = e^x\, dx$, so

$$\int \frac{e^x}{e^{2x} + 1}\, dx = \int \frac{du}{u^2 + 1}$$

$$= \tan^{-1} u + C = \tan^{-1}(e^x) + C$$

25. Let $u = 1 - x^2$. Then $x^2 = 1 - u$ and $2x\, dx = -du$, so

$$\int x^3(1 - x^2)^{3/2}\, dx = \int (1 - x^2)^{3/2} x^2 \cdot x\, dx$$

$$= \int u^{3/2}(1 - u)\left(-\frac{1}{2}\right) du$$

$$= \frac{1}{2}\int (u^{5/2} - u^{3/2})\, du$$

$$= \frac{1}{2}\left[\frac{2}{7}u^{7/2} - \frac{2}{5}u^{5/2}\right] + C$$

$$= \frac{1}{7}(1 - x^2)^{7/2} - \frac{1}{5}(1 - x^2)^{5/2} + C$$

26. Let $u = \sqrt{x}$. Then $du = \dfrac{dx}{2\sqrt{x}}$, so

$$\int \frac{\cos \sqrt{x}}{\sqrt{x}}\, dx = \int \cos u \cdot 2du$$

$$= 2 \sin u + C = 2 \sin \sqrt{x} + C$$

27. Let $u = 2x + 3$. Then $du = 2dx$, so

$$\int \sin(2x + 3)\, dx = \int \sin u \left(\frac{1}{2}du\right)$$

$$= -\frac{1}{2}\cos u + C$$

$$= -\frac{1}{2}\cos(2x + 3) + C$$

28. Let $u = 7 - 3x$. Then $du = -3dx$, so

$$\int \cos(7 - 3x)\, dx = \int \cos u \left(-\frac{1}{3}du\right)$$

$$= -\frac{1}{3}\sin u + C$$

$$= -\frac{1}{3}\sin(7 - 3x) + C$$

29. Let $u = \pi t$, so $du = \pi\, dt$. When $t = 0$, $u = 0$; when $t = 1$, $u = \pi$. Therefore,

$$\int_0^1 \cos \pi t\, dt = \int_0^\pi \cos u \left(\frac{1}{\pi}\, du\right)$$

$$= \frac{1}{\pi} [\sin u]_0^\pi = \frac{1}{\pi}(0 - 0) = 0$$

30. Let $u = 4t$, so $du = 4\, dt$. When $t = 0$, $u = 0$; when $t = \dfrac{\pi}{4}$, $u = \pi$. Therefore,

$$\int_0^{\pi/4} \sin 4t\, dt = \int_0^\pi \sin u \left(\frac{1}{4}\, du\right)$$

$$= -\frac{1}{4} [\cos u]_0^\pi = -\frac{1}{4}(-1 - 1) = \frac{1}{2}$$

31. Let $u = 1 + \dfrac{1}{x}$, so $du = -\dfrac{dx}{x^2}$. When $x = 1$, $u = 2$; when $x = 4$, $u = \dfrac{5}{4}$. Therefore,

$$\int_1^4 \frac{1}{x^2}\sqrt{1 + \frac{1}{x}}\, dx = \int_2^{5/4} u^{1/2}(-du)$$

$$= \int_{5/4}^2 u^{1/2}\, du = \left[\frac{2}{3} u^{3/2}\right]_{5/4}^2$$

$$= \frac{2}{3}\left(2\sqrt{2} - \frac{5\sqrt{5}}{8}\right)$$

$$= \frac{4\sqrt{2}}{3} - \frac{5\sqrt{5}}{12}$$

32. Let $u = 2x + 3$, so $du = 2dx$. When $x = 0$, $u = 3$; when $x = 3$, $u = 9$. Therefore,

$$\int_0^3 \frac{dx}{2x + 3} = \int_3^9 \frac{\frac{1}{2}du}{u}$$

$$= \left[\frac{1}{2}\ln u\right]_3^9 = \frac{1}{2}(\ln 9 - \ln 3)$$

$$= \frac{1}{2}\ln \frac{9}{3} = \frac{1}{2}\ln 3 \quad (\text{or } \ln \sqrt{3})$$

33. Let $u = 2x - 1$. Then $du = 2dx$, so

$$\int_0^1 (2x - 1)^{100}\, dx = \int_{-1}^1 u^{100}\left(\frac{1}{2}\, du\right)$$

$$= \int_0^1 u^{100}\, du \begin{bmatrix}\text{since the integrand} \\ \text{is an even function}\end{bmatrix}$$

$$= \left[\frac{1}{101} u^{101}\right]_0^1 = \frac{1}{101}$$

34. Let $u = 1 - 2x$. Then $du = -2dx$, so

$$\int_0^{-4} \sqrt{1 - 2x}\, dx = \int_1^9 u^{1/2}\left(-\frac{1}{2}\, du\right)$$

$$= -\frac{1}{2} \cdot \frac{2}{3} u^{3/2}\Big|_1^9$$

$$= -\frac{1}{3}(27 - 1) = -\frac{26}{3}$$

35. Let $u = x^4 + x$. Then $du = (4x^3 + 1)\, dx$, so

$$\int_0^1 (x^4 + x)^5 (4x^3 + 1)\, dx = \int_0^2 u^5\, du$$

$$= \left[\frac{u^6}{6}\right]_0^2 = \frac{2^6}{6} = \frac{32}{3}$$

36. Let $u = x^3 - x$. Then $du = (3x^2 - 1)dx$, so

$$\int_2^3 \frac{3x^2 - 1}{(x^3 - x)^2}\, dx = \int_6^{24} \frac{du}{u^2}$$

$$= \left[-\frac{1}{u}\right]_6^{24} = -\frac{1}{24} + \frac{1}{6} = \frac{1}{8}$$

6 | APPLICATIONS OF INTEGRATION

1–19 ■ Sketch the region bounded by the given curves and find the area of the region.

1. $y = x^4$, $y = -x - 1$, $x = -2$, $x = 0$

2. $y^2 = x$, $y = x + 5$, $y = -1$, $y = 2$

3. $x + y^2 = 0$, $x = y^2 + 1$, $y = 0$, $y = 3$

4. $y = x^2 - 4x$, $y = 2x$

5. $x^2 + 2x + y = 0$, $x + y + 2 = 0$

6. $y = 4 - x^2$, $y = x + 2$, $x = -3$, $x = 0$

7. $y = x^2 + 2x + 2$, $y = x + 4$, $x = -3$, $x = 2$

8. $y = x^3 - 4x^2 + 3x$, $y = x^2 - x$

9. $y = x$, $y = \sin x$, $x = -\pi/4$, $x = \pi/2$

10. $y = \sin x$, $y = \cos 2x$, $x = 0$, $x = \pi/4$

11. $y = |x|$, $y = (x + 1)^2 - 7$, $x = -4$

12. $y = |x - 1|$, $y = x^2 - 3$, $x = 0$

13. $x = 3y$, $x + y = 0$, $7x + 3y = 24$

14. $y = x\sqrt{1 - x^2}$, $y = x - x^3$

15. $y = 1/x$, $y = 1/x^2$, $x = 1$, $x = 2$

16. $y = x^2$, $y = 2/(x^2 + 1)$

17. $y = 2^x$, $y = 5^x$, $x = -1$, $x = 1$

18. $y = e^x$, $y = e^{3x}$, $x = 1$

19. $y = e^x$, $y = e^{-x}$, $x = -2$, $x = 1$

20. A particle is moved along the x-axis by a force that measures $5x^2 + 1$ pounds at a point x feet from the origin. Find the work done in moving the particle from the origin to a distance of 10 ft.

21. A uniform cable hanging over the edge of a tall building is 40 ft long and weighs 60 lb. How much work is required to pull 10 ft of the cable to the top?

22–26 ■ Find the volume of the solid obtained by rotating the region bounded by the given curves about the specified line. Sketch the region, the solid, and a typical disk or washer.

22. $y^2 = x^3$, $x = 4$, $y = 0$; about the x-axis

23. $x + y = 1$, $x = 0$, $y = 0$; about the x-axis

24. $y = x^2$, $y = 4$, $x = 0$, $x = 2$; about the y-axis

25. $y = x^2 + 1$, $y = 3 - x^2$; about the x-axis

26. $y = 2x - x^2$, $y = 0$, $x = 0$, $x = 1$; about the y-axis

27–38 ■ Refer to the figure and find the volume generated by rotating the given region about the given line.

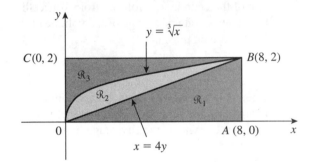

27. $\mathcal{R}_1$ about OA 28. $\mathcal{R}_1$ about OC

29. $\mathcal{R}_1$ about AB 30. $\mathcal{R}_1$ about BC

31. $\mathcal{R}_2$ about OA 32. $\mathcal{R}_2$ about OC

33. $\mathcal{R}_2$ about BC 34. $\mathcal{R}_2$ about AB

35. $\mathcal{R}_3$ about OA 36. $\mathcal{R}_3$ about OC

37. $\mathcal{R}_3$ about BC 38. $\mathcal{R}_3$ about AB

39–45 ■ Use the method of cylindrical shells to find the volume generated by rotating the region bounded by the given curves about the y-axis.

39. $y = x^2 - 6x + 10$, $y = -x^2 + 6x - 6$

40. $y^2 = x$, $x = 2y$

41. $y = x^2$, $y = 4$, $x = 0$

42. $y = x^2 - x^3$, $y = 0$

43. $y = \sqrt{4 + x^2}$, $y = 0$, $x = 0$, $x = 4$

44. $y = -x^2 + 4x - 3$, $y = 0$

45. $y = x - 2$, $y = \sqrt{x - 2}$

49–51 ■ Find the length of the curve.

49. $y = \frac{1}{3}(x^2 + 2)^{3/2}, \quad 0 \le x \le 1$

50. $y = \frac{x^4}{4} + \frac{1}{8x^2}, \quad 1 \le x \le 3$

51. $y = \ln(\sin x), \quad \pi/6 \le x \le \pi/3$

CHALLENGE

52. A cylindrical glass of radius r and height L is filled with water and then tilted until the water remaining in the glass exactly covers its base.

(a) Determine a way to "slice" the water into parallel rectangular cross-sections and then *set up* a definite integral for the volume of the water in the glass.

(b) Determine a way to "slice" the water into parallel cross-sections that are trapezoids and then *set up* a definite integral for the volume of the water.

(c) Find the volume of water in the glass by evaluating one of the integrals in part (a) or part (b).

(d) Find the volume of the water in the glass from purely geometric considerations.

(e) Suppose the glass is tilted until the water exactly covers half the base. In what direction can you "slice" the water into triangular cross-sections? Rectangular cross-sections? Cross-sections that are segments of circles? Find the volume of water in the glass.

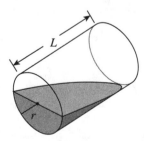
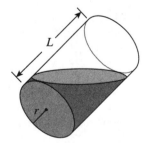

CHALLENGE

46. A *clepsydra*, or water clock, is a glass container with a small hole in the bottom through which water can flow. The "clock" is calibrated for measuring time by placing markings on the container corresponding to water levels at equally spaced times. Let $x = f(y)$ be continuous on the interval $[0, b]$ and assume that the container is formed by rotating the graph of f about the y-axis. Let V denote the volume of water and h the height of the water level at time t.

(a) Determine V as a function of h.

(b) Show that

$$\frac{dV}{dt} = \pi [f(h)]^2 \frac{dh}{dt}$$

(c) Suppose that A is the area of the hole in the bottom of the container. It follows from Torricelli's Law that the rate of change of the volume of the water is given by

$$\frac{dV}{dt} = kA\sqrt{h}$$

where k is a negative constant. Determine a formula for the function f such that dh/dt is a constant C. What is the advantage in having $dh/dt = C$?

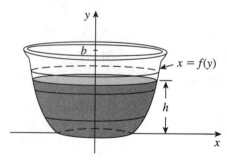

CHALLENGE

47. A solid is generated by rotating about the x-axis the region under the curve $y = f(x)$, where f is a positive function and $x \ge 0$. The volume generated by the part of the curve from $x = 0$ to $x = b$ is b^2 for all $b > 0$, Find the function f.

48. Find the length of the arc of the given curve from point A to point B.

$y = 1 - x^{2/3}; A(1,0), B(8, -3)$

CHALLENGE

53. (a) Show that the volume of a segment of height h of a sphere of radius r is

$$V = \frac{1}{3}\pi h^2(3r - h)$$

(b) Show that if a sphere of radius 1 is sliced by a plane at a distance x from the center in such a way that the volume of one segment is twice the volume of the other, then x is a solution of the equation

$$3x^3 - 9x + 2 = 0$$

where $0 < x < 1$. Use Newton's method to find x accurate to four decimal places.

(c) Using the formula for the volume of a segment of a sphere, it can be shown that the depth x to which a floating sphere of radius r sinks in water is a root of the equation

$$x^3 - 3rx^2 + 4r^3s = 0$$

where s is the specific gravity of the sphere. Suppose a wooden sphere of radius 0.5 m has specific gravity 0.75. Calculate, to four-decimal-place accuracy, the depth to which the sphere will sink.

(d) A hemispherical bowl has radius 5 inches and water is running into the bowl at the rate of 0.2 in³/s.

　(i) How fast is the water level in the bowl rising at the instant the water is 3 inches deep?

　(ii) At a certain instant, the water is 4 inches deep. How long will it take to fill the bowl?

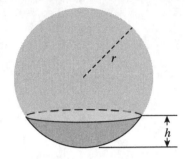

ANSWERS TO SELECTED EXERCISES

1. $\dfrac{32}{5}$

2. $\dfrac{33}{2}$

3. 21

4. 36

5. $\dfrac{9}{2}$

6. $\dfrac{31}{6}$

7. $\dfrac{49}{6}$

8. $\dfrac{71}{6}$

9. $\dfrac{5}{32}\pi^2 + \dfrac{1}{\sqrt{2}} - 2$

10. $\dfrac{1}{2}(3\sqrt{3} - \sqrt{2} - 3)$

11. 34

12. $\dfrac{13}{3}$

13. 12

14. $\dfrac{1}{6}$

15. $\ln 2 - \dfrac{1}{2}$

16. $\pi - \dfrac{2}{3}$

17. $\dfrac{16}{5\ln 5} - \dfrac{1}{2\ln 2}$

18. $\dfrac{1}{3}e^3 - e + \dfrac{2}{3}$

19. $e^2 + e + e^{-1} + e^{-2} - 4$

20. $\dfrac{5030}{3}$ ft-lb

21. 525 ft-lb

22. 64π

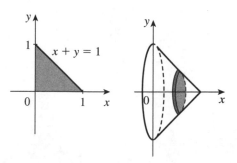

23. $\dfrac{\pi}{3}$

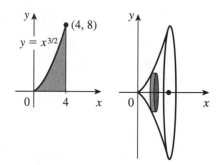

24. 8π

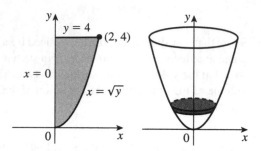

25. $\dfrac{32}{3}\pi$

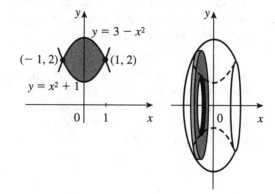

26. $\dfrac{5}{6}\pi$

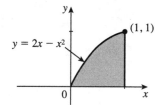

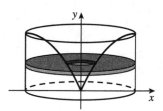

27. $\dfrac{32}{3}\pi$

28. $\dfrac{256}{3}\pi$

29. $\dfrac{128}{3}\pi$

30. $\dfrac{64}{3}\pi$

31. $\dfrac{128}{15}\pi$

32. $\dfrac{512}{21}\pi$

33. $\dfrac{112}{15}\pi$

34. $\dfrac{832}{21}\pi$

35. $\dfrac{64}{5}\pi$

36. $\dfrac{128}{7}\pi$

37. $\dfrac{16}{5}\pi$

38. $\dfrac{320}{7}\pi$

39. 16π

40. $\dfrac{64}{15}\pi$

41. 8π

42. $\dfrac{1}{10}\pi$

43. $\dfrac{16}{3}\pi(5\sqrt{5}-1)$

44. $\dfrac{16\pi}{3}$

45. $\dfrac{4}{5}\pi$

46. (a) $V = \displaystyle\int_0^h \pi[f(y)]^2 dy$

(c) $f(y) = \sqrt{kA/(\pi C)}\,y^{1/4}$

Advantage: the markings on the container are equally spaced.

47. $f(x) = \sqrt{2x/\pi}$

48. $\dfrac{1}{27}(80\sqrt{10}-13\sqrt{13})$

49. $\dfrac{4}{3}$

50. $\dfrac{181}{9}$

51. $\ln\left(1 + \dfrac{2}{\sqrt{3}}\right)$

53. (b) 0.2261

6 | SOLUTIONS TO SELECTED EXERCISES

1. $A = \int_{-2}^{0} \left[x^4 - (-x - 1) \right] dx = \int_{-2}^{0} (x^4 + x + 1)\, dx$

$= \left[\frac{1}{5}x^5 + \frac{1}{2}x^2 + x \right]_{-2}^{0} = 0 - \left(-\frac{32}{5} + 2 - 2 \right)$

$= \frac{32}{5}$

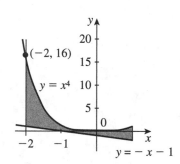

2. $A = \int_{-1}^{2} \left[y^2 - (y - 5) \right] dy = \left[\frac{1}{3}y^3 - \frac{1}{2}y^2 + 5y \right]_{-1}^{2}$

$= \left(\frac{8}{3} - 2 + 10 \right) - \left(-\frac{1}{3} - \frac{1}{2} - 5 \right) = \frac{33}{2}$

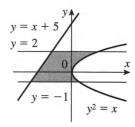

3. $A = \int_{0}^{3} \left[(y^2 + 1) - (-y^2) \right] dy = \int_{0}^{3} (2y^2 + 1)\, dy$

$= \left[\frac{2}{3}y^3 + y \right]_{0}^{3} = 18 + 3 = 21$

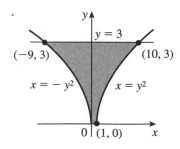

4. $A = \int_{0}^{6} \left[2x - (x^2 - 4x) \right] dx = \int_{0}^{6} (6x - x^2)\, dx$

$= \left[3x^2 - \frac{1}{3}x^3 \right]_{0}^{6} = 108 - 72 = 36$

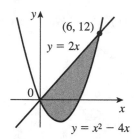

5. $A = \int_{-2}^{1} \left[-x^2 - 2x - (-x - 2) \right] dx$

$= \int_{-2}^{1} (-x^2 - x + 2)\, dx = \left[-\frac{1}{3}x^3 - \frac{1}{2}x^2 + 2x \right]_{-2}^{1}$

$= \left(-\frac{1}{3} - \frac{1}{2} - 2 \right) - \left(\frac{8}{3} - 2 - 4 \right) = \frac{9}{2}$

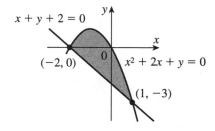

6. $A = \int_{-3}^{0} \left| (4 - x^2) - (x + 2) \right| dx$

$= \int_{-3}^{-2} \left[(x + 2) - (4 - x^2) \right] dx$

$+ \int_{-2}^{0} \left[(4 - x^2) - (x + 2) \right] dx$

$= \int_{-3}^{-2} (x^2 + x - 2)\, dx + \int_{-2}^{0} (-x^2 - x + 2)\, dx$

$= \left[\frac{1}{3}x^3 + \frac{1}{2}x^2 - 2x \right]_{-3}^{-2} + \left[-\frac{1}{3}x^3 - \frac{1}{2}x^2 + 2x \right]_{-2}^{0}$

$= \left(-\frac{8}{3} + 2 + 4 \right) - \left(-9 + \frac{9}{2} + 6 \right)$

$+ 0 - \left(\frac{8}{3} - 2 - 4 \right) = \frac{31}{6}$

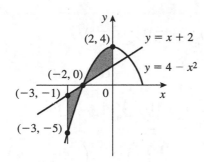

7. $A = \displaystyle\int_{-3}^{-2} \big[(x^2 + 2x + 2) - (x + 4)\big]\,dx$

$\qquad + \displaystyle\int_{-2}^{1} \big[(x + 4) - (x^2 + 2x + 2)\big]\,dx$

$\qquad + \displaystyle\int_{1}^{2} \big[(x^2 + 2x + 2) - (x + 4)\big]\,dx$

$\quad = \displaystyle\int_{-3}^{-2} (x^2 + x - 2)\,dx + \int_{-2}^{1} (-x^2 - x + 2)\,dx$

$\qquad + \displaystyle\int_{1}^{2} (x^2 + x - 2)\,dx$

$\quad = \left[\dfrac{1}{3}x^3 + \dfrac{1}{2}x^2 - 2x\right]_{-3}^{-2} + \left[-\dfrac{1}{3}x^3 - \dfrac{1}{2}x^2 + 2x\right]_{-2}^{1}$

$\qquad + \left[\dfrac{1}{3}x^3 + \dfrac{1}{2}x^2 - 2x\right]_{1}^{2}$

$\quad = \left[\left(-\dfrac{8}{3} + 2 + 4\right) - \left(-9 + \dfrac{9}{2} + 6\right)\right]$

$\qquad + \left[\left(-\dfrac{1}{3} - \dfrac{1}{2} + 2\right) - \left(\dfrac{8}{3} - 2 - 4\right)\right]$

$\qquad + \left[\left(\dfrac{8}{3} + 2 - 4\right) - \left(\dfrac{1}{3} + \dfrac{1}{2} - 2\right)\right] = \dfrac{49}{6}$

8. $A = \displaystyle\int_{0}^{1} \big[(x^3 - 4x^2 + 3x) - (x^2 - x)\big]\,dx$

$\qquad + \displaystyle\int_{1}^{4} \big[x^2 - x - (x^3 - 4x^2 + 3x)\big]\,dx$

$\quad = \displaystyle\int_{0}^{1} (x^3 - 5x^2 + 4x)\,dx + \int_{1}^{4} (-x^3 + 5x^2 - 4x)\,dx$

$\quad = \left[\dfrac{1}{4}x^4 - \dfrac{5}{3}x^3 + 2x^2\right]_{0}^{1} + \left[-\dfrac{1}{4}x^4 + \dfrac{5}{3}x^3 - 2x^2\right]_{1}^{4}$

$\quad = \left(\dfrac{1}{4} - \dfrac{5}{3} + 2\right) - 0 + \left(-64 + \dfrac{320}{3} - 32\right)$

$\qquad - \left(-\dfrac{1}{4} + \dfrac{5}{3} - 2\right) = \dfrac{71}{6}$

9. $A = \displaystyle\int_{-\pi/4}^{0} (\sin x - x)\,dx + \int_{0}^{\pi/2} (x - \sin x)\,dx$

$\quad = \left[-\cos x - \dfrac{1}{2}x^2\right]_{-\pi/4}^{0} + \left[\dfrac{1}{2}x^2 + \cos x\right]_{0}^{\pi/2}$

$\quad = 1 - \left(-\dfrac{1}{\sqrt{2}} - \dfrac{\pi^2}{32}\right) + \dfrac{\pi^2}{8} - 1 = \dfrac{5}{32}\pi^2 + \dfrac{1}{\sqrt{2}} - 2$

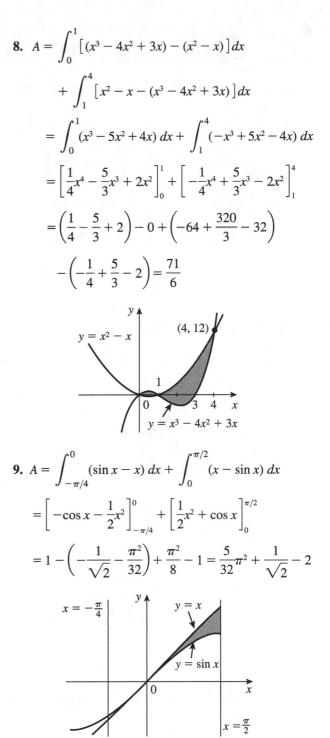

10. $\sin x = \cos 2x = 1 - 2\sin^2 x \Leftrightarrow$

$2\sin^2 x + \sin x - 1 = 0 \Leftrightarrow$

$(2\sin x - 1)(\sin x + 1) = 0 \Leftrightarrow \sin x = \dfrac{1}{2} \text{ or } -1 \Leftrightarrow$

$x = \dfrac{\pi}{6}.$

$A = \displaystyle\int_0^{\pi/6} (\cos 2x - \sin x)\,dx + \int_{\pi/6}^{\pi/4} (\sin x - \cos 2x)\,dx$

$= \left[\dfrac{1}{2}\sin 2x + \cos x\right]_0^{\pi/6} - \left[\dfrac{1}{2}\sin 2x + \cos x\right]_{\pi/6}^{\pi/4}$

$= \left(\dfrac{1}{2}\cdot\dfrac{\sqrt{3}}{2} + \dfrac{\sqrt{3}}{2}\right) - 1 - 1\left(\dfrac{1}{2} + \dfrac{\sqrt{2}}{2}\right)$

$\quad + \left(\dfrac{1}{2}\cdot\dfrac{\sqrt{3}}{2} + \dfrac{\sqrt{3}}{2}\right)$

$= \dfrac{1}{2}(3\sqrt{3} - \sqrt{2} - 3)$

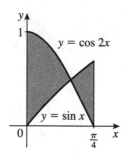

11. $A = \displaystyle\int_{-4}^0 \left(-x - \left[(x+1)^2 - 7\right]\right) dx$

$\quad + \displaystyle\int_0^2 \left(x - \left[(x+1)^2 - 7\right]\right) dx$

$= \displaystyle\int_{-4}^0 (-x^2 - 3x + 6)\,dx + \int_0^2 (-x^2 - x + 6)\,dx$

$= \left[-\dfrac{1}{3}x^3 - \dfrac{3}{2}x^2 + 6x\right]_{-4}^0 + \left[-\dfrac{1}{3}x^3 - \dfrac{1}{2}x^2 + 6x\right]_0^2$

$= 0 - \left(\dfrac{64}{3} - 24 - 24\right) + \left(-\dfrac{8}{3} - 2 + 12\right) - 0 = 34$

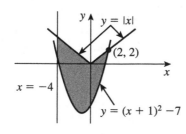

12. $A = \displaystyle\int_0^1 \left[(1-x) - (x^2 - 3)\right] dx$

$\quad + \displaystyle\int_1^2 \left[(x-1) - (x^2 - 3)\right] dx$

$= \left[-\dfrac{1}{3}x^3 - \dfrac{1}{2}x^2 + 4x\right]_0^1 + \left[-\dfrac{1}{3}x^3 + \dfrac{1}{2}x^2 + 2x\right]_1^2$

$= \left(-\dfrac{1}{3} - \dfrac{1}{2} + 4\right) - 0 + \left(-\dfrac{8}{3} + 2 + 4\right)$

$\quad - \left(-\dfrac{1}{3} + \dfrac{1}{2} + 2\right) = \dfrac{13}{3}$

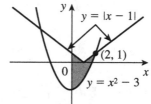

13. $A = \displaystyle\int_0^3 \left[\dfrac{1}{3}x - (-x)\right] dx + \int_3^6 \left[\left(8 - \dfrac{7}{3}x\right) - (-x)\right] dx$

$= \displaystyle\int_0^3 \dfrac{4}{3}x\,dx + \int_3^6 \left(-\dfrac{4}{3}x + 8\right) dx$

$= \left[\dfrac{2}{3}x^2\right]_0^3 + \left[-\dfrac{2}{3}x^2 + 8x\right]_3^6$

$= (6 - 0) + (24 - 18) = 12$

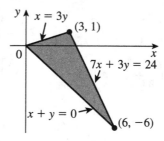

14. $A = \displaystyle\int_{-1}^1 \left|x\sqrt{1-x^2} - (x - x^3)\right| dx$

$= \displaystyle\int_{-1}^0 (x - x^3 - x\sqrt{1-x^2})\,dx$

$\quad + \displaystyle\int_0^1 (x\sqrt{1-x^2} - x + x^3)\,dx$

$= 2\displaystyle\int_0^1 (x\sqrt{1-x^2} - x + x^3)\,dx \text{ (by symmetry)}$

$= 2\left[-\dfrac{1}{3}(1-x^2)^{3/2} - \dfrac{1}{2}x^2 + \dfrac{1}{4}x^4\right]_0^1$

$= 2\left[\left(-\dfrac{1}{2} + \dfrac{1}{4}\right) + \dfrac{1}{3}\right] = \dfrac{1}{6}$

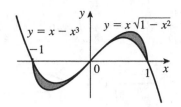

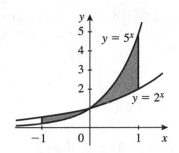

15. $A = \int_1^2 \left(\frac{1}{x} - \frac{1}{x^2}\right) dx = \left[\ln x + \frac{1}{x}\right]_1^2$

$= \left(\ln 2 + \frac{1}{2}\right) - (\ln 1 + 1) = \ln 2 - \frac{1}{2}$

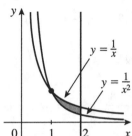

18. $A = \int_0^1 (e^{3x} - e^x) dx = \left[\frac{1}{3}e^{3x} - e^x\right]_0^1$

$= \left(\frac{1}{3}e^3 - e\right) - \left(\frac{1}{3} - 1\right) = \frac{1}{3}e^3 - e + \frac{2}{3}$

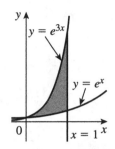

16. $A = 2\int_0^1 \left(\frac{2}{x^2+1} - x^2\right) dx = \left[4\tan^{-1}x - \frac{2}{3}x^3\right]_0^1$

$= 4 \cdot \frac{\pi}{4} - \frac{2}{3} = \pi - \frac{2}{3}$

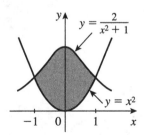

19. $A = \int_{-2}^0 (e^{-x} - e^x) dx + \int_0^1 (e^x - e^{-x}) dx$

$= \left[-e^{-x} - e^x\right]_{-2}^0 + \left[e^x + e^{-x}\right]_0^1$

$= (-1-1) - (-e^2 - e^{-2}) + (e + e^{-1}) - (1+1)$

$= e^2 + e + e^{-1} + e^{-2} - 4$

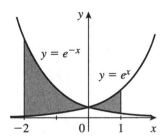

17. $A = \int_{-1}^0 (2^x - 5^x) dx + \int_0^1 (5^x - 2^x) dx$

$= \left[\frac{2^x}{\ln 2} - \frac{5^x}{\ln 5}\right]_{-1}^0 + \left[\frac{5^x}{\ln 5} - \frac{2^x}{\ln 2}\right]_0^1$

$= \left(\frac{1}{\ln 2} - \frac{1}{\ln 5}\right) - \left(\frac{1/2}{\ln 2} - \frac{1/5}{\ln 5}\right)$

$+ \left(\frac{5}{\ln 5} - \frac{2}{\ln 2}\right) - \left(\frac{1}{\ln 5} - \frac{1}{\ln 2}\right)$

$= \frac{16}{5\ln 5} - \frac{1}{2\ln 2}$

20. $W = \int_a^b f(x) dx$

$= \int_0^{10} (5x^2 + 1) dx$

$= \left[\frac{5}{3}x^3 + x\right]_0^{10} = \frac{5000}{3} + 10$

$= \frac{5030}{3}$ ft-lb

21. Each part of the top 10 ft of cable is lifted a distance x_i^* equal to its distance from the top. The cable weighs $\dfrac{60}{40} = 1.5$ lb/ft, so the work done on the ith subinterval is $\dfrac{3}{2}x_i^*\Delta x$. The remaining 30 ft of cable is lifted 10 ft. Thus,

$$W = \lim_{n\to\infty}\sum_{i=1}^{n}\left(\frac{3}{2}x_i^*\Delta x + \frac{3}{2}\cdot 10\Delta x\right)$$

$$= \int_0^{10}\frac{3}{2}x\,dx + \int_{10}^{40}\frac{3}{2}\cdot 10\,dx$$

$$= \left[\frac{3}{4}x^2\right]_0^{10} + \left[15x\right]_{10}^{40}$$

$$= \frac{3}{4}(100) + 15(30)$$

$$= 75 + 450$$

$$= 525 \text{ ft-lb}$$

22. $V = \displaystyle\int_0^4 \pi\,(x^{3/2})^2\,dx = \pi\left[\frac{1}{4}x^4\right]_0^4 = 64\pi$

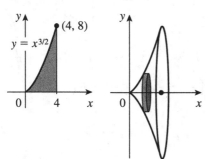

23. $V = \displaystyle\int_0^1 \pi(-x+1)^2\,dx = \pi\int_0^1 (x^2 - 2x + 1)\,dx$

$$= \pi\left[\frac{1}{3}x^3 - x^2 + x\right]_0^1 = \pi\left(\frac{1}{3} - 1 + 1\right) = \frac{\pi}{3}$$

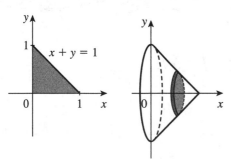

24. $V = \displaystyle\int_0^4 \pi\left(\sqrt{y}\right)^2 dy = \pi\int_0^4 y\,dy = \pi\left[\frac{1}{2}y^2\right]_0^4 = 8\pi$

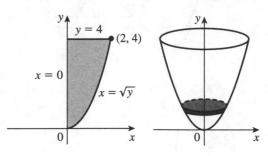

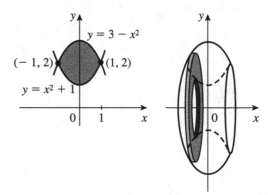

25. $V = \pi\displaystyle\int_{-1}^1 \left[(3 - x^2)^2 - (x^2 + 1)^2\right]dx$

$$= \pi\int_{-1}^1 (8 - 8x^2)\,dx = 2\pi\int_0^1 (8 - 8x^2)\,dx$$

$$= 2\pi\left[8x - \frac{8}{3}x^3\right]_0^1 = 2\pi\left(8 - \frac{8}{3}\right) = \frac{32}{3}\pi$$

26. $V = \pi\displaystyle\int_0^1 \left[1^2 - (1 - \sqrt{1-y})^2\right]dy$

$$= \pi\int_0^1 (2\sqrt{1-y} - 1 + y)\,dy$$

$$= \pi\left[-\frac{4}{3}(1-y)^{3/2} - y + \frac{1}{2}y^2\right]_0^1$$

$$= \pi\left[\left(0 - 1 + \frac{1}{2}\right) - \left(-\frac{4}{3} - 0 + 0\right)\right] = \frac{5}{6}\pi$$

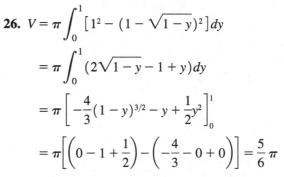

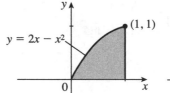

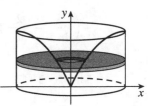

27. $V = \pi \int_0^8 \left(\frac{1}{4}x\right)^2 dx = \frac{\pi}{16}\left[\frac{1}{3}x^3\right]_0^8 = \frac{32}{3}\pi$

28. $V = \pi \int_0^2 \left[8^2 - (4y)^2\right] dy = \pi\left[64y - \frac{16}{3}y^3\right]_0^2$

$= \pi\left(128 - \frac{128}{3}\right) = \frac{256}{3}\pi$

29. $V = \pi \int_0^2 (8 - 4y)^2 dy = \pi\left[64y - 32y^2 + \frac{16}{3}y^3\right]_0^2$

$= \pi\left(128 - 128 + \frac{128}{3}\right) = \frac{128}{3}\pi$

30. $V = \pi \int_0^8 \left[2^2 - \left(2 - \frac{1}{4}x\right)^2\right] dx = \pi \int_0^8 \left(x - \frac{1}{16}x^2\right) dx$

$= \pi\left[\frac{1}{2}x^2 - \frac{1}{48}x^3\right]_0^8 = \pi\left(32 - \frac{32}{3}\right) = \frac{64}{3}\pi$

31. $V = \pi \int_0^8 \left[(\sqrt[3]{x})^2 - \left(\frac{1}{4}x\right)^2\right] = \pi \int_0^8 \left(x^{2/3} - \frac{1}{16}x^2\right) dx$

$= \pi\left[\frac{3}{5}x^{5/3} - \frac{1}{48}x^3\right]_0^8 = \pi\left(\frac{96}{5} - \frac{32}{3}\right) = \frac{128}{15}\pi$

32. $V = \pi \int_0^2 \left[(4y)^2 - (y^3)^2\right] dy = \pi \int_0^2 (16y^2 - y^6) dy$

$= \pi\left[\frac{16}{3}y^3 - \frac{1}{7}y^7\right]_0^2 = \pi\left(\frac{128}{3} - \frac{128}{7}\right) = \frac{512}{21}\pi$

33. $V = \pi \int_0^8 \left[\left(2 - \frac{1}{4}x\right)^2 - (2 - \sqrt[3]{x})^2\right] dx$

$= \pi \int_0^8 \left(-x + \frac{1}{16}x^2 + 4x^{1/3} - x^{2/3}\right) dx$

$= \pi\left[-\frac{1}{2}x^2 + \frac{1}{48}x^3 + 3x^{4/3} - \frac{3}{5}x^{5/3}\right]_0^8$

$= \pi\left(-32 + \frac{32}{3} + 48 - \frac{96}{5}\right) = \frac{112}{15}\pi$

34. $V = \pi \int_0^2 \left[(8 - y^3)^2 - (8 - 4y)^2\right] dy$

$= \pi \int_0^2 (-16y^3 + y^6 + 64y - 16y^2) dy$

$= \pi\left[-4y^4 + \frac{1}{7}y^7 + 32y^2 - \frac{16}{3}y^3\right]_0^2$

$= \pi\left(-64 + \frac{128}{7} + 128 - \frac{128}{3}\right) = \frac{832}{21}\pi$

35. $V = \pi \int_0^8 (2^2 - x^{2/3}) dx = \pi\left[4x - \frac{3}{5}x^{5/3}\right]_0^8$

$= \pi\left(32 - \frac{96}{5}\right) = \frac{64}{5}\pi$

36. $V = \pi \int_0^2 (y^3)^2 dy = \pi\left[\frac{1}{7}y^7\right]_0^2 = \frac{128}{7}\pi$

37. $V = \pi \int_0^8 (2 - \sqrt[3]{x})^2 dx = \pi \int_0^8 (4 - 4x^{1/3} + x^{2/3}) dx$

$= \pi\left[4x - 3x^{4/3} + \frac{3}{5}x^{5/3}\right]_0^8$

$= \pi\left(32 - 48 + \frac{96}{5}\right) = \frac{16}{5}\pi$

38. $V = \pi \int_0^2 \left[8^2 - (8 - y^3)^2\right] dy = \pi \int_0^2 (16y^3 - y^6) \, dy$

$= \pi\left[4y^4 - \frac{1}{7}y^7\right]_0^2 = \pi\left(64 - \frac{128}{7}\right) = \frac{320}{7}\pi$

39. $V = \int_2^4 2\pi x\left[(-x^2 + 6x - 6) - (x^2 - 6x + 10)\right] dx$

$= 2\pi \int_2^4 x\,(-2x^2 + 12x - 16) \, dx$

$= 4\pi \int_2^4 (-x^3 + 6x^2 - 8x) \, dx$

$= 4\pi\left[-\frac{1}{4}x^4 + 2x^3 - 4x^2\right]_2^4$

$= 4\pi\left[(-64 + 128 - 64) - (-4 + 16 - 16)\right] = 16\pi$

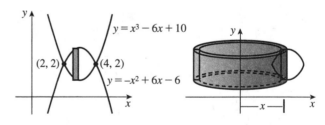

40. $V = \int_0^4 2\pi x\left(\sqrt{x} - \frac{1}{2}x\right) dx = 2\pi \int_0^4 x^{3/2} dx - \pi \int_0^4 x^2 \, dx$

$= 2\pi\left[\frac{2}{5}x^{5/2}\right]_0^4 - \pi\left[\frac{1}{3}x^3\right]_0^4 = \frac{4}{5}\pi(32) - \frac{64}{3}\pi = \frac{64}{15}\pi$

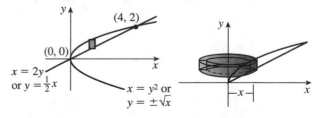

41. $V = \int_0^2 2\pi x(4 - x^2)\,dx = 2\pi \int_0^2 (4x - x^3)\,dx$

$$= 2\pi\left[2x^2 - \frac{1}{4}x^4\right]_0^2 = 2\pi(8 - 4) = 8\pi$$

Note: If we integrated from –2 to 2, we would be generating the volume twice.

42. $V = \int_0^1 2\pi x(x^2 - x^3)\,dx = 2\pi \int_0^1 (x^3 - x^4)\,dx$

$$= 2\pi\left[\frac{1}{4}x^4 - \frac{1}{5}x^5\right]_0^1 = 2\pi\left(\frac{1}{4} - \frac{1}{5}\right) = \frac{1}{10}\pi$$

43. $V = \int_0^4 2\pi x\sqrt{4 + x^2}\,dx = \pi \int_0^4 \sqrt{x^2 + 4}\,2x\,dx$

$$= \left[\frac{2}{3}\pi(x^2 + 4)^{3/2}\right]_0^4 = \frac{2\pi}{3}(20\sqrt{20} - 8)$$

$$= \frac{16}{3}\pi(5\sqrt{5} - 1)$$

44. $V = \int_1^3 2\pi x(-x^2 + 4x - 3)\,dx$

$$= 2\pi\left[-\frac{1}{4}x^4 + \frac{4}{3}x^3 - \frac{3}{2}x^2\right]_1^3$$

$$= 2\pi\left[\left(-\frac{81}{4} + 36 - \frac{27}{2}\right) - \left(-\frac{1}{4} + \frac{4}{3} - \frac{3}{2}\right)\right] = \frac{16\pi}{3}$$

45. $V = \int_2^3 2\pi x\left[\sqrt{x - 2} - (x - 2)\right]dx$

$$= \int_0^1 2\pi(u + 2)(\sqrt{u} - u)\,du\,[u = x - 2]$$

$$= 2\pi \int_0^1 (u^{3/2} - u^2 + 2u^{1/2} - 2u)\,du$$

$$= 2\pi\left[\frac{2}{5}u^{5/2} - \frac{1}{3}u^3 + \frac{4}{3}u^{3/2} - u^2\right]_0^1$$

$$= 2\pi\left(\frac{2}{5} - \frac{1}{3} + \frac{4}{3} - 1\right) = \frac{4}{5}\pi$$

46. (a) Stacking disks along the *y*-axis gives us

$$V = \int_0^h \pi[f(y)]^2\,dy.$$

(b) Using the Chain Rule, $\dfrac{dV}{dt} = \dfrac{dV}{dh}\cdot\dfrac{dh}{dt} = \pi[f(h)]^2\dfrac{dh}{dt}.$

(c) $kA\sqrt{h} = \pi[f(h)]^2\dfrac{dh}{dt}$. Set $\dfrac{dh}{dt} = C$;

$$\pi[f(h)]^2 C = kA\sqrt{h} \Rightarrow [f(h)]^2 = \frac{kA}{\pi C}\sqrt{h} \Rightarrow$$

$$f(h) = \sqrt{\frac{kA}{\pi C}}h^{1/4}; \text{ that is, } f(y) = \sqrt{\frac{kA}{\pi c}}y^{1/4}.$$

The advantage of having $\dfrac{dh}{dt} = C$ is that the markings on the container are equally spaced.

47. The volume generated from $x = 0$ to $x = b$ is

$\int_0^b \pi[f(x)]^2 dx$. Hence, we are given that

$b^2 = \int_0^b \pi[f(x)]^2 dx$ for all $b > 0$. Differentiating both sides of this equation using the Fundamental Theorem of Calculus gives $2b = \pi[f(b)]^2 \Rightarrow$ $f(b) = \sqrt{2b/\pi}$, since f is positive. Therefore, $f(x) = \sqrt{2x/\pi}$.

48. $y = 1 - x^{2/3} \Rightarrow dy/dx = -\dfrac{2}{3}x^{-1/3} \Rightarrow$

$1 + (dy/dx)^2 = 1 + \dfrac{4}{9}x^{-2/3}$. So

$$L = \int_1^8 \sqrt{1 + \frac{4}{9x^{2/3}}}\,dx = \int_1^8 \frac{\sqrt{9x^{2/3} + 4}}{3x^{1/3}}\,dx$$

$$= \frac{1}{18}\int_{13}^{40} \sqrt{u}\,du\ \left(u = 9x^{2/3} + 4,\ du = 6x^{-1/3}dx\right)$$

$$= \frac{1}{27}\left[u^{3/2}\right]_{13}^{40} = \frac{1}{27}\left(80\sqrt{10} - 13\sqrt{13}\right)$$

Or: Let $u = x^{1/3}$.

49. $y = \dfrac{1}{3}(x^2 + 2)^{3/2} \Rightarrow$

$dy/dx = \dfrac{1}{2}(x^2 + 2)^{1/2}(2x) = x\sqrt{x^2 + 2} \Rightarrow$

$1 + (dy/dx)^2 = 1 + x^2(x^2 + 2) = (x^2 + 1)^2$. So

$$L = \int_0^1 (x^2 + 1)\,dx = \left[\frac{1}{3}x^3 + x\right]_0^1 = \frac{4}{3}.$$

50. $y = \dfrac{x^4}{4} + \dfrac{1}{8x^2} \Rightarrow \dfrac{dy}{dx} = x^3 - \dfrac{1}{4x^3} \Rightarrow$

$1 + \left(\dfrac{dy}{dx}\right)^2 = 1 + x^6 - \dfrac{1}{2} + \dfrac{1}{16x^6} = x^6 + \dfrac{1}{2} + \dfrac{1}{16x^6}$. So

$L = \displaystyle\int_1^3 \left(x^3 + \dfrac{1}{4}x^{-3}\right) dx = \left[\dfrac{1}{4}x^4 - \dfrac{1}{8}x^{-2}\right]_1^3$

$\quad = \left(\dfrac{81}{4} - \dfrac{1}{72}\right) - \left(\dfrac{1}{4} - \dfrac{1}{8}\right) = \dfrac{181}{9}$

51. $y = \ln(\sin x) \Rightarrow \dfrac{dy}{dx} = \dfrac{\cos x}{\sin x} = \cot x \Rightarrow$

$1 + \left(\dfrac{dy}{dx}\right)^2 = 1 + \cot^2 x = \csc^2 x$. So

$L = \displaystyle\int_{\pi/6}^{\pi/3} \csc x\, dx = \big[\ln(\csc x - \cot x)\big]_{\pi/6}^{\pi/3}$

$\quad = \ln\left(\dfrac{2}{\sqrt{3}} - \dfrac{1}{\sqrt{3}}\right) - \ln(2 - \sqrt{3})$

$\quad = \ln\dfrac{1}{\sqrt{3}(2 - \sqrt{3})} = \ln\dfrac{2 + \sqrt{3}}{\sqrt{3}} = \ln\left(1 + \dfrac{2}{\sqrt{3}}\right)$

53. (a) $V = \pi h^2(r - h/3) = \dfrac{1}{3}\pi h^2(3r - h)$.

(b) The smaller segment has height $h = 1 - x$ and so by part (a) its volume is

$V = \dfrac{1}{3}\pi(1 - x)^2\big[3(1) - (1 - x)\big]$

$\quad = \dfrac{1}{3}\pi(x - 1)^2(x + 2)$. This volume must be $\dfrac{1}{3}$

of the total volume of the sphere, which is

$\dfrac{4}{3}\pi(1)^3$. So $\dfrac{1}{3}\pi(x - 1)^2(x + 2) = \dfrac{1}{3}\left(\dfrac{4}{3}\pi\right) \Rightarrow$

$(x^2 - 2x + 1)(x + 2) = \dfrac{4}{3} \Rightarrow$

$x^3 - 3x + 2 = \dfrac{4}{3} \Rightarrow 3x^3 - 9x + 2 = 0$.

Using Newton's method with

$f(x) = 3x^3 - 9x + 2$, $f'(x) = 9x^2 - 9$, we get

$x_{n+1} = x_n - \dfrac{3x_n^3 - 9x_n + 2}{9x_n^2 - 9}$. Taking $x_1 = 0$, we

get $x_2 \approx 0.2222$, and $x_3 \approx 0.2261 \approx x_4$, so, correct to four decimal places, $x \approx 0.2261$.

(c) With $r = 0.5$ and $s = 0.75$, the equation $x^3 - 3rx^2 + 4r^3s = 0$ becomes

$x^3 - 3(0.5)x^2 + 4(0.5)^3(0.75) = 0 \Rightarrow$

$x^3 - \dfrac{3}{2}x^2 + 4\left(\dfrac{1}{8}\right)\dfrac{3}{4} = 0 \Rightarrow 8x^3 - 12x^2 + 3 = 0$.

We use Newton's method with

$f(x) = 8x^3 - 12x^2 + 3$, $f'(x) = 24x^2 - 24x$, so

$x_{n+1} = x_n - \dfrac{8x_n^3 - 12x_n^2 + 3}{24x_n^2 - 24x_n}$. Take $x_1 = 0.5$. Then

$x_2 \approx 0.6667$, and $x_3 \approx 0.6736 \approx x_4$. So to four decimal places the depth is 0.6736 m.

(d) (i) From part (a) with $r = 5$ in. the volume of

water in the bowl is $V = \dfrac{1}{3}\pi h^2(3r - h)$

$\quad = \dfrac{1}{3}\pi h^2(15 - h) = 5\pi h^2 - \dfrac{1}{3}\pi h^3$. We are given

that $\dfrac{dV}{dt} = 0.2$ m^3/s and we want to find $\dfrac{dh}{dt}$

when $h = 3$. Now $\dfrac{dV}{dt} = 10\pi h\dfrac{dh}{dt} - \pi h^2\dfrac{dh}{dt}$,

so $\dfrac{dh}{dt} = \dfrac{0.2}{\pi(10h - h^2)}$. When $h = 3$, we have

$\dfrac{dh}{dt} = \dfrac{0.2}{\pi(10 \cdot 3 - 3^2)} = \dfrac{1}{105\pi} \approx 0.003$ in/s.

(ii) From part (a), the volume of water required to fill the bowl from the instant that the water is 4 in. deep is $V = \dfrac{1}{2} \cdot \dfrac{4}{3}\pi(5)^3 - \dfrac{1}{3}\pi(4)^2(15 - 4) =$

$\dfrac{2}{3} \cdot 125\pi - \dfrac{16}{3} \cdot 11\pi = \dfrac{74}{3}\pi$. To find the time

required to fill the bowl we divide this

volume by the rate: Time $= \dfrac{74\pi/3}{0.2} = \dfrac{370\pi}{3} \approx$

387 s ≈ 6.5 min

7 | TECHNIQUES OF INTEGRATION

1–15 ■ Evaluate the integral.

1. $\int xe^{2x}\,dx$

2. $\int x\cos x\,dx$

3. $\int x\sin 4x\,dx$

4. $\int x^2\cos 3x\,dx$

5. $\int x^2\sin ax\,dx$

6. $\int \theta\sin\theta\cos\theta\,d\theta$

7. $\int t^2\ln t\,dt$

8. $\int e^{-\theta}\cos 3\theta\,d\theta$

9. $\int_0^1 te^{-t}\,dt$

10. $\int_1^4 \ln\sqrt{x}\,dx$

11. $\int_0^{x/2} x\cos 2x\,dx$

12. $\int_0^1 x^2e^{-x}\,dx$

13. $\int x^3e^x\,dx$

14. $\int \sin(\ln x)\,dx$

15. $\int x\tan^{-1}x\,dx$

16–31 ■ Evaluate the integral.

16. $\int \sin^3 x\,dx$

17. $\int \sin^3 x\cos^4 x\,dx$

18. $\int \sin^4 x\cos^3 x\,dx$

19. $\int \cos^5 x\sin^5 x\,dx$

20. $\int_0^{\pi/2} \sin^2 3x\,dx$

21. $\int_0^{\pi/2} \cos^2 x\,dx$

22. $\int \cos^4 t\,dt$

23. $\int \sin^6 \pi x\,dx$

24. $\int \tan x\sec^6 x\,dx$

25. $\int \tan^3 x\sec^6 x\,dx$

26. $\int \sec^4 x\,dx$

27. $\int_0^{\pi/4} \sec^6 x\,dx$

28. $\int_{1/2}^{\sqrt{3}/2} \frac{1}{x^2\sqrt{1-x^2}}\,dx$

29. $\int_0^2 x^3\sqrt{4-x^2}\,dx$

30. $\int \frac{x}{\sqrt{1-x^2}}\,dx$

31. $\int x\sqrt{4-x^2}\,dx$

32–49 ■ Write out the form of the partial fraction decomposition of the function. Do not determine the numerical values of the coefficients.

32. $\dfrac{3}{(2x+3)(x-1)}$

33. $\dfrac{5}{2x^2-3x-2}$

34. $\dfrac{x^2+9x-12}{(3x-1)(x+6)^2}$

35. $\dfrac{z^2-4z}{(3z+5)^3(z+2)}$

36. $\dfrac{1}{x^4-x^3}$

37. $\dfrac{x^4+x^3-x^2-x+1}{x^3-x}$

38. $\dfrac{x^2+1}{x^2-1}$

39. $\dfrac{x^3-4x^2+2}{(x^2+1)(x^2+2)}$

40. $\dfrac{x+1}{x^2+2x}$

41. $\dfrac{7}{2x^2+5x-12}$

42. $\dfrac{1}{(x-1)(x+2)}$

43. $\dfrac{x^2+3x-4}{(2x-1)^2(2x+3)}$

44. $\dfrac{x^3-x^2}{(x-6)(5x+3)^3}$

45. $\dfrac{1}{x^6-x^3}$

46. $\dfrac{19x}{(x-1)^3(4x^2+5x+3)^2}$

47. $\dfrac{x^3+x^2+1}{x^4+x^3+2x^2}$

48. $\dfrac{3-11x}{(x-2)^3(x^2+1)(2x^2+5x+7)^2}$

49. $\dfrac{x^4}{(x^2+9)^3}$

59

CHALLENGE

50. Three mathematics students have ordered a 14-inch pizza. Instead of slicing it in the traditional way, they decide to slice it by parallel cuts, as shown in the figure. Being mathematics majors, they are able to determine where to slice so that each gets the same amount of pizza. Where are the cuts made?

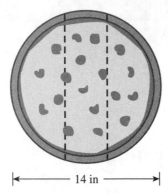

|←——— 14 in ———→|

CHALLENGE

51. Evaluate $\displaystyle\int \frac{1}{x^7 - x}\, dx$.

The straightforward approach would be to start with partial fractions, but that would be brutal. Try a substitution.

CHALLENGE

52. Evaluate $\displaystyle\int_0^1 \left(\sqrt[3]{1 - x^7} - \sqrt[7]{1 - x^3} \right) dx$.

CHALLENGE

53. The circle with radius 1 shown in the figure touches the curve $y = |2x|$ twice. Find the area of the region that lies between the two curves.

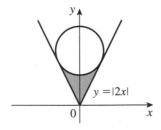

CHALLENGE

54. A rocket is fired straight up, burning fuel at the constant rate of b kilograms per second. Let $v = v(t)$ be the velocity of the rocket at time t and suppose that the velocity u of the exhaust gas is constant. Let $M = M(t)$ be the mass of the rocket at time t and note that M decreases as the fuel burns. If we neglect air resistance, it follows from Newton's Second Law that

$$F = M\frac{dv}{dt} - ub$$

where the force $F = -Mg$. Thus

1 $$M\frac{dv}{dt} - ub = -Mg$$

Let M_1 be the mass of the rocket without fuel, M_2 the initial mass of the fuel, and $M_0 = M_1 + M_2$. Then, until the fuel runs out at time $t = M_2 b$, the mass is $M = M_0 - bt$.

(a) Substitute $M = M_0 - bt$ into Equation 1 and solve the resulting equation for v. Use the initial condition $v(0) = 0$ to evaluate the constant.

(b) Determine the velocity of the rocket at time $t = M_2/b$. This is called the *burnout velocity*.

(c) Determine the height of the rocket $y = y(t)$ at the burnout time.

(d) Find the height of the rocket at any time t.

7 | ANSWERS TO SELECTED EXERCISES

1. $\frac{1}{2}xe^{2x} - \frac{1}{4}e^{2x} + C$

2. $x \sin x + \cos x + C$

3. $-\frac{1}{4}x\cos 4x + \frac{1}{16}\sin 4x + C$

4. $\frac{1}{3}x^2 \sin 3x + \frac{2}{9}x\cos 3x - \frac{2}{27}\sin 3x + C$

5. $-\frac{x^2}{a}\cos ax + \frac{2x}{a^2}\sin ax + \frac{2}{a^3}\cos ax + C$

6. $\frac{1}{8}(\sin 2\theta - 2\theta\cos 2\theta) + C$

7. $\frac{1}{9}t^3(3\ln t - 1) + C$

8. $\frac{1}{10}e^{-\theta}(3\sin 3\theta - \cos 3\theta) + C$

9. $1 - 2/e$

10. $2\ln 4 - \frac{3}{2}$

11. $-\frac{1}{2}$

12. $2 - 5/e$

13. $\frac{1}{2}e^{x^2}(x^2 - 1) + C$

14. $\frac{1}{2}x\left[\sin(\ln x) - \cos(\ln x)\right] + C$

15. $\frac{1}{2}(x^2\tan^{-1}x + \tan^{-1}x - x) + C$

16. $-\cos x + \frac{1}{3}\cos^3 x + C$

17. $\frac{1}{7}\cos^7 x - \frac{1}{5}\cos^5 x + C$

18. $\frac{1}{5}\sin^5 x - \frac{1}{7}\sin^7 x + C$

19. $\frac{1}{10}\sin^{10}x - \frac{1}{4}\sin^8 x + \frac{1}{6}\sin^6 x + C$

20. $\frac{\pi}{4}$

21. $\frac{\pi}{4}$

22. $\frac{3}{8}t + \frac{1}{4}\sin 2t + \frac{1}{32}\sin 4t + C$

23. $\frac{5}{16}x - \frac{1}{4\pi}\sin 2\pi x + \frac{3}{64\pi}\sin 4\pi x + \frac{1}{48\pi}\sin^3 2\pi x + C$

24. $\frac{1}{6}\sec^6 x + C$ or $\frac{1}{2}\tan^2 x + \frac{1}{2}\tan^4 x + \frac{1}{2}\tan^6 x + C$

25. $\frac{1}{8}\sec^8 x - \frac{1}{6}\sec^6 x + C$ or

$\frac{1}{8}\tan^2 x + \frac{1}{3}\tan^6 x + \frac{1}{4}\tan^4 x + C$

26. $\frac{1}{3}\tan^3 x + \tan x + C$

27. $\frac{28}{15}$

28. $\frac{2}{\sqrt{3}}$

29. $\frac{64}{15}$

30. $-\sqrt{1 - x^2} + C$

31. $-\frac{1}{3}(4 - x^2)^{3/2} + C$

32. $\frac{A}{2x + 3} + \frac{B}{x - 1}$

33. $\frac{A}{2x + 1} + \frac{B}{x - 2}$

34. $\frac{A}{3x - 1} + \frac{B}{x + 6} + \frac{C}{(x + 6)^2}$

35. $\frac{A}{3z + 5} + \frac{B}{(3z + 5)^2} + \frac{C}{(3z + 5)^3} + \frac{D}{z + 2}$

36. $\frac{A}{x} + \frac{B}{x^2} + \frac{C}{x^3} + \frac{D}{x - 1}$

37. $x + 1 + \frac{A}{x} + \frac{B}{x + 1} + \frac{C}{x - 1}$

38. $1 + \frac{A}{x - 1} + \frac{B}{x + 1}$

39. $\frac{Ax + B}{x^2 + 1} + \frac{Cx + D}{x^2 + 2}$

40. $\frac{A}{x} + \frac{B}{x + 2}$

41. $\frac{A}{2x - 3} + \frac{B}{x + 4}$

42. $\frac{A}{x - 1} + \frac{B}{x + 2}$

43. $\frac{A}{2x - 1} + \frac{B}{(2x - 1)^2} + \frac{C}{2x + 3}$

44. $\frac{A}{x - 6} + \frac{B}{5x + 3} + \frac{C}{(5x + 3)^2} + \frac{D}{(5x + 3)^3}$

45. $\frac{A}{x} + \frac{B}{x^2} + \frac{C}{x^3} + \frac{D}{x - 1} + \frac{Ex + F}{x^2 + x + 1}$

46. $\frac{A}{x - 1} + \frac{B}{(x - 1)^2} + \frac{C}{(x - 1)^3}$

$+ \frac{Dx + E}{4x^2 + 5x + 3} + \frac{Fx + G}{(4x^2 + 5x + 3)^2}$

47. $\dfrac{A}{x} + \dfrac{B}{x^2} + \dfrac{Cx + D}{x^2 + x + 2}$

48. $\dfrac{A}{x - 2} + \dfrac{B}{(x - 2)^2} + \dfrac{C}{(x - 2)^3} + \dfrac{Dx + E}{x^2 + 1}$

$\qquad + \dfrac{Fx + G}{2x^2 + 5x + 7} + \dfrac{Hx + I}{(2x^2 + 5x + 7)^2}$

49. $\dfrac{Ax + B}{x^2 + 9} + \dfrac{Cx + D}{(x^2 + 9)^2} + \dfrac{Ex + F}{(x^2 + 9)^3}$

50. About 1.85 inches from the center

52. 0

53. $2 - \sin^{-1}(2/\sqrt{5})$

7 | SOLUTIONS TO SELECTED EXERCISES

1. Let $u = x, dv = e^{2x}dx \Rightarrow$

$du = dx, v = \frac{1}{2}e^{2x}$. Then

$$\int xe^{2x}dx = \frac{1}{2}xe^{2x} - \int \frac{1}{2}e^{2x}dx = \frac{1}{2}xe^{2x} - \frac{1}{4}e^{2x} + C.$$

2. Let $u = x, dv = \cos x\,dx \Rightarrow du = dx,$
$v = \sin x$. Then

$$\int x \cos x\,dx = x\sin x - \int \sin x\,dx$$
$$= x \sin x + \cos x + C.$$

3. Let $u = x, dv = \sin 4x\,dx \Rightarrow$

$du = dx, v = -\frac{1}{4}\cos 4x.$

Then

$$\int x \sin 4x\,dx = -\frac{1}{4}x\cos 4x - \int \left(-\frac{1}{4}\cos 4x\right)dx$$
$$= -\frac{1}{4}x\cos 4x + \frac{1}{16}\sin 4x + C$$

4. Let $u = x^2, dv = \cos 3x\,dx \Rightarrow$

$du = 2x\,dx, v = \frac{1}{3}\sin 3x$. Then

$$I = \int x^2 \cos 3x\,dx = \frac{1}{3}x^2 \sin 3x - \frac{2}{3}\int x \sin 3x\,dx$$

Next let $U = x, dV = \sin 3x\,dx \Rightarrow dU = dx,$

$V = -\frac{1}{3}\cos 3x$ to get

$$\int x \sin 3x\,dx = -\frac{1}{3}x\cos 3x + \frac{1}{3}\int \cos 3x\,dx$$
$$= -\frac{1}{3}x\cos 3x + \frac{1}{9}\sin 3x + C_1$$

Substituting for $\int x \sin 3x\,dx$, we get

$$I = \frac{1}{3}x^2 \sin 3x - \frac{2}{3}\left(-\frac{1}{3}x\cos 3x + \frac{1}{9}\sin 3x + C_1\right)$$
$$= \frac{1}{3}x^2 \sin 3x + \frac{2}{9}x\cos 3x - \frac{2}{27}\sin 3x + C$$

where $C = -\frac{2}{3}C_1.$

5. Let $u = x^2, dv = \sin ax\,dx \Rightarrow du = 2x\,dx,$

$v = -\frac{1}{a}\cos ax$. Then

$$I = \int x^2 \sin ax\,dx$$
$$= -\frac{x^2}{a}\cos ax - \int \left(-\frac{1}{a}\right)\cos ax\,(2x\,dx)$$
$$= -\frac{x^2}{a}\cos ax + \frac{2}{a}\int x \cos ax\,dx.$$

Let $U = x, dV = \cos ax\,dx \Rightarrow dU = dx,$

$V = \frac{1}{a}\sin ax$. Then

$$\int x \cos ax\,dx = \frac{x}{a}\sin ax - \int \frac{1}{a}\sin ax\,dx$$
$$= \frac{x}{a}\sin ax + \frac{1}{a^2}\cos ax + C_1$$

So

$$I = -\frac{x^2}{a}\cos ax + \frac{2}{a}\left(\frac{x}{a}\sin ax + \frac{1}{a^2}\cos ax + C_1\right)$$
$$= -\frac{x^2}{a}\cos ax + \frac{2x}{a^2}\sin ax + \frac{2}{a^3}\cos ax + C$$

6. $I = \int \theta \sin \theta \cos \theta\,d\theta = \frac{1}{4}\int 2\theta \sin 2\theta\,d\theta$

$$= \frac{1}{8}\int t \sin t\,dt \text{ (Put } t = 2\theta \Rightarrow dt = d\theta/2.\text{)}$$

Let $u = t, dv = \sin t\,dt \Rightarrow du = dt, v = -\cos t$. Then

$$I = \frac{1}{8}\left(-t\cos t + \int \cos t\,dt\right)$$
$$= \frac{1}{8}(-t\cos t + \sin t) + C$$
$$= \frac{1}{8}(\sin 2\theta - 2\theta \cos 2\theta) + C$$

7. Let $u = \ln t, dv = t^2 dt \Rightarrow du = dt/t, v = \frac{1}{3}t^3$. Then

$$\int t^2 \ln t\,dt = \frac{1}{3}t^3 \ln t - \int \frac{1}{3}t^3(1/t)dt =$$

$$\frac{1}{3}t^3 \ln t - \frac{1}{9}t^3 + C = \frac{1}{9}t^3(3\ln t - 1) + C.$$

8. Let $u = \cos 3\theta, dv = e^{-\theta}d\theta \Rightarrow$
$du = -3\sin 3\theta\,d\theta, v = -e^{-\theta}$ Then

$$I = \int e^{-\theta}\cos 3\theta\,d\theta = -e^{-\theta}\cos 3\theta - 3\int e^{-\theta}\sin 3\theta\,d\theta.$$

Integrate by parts again:

$$I = -e^{-\theta} \cos 3\theta + 3e^{-\theta} \sin 3\theta - \int e^{-\theta} 9 \cos 3\theta \, d\theta,$$

so $10 \int e^{-\theta} \cos 3\theta d\theta = e^{-\theta} (3 \sin 3\theta - \cos 3\theta) + C_1$

and $I = \dfrac{1}{10} e^{-\theta} (3 \sin 3\theta - \cos 3\theta) + C$, where

$C = C_1/10$.

9. Let $u = t$, $dv = e^{-t} dt \Rightarrow du = dt$, $v = -e^{-t}$. By Formula 6,

$$\int_0^1 te^{-t} dt = \left[-te^{-t} \right]_0^1 + \int_0^1 e^{-t} dt$$

$$= -1/e + \left[-e^{-t} \right]_0^1 = -1/e - 1/e + 1$$

$$= 1 - 2/e$$

10. $I = \displaystyle\int_1^4 \ln \sqrt{x} \, dx = \dfrac{1}{2} \int_1^4 \ln x \, dx = \dfrac{1}{2} \left[x \ln x - x \right]_1^4.$

So $I = \dfrac{1}{2} \left[(4 \ln 4 - 4) - (0 - 1) \right] = 2 \ln 4 - \dfrac{3}{2}.$

11. Let $u = x, dv = \cos 2x \, dx \Rightarrow du = dx$,

$v = \dfrac{1}{2} \sin 2x \, dx$. Then

$$\int_0^{\pi/2} x \cos 2x \, dx = \left[\dfrac{1}{2} x \sin 2x \right]_0^{\pi/2} - \dfrac{1}{2} \int_0^{\pi/2} \sin 2x \, dx$$

$$= 0 + \left[\dfrac{1}{4} \cos 2x \right]_0^{\pi/2}$$

$$= \dfrac{1}{4} (-1 - 1) = -\dfrac{1}{2}$$

12. Let $u = x^2, dv = e^{-x} dx \Rightarrow du = 2x \, dx, v = -e^{-x}.$ Then

$$I = \int_0^1 x^2 e^{-x} dx = \left[-x^2 e^{-x} \right]_0^1 + \int_0^1 2x e^{-x} dx$$

$$= -1/e + \int_0^1 2x e^{-x} dx$$

Now use parts again with $u = 2x$, $dv = e^{-x}$. Then

$$I = -1/e - \left[2xe^{-x} \right]_0^1 + \int_0^1 2e^{-x} dx$$

$$= -1/e - 2/e - \left[2e^{-x} \right]_0^1 = -3/e - 2/e + 2$$

$$= 2 - 5/e$$

13. Substitute $t = x^2 \Rightarrow dt = 2x \, dx$. Then use parts with $u = t, dv = e^t dt \Rightarrow du = dt, v = e^t$. Thus,

$$\int x^3 e^{x^2} dx = \dfrac{1}{2} \int te^t dt = \dfrac{1}{2} te^t - \dfrac{1}{2} \int e^t dt$$

$$= \dfrac{1}{2} te^t - \dfrac{1}{2} e^t + C = \dfrac{1}{2} e^{x^2} (x^2 - 1) + C$$

14. Let $w = \ln x$, so that $x = e^w$ and $dx = e^w$. Then

$$\int \sin (\ln x) \, dx = \int e^w \sin w \, dw$$

$$= \dfrac{1}{2} e^w (\sin w - \cos w) + C$$

$$= \dfrac{1}{2} x \left[\sin (\ln x) - \cos (\ln x) \right] + C$$

15. Let $u = \tan^{-1} x, dv = x \, dx \Rightarrow du = dx/(1 + x^2),$

$v = \dfrac{1}{2} x^2.$

Then $\displaystyle\int x \tan^{-1} x \, dx = \dfrac{1}{2} x^2 \tan^{-1} x - \dfrac{1}{2} \int \dfrac{x^2}{1 + x^2} dx.$

But

$$\int \dfrac{x^2}{1 + x^2} dx = \int \dfrac{(1 + x^2) - 1}{1 + x^2} dx$$

$$= \int 1 \, dx - \int \dfrac{1}{1 + x^2} dx$$

$$= x - \tan^{-1} x + C_1$$

so

$$\int x \tan^{-1} x \, dx = \dfrac{1}{2} x^2 \tan^{-1} x - \dfrac{1}{2} (x - \tan^{-1} x + C_1)$$

$$= \dfrac{1}{2} (x^2 \tan^{-1} x + \tan^{-1} x - x) + C$$

16. $\displaystyle\int \sin^3 x \, dx = \int (1 - \cos^2 x) \sin x \, dx$

$$= \int \sin x \, dx + \int \cos^2 x \, (-\sin x) dx$$

$$= -\cos x + \dfrac{1}{3} \cos^3 x + C$$

by the substitution $u = \cos x$ in the second integral.

17. Let $u = \cos x \Rightarrow du = -\sin x \, dx$. Then

$$\int \sin^3 x \cos^4 x \, dx = \int \cos^4 x \, (1 - \cos^2 x) \sin x \, dx$$

$$= \int u^4 (1 - u^2)(-du) = \int (u^6 - u^4) du$$

$$= \dfrac{1}{7} u^7 - \dfrac{1}{5} u^5 + C = \dfrac{1}{7} \cos^7 x - \dfrac{1}{5} \cos^5 x + C$$

18. Let $u = \sin x \Rightarrow du = \cos x\, dx$. Then

$$\int \sin^4 x \cos^3 x\, dx = \int \sin^4 x\, (1 - \sin^2 x) \cos x\, dx$$

$$= \int (u^4 - u^6)\, du = \frac{1}{5}u^5 - \frac{1}{7}u^7 + C$$

$$= \frac{1}{5}\sin^5 x - \frac{1}{7}\sin^7 x + C$$

19. Let $u = \sin x \Rightarrow du = \cos x\, dx$. Then

$$\int \cos^5 x \sin^5 x\, dx = \int u^5 (1 - u^2)^2\, du$$

$$= \int u^5 (1 - 2u^2 + u^4)\, du = \int (u^5 - 2u^7 + u^9)\, du$$

$$= \frac{1}{10}u^{10} - \frac{1}{4}u^8 + \frac{1}{6}u^6 + C$$

$$= \frac{1}{10}\sin^{10} x - \frac{1}{4}\sin^8 x + \frac{1}{6}\sin^6 x + C$$

Or: Let $v = \cos x$, $dv = -\sin x\, dx$. Then

$$\int \cos^5 x \sin^5 x\, dx = \int v^5 (1 - v^2)^2 (-dv)$$

$$= \int (-v^5 + 2v^7 - v^9)\, dv = -\frac{1}{10}v^{10} + \frac{1}{4}v^8 - \frac{1}{6}v^6 + C$$

$$= -\frac{1}{10}\cos^{10} x + \frac{1}{4}\cos^8 x - \frac{1}{6}\cos^6 x + C$$

20. $\displaystyle\int_0^{\pi/2} \sin^2 3x\, dx = \int_0^{\pi/2} \frac{1}{2}(1 - \cos 6x)\, dx$

$$= \left[\frac{1}{2}x - \frac{1}{12}\sin 6x\right]_0^{\pi/2} = \frac{\pi}{4}$$

21. $\displaystyle\int_0^{\pi/2} \cos^2 x\, dx = \int_0^{\pi/2} \frac{1}{2}(1 + \cos 2x)\, dx$

$$= \left[\frac{1}{2}x + \frac{1}{4}\sin 2x\right]_0^{\pi/2} = \frac{\pi}{4}$$

22. $\displaystyle\int \cos^4 t\, dt = \int \left[\frac{1}{2}(1 + \cos 2t)\right]^2 dt$

$$= \frac{1}{4}\int (1 + 2\cos 2t + \cos^2 2t)\, dt$$

$$= \frac{1}{4}t + \frac{1}{4}\sin 2t + \frac{1}{4}\int \frac{1}{2}(1 + \cos 4t)\, dt$$

$$= \frac{1}{4}\left[t + \sin 2t + \frac{1}{2}t + \frac{1}{8}\sin 4t\right] + C$$

$$= \frac{3}{8}t + \frac{1}{4}\sin 2t + \frac{1}{32}\sin 4t + C$$

23. $\displaystyle\int \sin^6 \pi x\, dx = \int (\sin^2 \pi x)^3\, dx$

$$= \int \left[\frac{1}{2}(1 - \cos 2\pi x)\right]^3 dx$$

$$= \frac{1}{8}\int (1 - 3\cos 2\pi x + 3\cos^2 2\pi x - \cos^3 2\pi x)\, dx$$

$$= \frac{1}{8}\int \left[1 - 3\cos 2\pi x + \frac{3}{2}(1 + \cos 4\pi x)\right.$$

$$\left. - (1 - \sin^2 2\pi x)\cos 2\pi x\right] dx$$

$$= \frac{1}{8}\int \left(\frac{5}{2} - 4\cos 2\pi x + \frac{3}{2}\cos 4\pi x\right.$$

$$\left. + \sin^2 2\pi x \cos 2\pi x\right) dx$$

$$= \frac{1}{8}\left[\frac{5}{2}x - \frac{4}{2\pi}\sin 2\pi x + \frac{3}{8\pi}\sin 4\pi x\right.$$

$$\left. + \frac{1}{3 \cdot 2\pi}\sin^3 2\pi x\right] + C$$

$$= \frac{5}{16}x - \frac{1}{4\pi}\sin 2\pi x + \frac{3}{64\pi}\sin 4\pi x$$

$$+ \frac{1}{48\pi}\sin^3 2\pi x + C$$

24. Let $u = \sec x \Rightarrow du = \sec x \tan x\, dx$. Then

$$\int \tan x \sec^6 x\, dx = \int \sec^5 x \sec x \tan x\, dx$$

$$= \int u^5\, du = \frac{1}{6}u^6 + C$$

$$= \frac{1}{6}\sec^6 x + C$$

Or: Let $u = \tan x$, $du = \sec^2 x$. Then

$$\int \tan x \sec^6 x\, dx = \int \tan x\, (1 + \tan^2 x)^2 \sec^2 x\, dx$$

$$= \int \tan x \sec^2 x\, dx + 2\int \tan^3 x \sec^2 x\, dx$$

$$+ \int \tan^5 x \sec^2 x\, dx$$

$$= \frac{1}{2}\tan^2 x + \frac{1}{2}\tan^4 x + \frac{1}{2}\tan^6 x + C$$

25. Let $u = \sec x \Rightarrow du = \sec x \tan x\, dx$. Then

$$\int \tan^3 x \sec^6 x\, dx = \int (\sec^2 x - 1)\sec^5 x \sec x \tan x\, dx$$

$$= \int (u^2 - 1)u^5\, du = \int (u^7 - u^5)\, du$$

$$= \frac{1}{8}u^8 - \frac{1}{6}u^6 + C$$

$$= \frac{1}{8}\sec^8 x - \frac{1}{6}\sec^6 x + C$$

Or:

$$\int \tan^3 x \sec^6 x \, dx = \int \tan^3 x \, (\tan^2 x + 1)^2 \sec^2 x \, dx$$

$$= \int v^3(v^2 + 1)^2 \, dv \, (\text{where } v = \tan x)$$

$$= \int (v^7 + 2v^5 + v^3) \, dv$$

$$= \frac{1}{8}v^8 + \frac{1}{3}v^6 + \frac{1}{4}v^4 + C_1$$

$$= \frac{1}{8}\tan^2 x + \frac{1}{3}\tan^6 x + \frac{1}{4}\tan^4 x + C_1$$

26. $\displaystyle \int \sec^4 x \, dx = \int (\tan^2 x + 1) \sec^2 x \, dx$

$$= \int \tan^2 x \sec^2 x \, dx + \int \sec^2 x \, dx$$

$$= \frac{1}{3}\tan^3 x + \tan x + C$$

27. $\displaystyle \int \sec^6 x \, dx = \int (\tan^2 x + 1)^2 \sec^2 x \, dx$

$$= \int \tan^4 x \sec^2 x \, dx + 2 \int \tan^2 x \sec^2 x \, dx$$

$$+ \int \sec^2 x \, dx$$

$$= \frac{1}{5}\tan^5 x + \frac{2}{3}\tan^3 x + \tan x + C$$

(Set $u = \tan x$ in the first two integrals.) Thus

$$\int_0^{\pi/4} \sec^6 x \, dx = \left[\frac{1}{5}\tan^5 x + \frac{2}{3}\tan^3 x + \tan x\right]_0^{\pi/4}$$

$$= \frac{1}{5} + \frac{2}{3} + 1 = \frac{28}{15}$$

28. Let $x = \sin\theta$, where $-\dfrac{\pi}{2} \le \theta \le \dfrac{\pi}{2}$. Then

$dx = \cos\theta \, d\theta$ and $\sqrt{1 - x^2} = |\cos\theta| = \cos\theta$

$\left(\text{since } \cos\theta > 0 \text{ for } \theta \text{ in } \left[-\dfrac{\pi}{2}, \dfrac{\pi}{2}\right]\right)$. Thus

$$\int_{1/2}^{\sqrt{3}/2} \frac{dx}{x^2\sqrt{1 - x^2}} = \int_{\pi/6}^{\pi/3} \frac{\cos\theta \, d\theta}{\sin^2\theta \, \cos\theta}$$

$$= \int_{\pi/6}^{\pi/3} \csc^2\theta \, d\theta = \left[-\cot\theta\right]_{\pi/6}^{\pi/3}$$

$$= -\frac{1}{\sqrt{3}} - (-\sqrt{3})$$

$$= \frac{3}{\sqrt{3}} - \frac{1}{\sqrt{3}} = \frac{2}{\sqrt{3}}$$

29. Let $x = 2\sin\theta$, $-\dfrac{\pi}{2} \le \theta \le \dfrac{\pi}{2}$. Then $dx = 2\cos\theta \, d\theta$

and $\sqrt{4 - x^2} = |2\cos\theta| = 2\cos\theta$, so

$$\int_0^2 x^3\sqrt{4 - x^2}\, dx = \int_0^{\pi/2} 8\sin^3\theta(2\cos\theta)(2\cos\theta)\, d\theta$$

$$= 32\int_0^{\pi/2} \cos^2\theta\,(1 - \cos^2\theta)\sin\theta \, d\theta$$

$$= 32\int_1^0 u^2(1 - u^2)(-du)\,(\text{where } u = \cos\theta)$$

$$= 32\int_0^1 (u^2 - u^4)\, du = 32\left[\frac{1}{3}u^3 - \frac{1}{5}u^5\right]_0^1$$

$$= 32\left(\frac{1}{3} - \frac{1}{5}\right) = \frac{64}{15}$$

30. Let $u = 1 - x^2$. Then $du = -2x\,dx$, so

$$\int \frac{x}{\sqrt{1 - x^2}}\, dx = -\frac{1}{2}\int \frac{du}{\sqrt{u}} = -\sqrt{u} + C$$

$$= -\sqrt{1 - x^2} + C$$

31. Let $u = 4 - x^2$. Then $du = -2x\,dx \Rightarrow$

$$\int x\sqrt{4 - x^2}\, dx = -\frac{1}{2}\int \sqrt{u}\, du = -\frac{1}{2}\cdot\frac{2}{3}u^{3/2} + C$$

$$= -\frac{1}{3}(4 - x^2)^{3/2} + C$$

32. $\displaystyle \frac{3}{(2x + 3)(x - 1)} = \frac{A}{2x + 3} + \frac{B}{x - 1}$

33. $\displaystyle \frac{5}{2x^2 - 3x - 2} = \frac{5}{(2x + 1)(x - 2)} = \frac{A}{2x + 1} + \frac{B}{x - 2}$

34. $\displaystyle \frac{x^2 + 9x - 12}{(3x - 1)(x + 6)^2} = \frac{A}{3x - 1} + \frac{B}{x + 6} + \frac{C}{(x + 6)^2}$

35. $\displaystyle \frac{z^2 - 4z}{(3z + 5)^3(z + 2)} = \frac{A}{3z + 5} + \frac{B}{(3z + 5)^2}$

$$+ \frac{C}{(3z + 5)^3} + \frac{D}{z + 2}$$

36. $\displaystyle \frac{1}{x^4 - x^3} = \frac{1}{x^3(x - 1)} = \frac{A}{x} + \frac{B}{x^2} + \frac{C}{x^3} + \frac{D}{x - 1}$

37. $\displaystyle \frac{x^4 + x^3 - x^2 - x + 1}{x^3 - x} = x + 1 + \frac{1}{x(x + 1)(x - 1)}$

$$= x + 1 + \frac{A}{x} + \frac{B}{x + 1} + \frac{C}{x - 1}$$

38. $\displaystyle \frac{x^2 + 1}{x^2 - 1} = 1 + \frac{2}{(x - 1)(x + 1)} = 1 + \frac{A}{x - 1} + \frac{B}{x + 1}$

39. $\displaystyle \frac{x^3 - 4x^2 + 2}{(x^2 + 1)(x^2 + 2)} = \frac{Ax + B}{x^2 + 1} + \frac{Cx + D}{x^2 + 2}$

40. $\dfrac{x+1}{x(x+2)} = \dfrac{A}{x} + \dfrac{B}{x+2}$

41. $\dfrac{7}{(2x-3)(x+4)} = \dfrac{A}{2x-3} + \dfrac{B}{x+4}$

42. $\dfrac{1}{(x-1)(x+2)} = \dfrac{A}{x-1} + \dfrac{B}{x+2}$

43. $\dfrac{x^2+3x-4}{(2x-1)^2(2x+3)} = \dfrac{A}{2x-1} + \dfrac{B}{(2x-1)^2} + \dfrac{C}{2x+3}$

44. $\dfrac{x^3-x^2}{(x-6)(5x+3)^3} = \dfrac{A}{x-6} + \dfrac{B}{5x+3}$

$$+ \dfrac{C}{(5x+3)^2} + \dfrac{D}{(5x+3)^3}$$

45. $\dfrac{1}{x^6-x^3} = \dfrac{1}{x^3(x^3-1)} = \dfrac{1}{x^3(x-1)(x^2+x+1)}$

$$= \dfrac{A}{x} + \dfrac{B}{x^2} + \dfrac{C}{x^3} + \dfrac{D}{x-1} + \dfrac{Ex+F}{x^2+x+1}$$

46. $\dfrac{19x}{(x-1)^3(4x^2+5x+3)^2} = \dfrac{A}{x-1} + \dfrac{B}{(x-1)^2}$

$$+ \dfrac{C}{(x-1)^3} + \dfrac{Dx+E}{4x^2+5x+3} + \dfrac{Fx+G}{(4x^2+5x+3)^2}$$

47. $\dfrac{x^3+x^2+1}{x^4+x^3+2x^2} = \dfrac{x^3+x^2+1}{x^2(x^2+x+2)}$

$$= \dfrac{A}{x} + \dfrac{B}{x^2} + \dfrac{Cx+D}{x^2+x+2}$$

48. $\dfrac{3-11x}{(x-2)^3(x^2+1)(2x^2+5x+7)^2}$

$$= \dfrac{A}{x-2} + \dfrac{B}{(x-2)^2} + \dfrac{C}{(x-2)^3}$$

$$+ \dfrac{Dx+E}{x^2+1} + \dfrac{Fx+G}{2x^2+5x+7} + \dfrac{Hx+1}{(2x^2+5x+7)^2}$$

49. $\dfrac{x^4}{(x^2+9)^3} = \dfrac{Ax+B}{x^2+9} + \dfrac{Cx+D}{(x^2+9)^2} + \dfrac{Ex+F}{(x^2+9)^3}$

50.

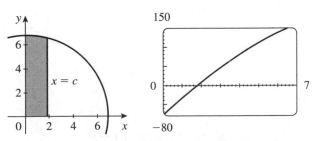

By symmetry, the problem can be reduced to finding the line $x = c$ such that the shaded area is one-third

of the area of the quarter-circle. The equation of the circle is $y = \sqrt{49 - x^2}$, so we require that

$$\int_0^c \sqrt{49-x^2}\, dx = \dfrac{1}{3} \cdot \dfrac{1}{4}\pi(7)^2 \Leftrightarrow$$

$$\left[\dfrac{1}{2}x\sqrt{49-x^2} + \dfrac{49}{2}\sin^{-1}(x/7)\right]_0^c = \dfrac{49}{12}\pi$$

[by Formula 30] $\Leftrightarrow \dfrac{1}{2}c\sqrt{49-c^2} + \dfrac{49}{2}\sin^{-1}(c/7)$

$= \dfrac{49}{12}\pi$. This equation would be difficult to solve

exactly, so we plot the left-hand side as a function of c, and find that the equation holds for $c \approx 1.85$. So the cuts should be made at distances of about 1.85 inches from the center of the pizza.

52. The given integral represents the difference of the shaded areas, which appears to be 0. It can be calculated by integrating with respect to either x or y, so we find x in terms of y for

each curve: $y = \sqrt[3]{1-x^7} \Rightarrow x = \sqrt[7]{1-y^3}$

and $y = \sqrt[7]{1-x^3} \Rightarrow x = \sqrt[3]{1-y^7}$, so

$$\int_0^1 \left(\sqrt[3]{1-y^7} - \sqrt[7]{1-y^3}\right) dy = \int_0^1 \left(\sqrt[7]{1-x^3}\right.$$

$$\left. -\sqrt[3]{1-x^7}\right) dx.$$ But this equation is of the form

$$z = -z.\ \text{So} \int_0^1 \left(\sqrt[3]{1-x^7} - \sqrt[7]{1-x^3}\right) dx = 0.$$

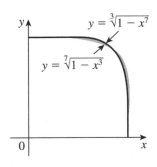

53. An equation of the circle with center $(0, c)$ and radius 1 is $x^2 + (y-c)^2 = 1^2$, so an equation of the lower semicircle is $y = c - \sqrt{1-x^2}$. At the points of tangency, the slopes of the line and semicircle must be equal. For $x \ge 0$, we must have

$$y' = 2 \Rightarrow \dfrac{x}{\sqrt{1-x^2}} = 2 \Rightarrow x = 2\sqrt{1-x^2} \Rightarrow$$

$$x^2 = 4(1-x^2) \Rightarrow 5x^2 = 4 \Rightarrow x^2 = \dfrac{4}{5} \Rightarrow$$

$$x = \dfrac{2}{5}\sqrt{5} \text{ and so } y = 2\left(\dfrac{2}{5}\sqrt{5}\right) = \dfrac{4}{5}\sqrt{5}.$$

The slope of the perpendicular line segment is $-\dfrac{1}{2}$, so an equation of the line segment is $y - \dfrac{4}{5}\sqrt{5} =$

$-\dfrac{1}{2}\left(x - \dfrac{2}{5}\sqrt{5}\right) \Leftrightarrow y = -\dfrac{1}{2}x + \dfrac{1}{5}\sqrt{5} + \dfrac{4}{5}\sqrt{5} \Leftrightarrow$

$y = -\dfrac{1}{2}x + \sqrt{5}$, so $c = \sqrt{5}$ and an equation of the

lower semicircle is $y = \sqrt{5} - \sqrt{1 - x^2}$. Thus, the shaded area is

$2\displaystyle\int_0^{(2/5)\sqrt{5}} \left[\left(\sqrt{5} - \sqrt{1 - x^2}\right) - 2x\right] dx \overset{30}{=}$

$2\left[\sqrt{5}x - \dfrac{x}{2}\sqrt{1 - x^2} - \dfrac{1}{2}\sin^{-1}x - x^2\right]_0^{(2/5)\sqrt{5}}$

$= 2\left[2 - \dfrac{\sqrt{5}}{5} \cdot \dfrac{1}{\sqrt{5}} - \dfrac{1}{2}\sin^{-1}\left(\dfrac{2}{\sqrt{5}}\right) - \dfrac{4}{5}\right] - 2(0)$

$= 2\left[1 - \dfrac{1}{2}\sin^{-1}\left(\dfrac{2}{\sqrt{5}}\right)\right] = 2 - \sin^{-1}\left(\dfrac{2}{\sqrt{5}}\right)$

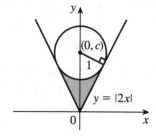

8 DIFFERENTIAL EQUATIONS

1. (a) A direction field for the differential equation $y' = 2y(y - 2)$ is shown. Sketch the graphs of the solutions that satisfy the given initial conditions.

   (i) $y(0) = 1$ (ii) $y(0) = 2.5$ (iii) $y(0) = -1$

   (b) Suppose the initial condition is $y(0) = c$. For what values of c is $\lim_{t\to\infty} y(t)$ finite? What are the equilibrium solutions?

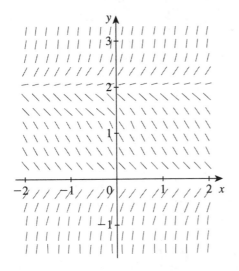

2–3 ■ Sketch a direction field for the differential equation. Then use it to sketch three solution curves.

2. $y' = x - y$

3. $y' = xy + y^2$

4–5 ■ Sketch the direction field of the given differential equation. Then use it to sketch a solution curve that passes through the given point.

4. $y' = y^2$, $(0, 1)$

5. $y' = x^2 + y$, $(1, 1)$

6–9 ■ Solve the differential equation.

6. $x^2 y' + y = 0$

7. $y' = \dfrac{\ln x}{xy + xy^3}$

8. $\dfrac{du}{dt} = e^{u + 2t}$

9. $\dfrac{dx}{dt} = 1 + t - x - tx$

10–15 ■ Find the solution of the differential equation that satisfies the given initial condition.

10. $\dfrac{dy}{dx} = \dfrac{1 + x}{xy}$, $x > 0$, $y(1) = -4$

11. $xe^{-t}\dfrac{dx}{dt} = t$, $x(0) = 1$

12. $x + 2y\sqrt{x^2 + 1}\,\dfrac{dy}{dx} = 0$, $y(0) = 1$

13. $e^y y' = \dfrac{3x^2}{1 + y}$, $y(2) = 0$

14. $\dfrac{du}{dt} = \dfrac{2t + 1}{2(u - 1)}$, $u(0) = -1$

15. $\dfrac{dy}{dt} = \dfrac{ty + 3t}{t^2 + 1}$, $y(2) = 2$

16–19 ■ Determine whether the differential equation is linear.

16. $y' + x^2 y = y^2$

17. $x^2 y' - y + x = 0$

18. $xy' = x - y$

19. $yy' = \sin x$

20–24 ■ Solve the initial-value problem.

20. $y' + y = x + e^x$, $y(0) = 0$

21. $xy' - 3y = x^2$, $x > 0$, $y(1) = 0$

22. $y' - 2xy = 2xe^{x^2}$, $y(0) = 3$

23. $(1 + x^2)y' + 2xy = 3\sqrt{x}$, $y(0) = 2$

24. $x^2\dfrac{dy}{dx} + 2xy = \cos x$, $y(\pi) = 0$

8 | ANSWERS TO SELECTED EXERCISES

1. (a) (i)

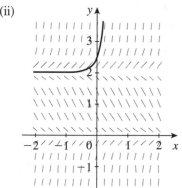

(ii)

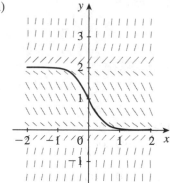

(iii)

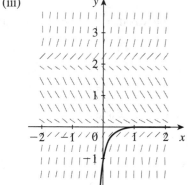

(b) $c \leq 2$; $y = 0$, $y = 2$

2.

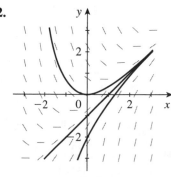

3.

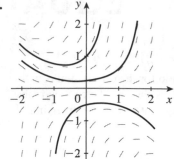

4.

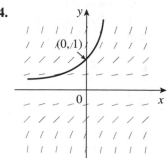

5.

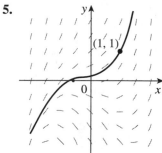

6. $y = Ce^{1/x}$

7. $y^2 + 1 = \sqrt{2(\ln x)^2 + C}$

8. $u = -\ln\left(C - \dfrac{1}{2}e^{2t}\right)$

9. $x = 1 + Ce^{-(t^2/2 + t)}$

10. $y^2 = 2\ln x + 2x + 14$

11. $x = \sqrt{2(t-1)e^t + 3}$

12. $y^2 = 2 - \sqrt{x^2 + 1}$

13. $ye^y = x^3 - 8$

14. $u = 1 - \sqrt{t^2 + t + 4}$

15. $y = -3 + \sqrt{5t^2 + 5}$

16. Not linear

17. Linear

18. Linear

19. Not linear

20. $y = x - 1 + \cosh x$

21. $y = -x^2 + x^3$

22. $y = (x^2 + 3)\,e^{x^2}$

23. $y = \dfrac{2x^{3/2} + 2}{1 + x^2}$

24. $y = \dfrac{\sin x}{x^2}$

8 | SOLUTIONS TO SELECTED EXERCISES

1. (a) (i)

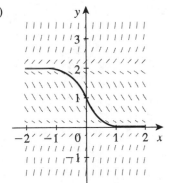

(ii)

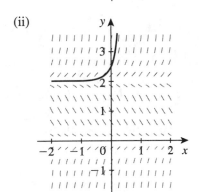

(iii)

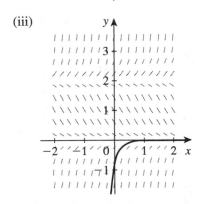

(b) For $c \leq 2$, $\lim_{t \to \infty} y(t)$ is finite. In fact, if $c = 2$ then $\lim_{t \to \infty} y(t) = 2$ and if $c < 2$ then $\lim_{t \to \infty} y(t) = 0$. The equilibrium solutions are $y = 0$ and $y = 2$.

2. $y' = x - y$

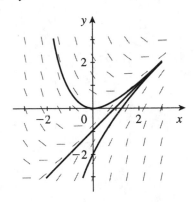

3. $y' = xy + y^2$

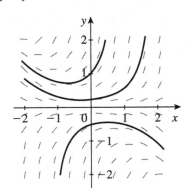

4.

x	y	$y' = y^2$
0	0	0
0	1	1
0	−1	1
1	0	0
−1	0	0
1	−1	1
1	1	1
1	2	4
1	−2	4
−1	2	4
−1	−2	4

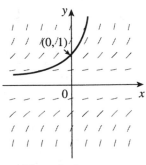

The solution curve through (0, 1)

5.

x	y	$y' = x^2 + y$
0	0	0
0	1	1
0	−1	−1
1	0	1
−1	0	1
1	1	2
−1	1	2
1	−1	0
−1	−1	0
2	0	4
2	1	5
2	−1	3

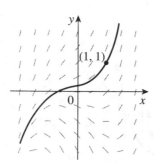

The solution curve
through (1, 1)

6. $x^2y' + y = 0 \Rightarrow \dfrac{dy}{dx} = -\dfrac{y}{x^2} \Rightarrow$

$\displaystyle\int \dfrac{dy}{y} = \int \dfrac{-dx}{x^2}$ $(y \neq 0) \Rightarrow \ln |y| = \dfrac{1}{x} + K \Rightarrow$

$|y| = e^K e^{1/x} \Rightarrow y = Ce^{1/x}$, where now we allow C to
be any constant.

7. $y' = \dfrac{\ln x}{xy + xy^3} = \dfrac{\ln x}{x(y + y^3)} \Rightarrow$

$\displaystyle\int (y + y^3)dy = \int \dfrac{\ln x}{x} dx \Rightarrow$

$\dfrac{y^2}{2} + \dfrac{y^4}{4} = \dfrac{1}{2}(\ln x)^2 + C_1 \Rightarrow$

$y^4 + 2y^2 = 2(\ln x)^2 + 2C_1 \Rightarrow$

$(y^2 + 1)^2 = 2(\ln x)^2 + K$ (where $K = 2C_1 + 1$)

$\Rightarrow y^2 + 1 = \sqrt{2(\ln x)^2 + K}$

8. $\dfrac{du}{dt} = e^{u + 2t} = e^u e^{2t} \Rightarrow \displaystyle\int e^{-u}du = \int e^{2t}dt \Rightarrow$

$-e^{-u} = \dfrac{1}{2}e^{2t} + C_1 \Rightarrow e^{-u} = -\dfrac{1}{2}e^{2t} + C$ (where

$C = -C_1$ and the right-hand side is positive, since
$e^{-u} > 0$)

$\Rightarrow -u = \ln\left(C - \dfrac{1}{2}e^{2t}\right) \Rightarrow u = -\ln\left(C - \dfrac{1}{2}e^{2t}\right)$

9. $\dfrac{dx}{dt} = 1 + t - x - tx = (1 + t)(1 - x) \Rightarrow$

$\displaystyle\int \dfrac{dx}{1 - x} = \int (1 + t)dt$ $(x \neq 1) \Rightarrow$

$-\ln |1 - x| = \dfrac{1}{2}t^2 + t + C \Rightarrow |1 - x| = e^{-(t^2/2 + t + C)}$

$\Rightarrow 1 - x = \pm e^{-(t^2/2 + t + C)} \Rightarrow$

$x = 1 + Ae^{-(t^2/2 + t)}$ (where $A = \pm e^C$ or 0)

10. $\dfrac{dy}{dx} = \dfrac{1 + x}{xy}, x > 0, y(1) = -4.$

$\displaystyle\int y \, dy = \int \dfrac{1 + x}{x} dx = \int\left(\dfrac{1}{x} + 1\right)dx \Rightarrow$

$\dfrac{1}{2}y^2 = \ln |x| + x + C = \ln x + x + C$ (since $x > 0$).

$y(1) = -4 \Rightarrow \dfrac{(-4)^2}{2} = \ln 1 + 1 + C \Rightarrow$

$8 = 0 + 1 + C \Rightarrow C = 7$, so $y^2 = 2 \ln x + 2x + 14.$

11. $xe^{-t}\dfrac{dx}{dt} = t, x(0) = 1. \displaystyle\int x \, dx = \int te^t \, dt \Rightarrow$

$\dfrac{1}{2}x^2 = (t - 1)e^t + C$ [integration by parts or
Formula 96].

$x(0) = 1$, so $\dfrac{1}{2} = (0 - 1)e^0 + C$ and $C = \dfrac{3}{2}$. Thus,

$x^2 = 2(t - 1)e^t + 3 \Rightarrow x = \sqrt{2(t - 1)e^t + 3}$ [use
the positive square root since $x(0) = +1$].

12. $x + 2y\sqrt{x^2 + 1}\dfrac{dy}{dx} = 0 \Rightarrow x \, dx +$

$2y\sqrt{x^2 + 1} \, dy = 0,$

$y(0) = 1. \displaystyle\int 2y \, dy = -\int \dfrac{x \, dx}{\sqrt{x^2 + 1}} \Rightarrow$

$y^2 = -\sqrt{x^2 + 1} + C. \ y(0) = 1 \Rightarrow 1 = -1 + C \Rightarrow$

$C = 2$, so $y^2 = 2 - \sqrt{x^2 + 1}.$

13. $e^y y' = \dfrac{3x^2}{1 + y}, y(2) = 0. \displaystyle\int e^y (1 + y) \, dy =$

$\displaystyle\int 3x^2 \, dx \Rightarrow$

$ye^y = x^3 + C. \ y(2) = 0$, so $0 = 2^3 + C$ and $C = -8.$
Thus $ye^y = x^3 - 8.$

14. $\dfrac{du}{dt} = \dfrac{2t + 1}{2(u - 1)}, u(0) = -1.$

$\displaystyle\int 2(u - 1) \, du = \int (2t + 1) \, dt \Rightarrow$

$u^2 - 2u = t^2 + t + C. \ u(0) = -1$ so
$(-1)^2 - 2(-1) = 0^2 + 0 + C$ and $C = 3.$ Thus

$u^2 - 2u = t^2 + t + 3$; the quadratic formula gives
$u = 1 - \sqrt{t^2 + t + 4}$.

15. $\dfrac{dy}{dt} = \dfrac{ty + 3t}{t^2 + 1} = \dfrac{t(y + 3)}{t^2 + 1}$,

$y\,(2) = 2$. $\displaystyle\int \dfrac{dy}{y + 3} = \int \dfrac{t\,dt}{t^2 + 1} \Rightarrow$

$\ln |y + 3| = \dfrac{1}{2} \ln (t^2 + 1) + C \Rightarrow y + 3 = A\sqrt{t^2 + 1}$.

$y\,(2) = 2 \Rightarrow 5 = A\sqrt{5} \Rightarrow A = \sqrt{5} \Rightarrow$
$y = -3 + \sqrt{5t^2 + 5}$.

16. $y' + x^2 y = y^2$ is not linear since it cannot be put into the standard linear form (1).

17. $x^2 y' - y + x = 0 \Rightarrow y' - \dfrac{1}{x^2} y = -\dfrac{1}{x}$, which is in the

standard linear form (1), and thus this differential equation is linear.

18. $xy' = x - y \Rightarrow xy' + y = x \Rightarrow y' + \dfrac{1}{x} y = 1$, which

is in the standard linear form (1), and thus this differential equation is linear.

19. $yy' = \sin x$ is not linear since it cannot be put into the standard linear form (1).

20. $I(x) = e^{\int dx} = e^x$. Multiplying the differential equation by

$I(x)$ gives $e^x y' + e^x y = e^x(x + e^x) \Rightarrow$
$(e^x y)' = e^x(x + e^x)$. Thus

$y = e^{-x} \left[\displaystyle\int e^x(x + e^x)dx + C \right]$

$= e^{-x} \left[xe^x - e^x + \dfrac{e^{2x}}{2} + C \right]$

$= x - 1 + \dfrac{e^x}{2} + \dfrac{C}{e^x}$

But $0 = y(0) = -1 + \dfrac{1}{2} + C$, so $C = \dfrac{1}{2}$, and the

solution to the initial-value problem is

$y = x - 1 + \dfrac{1}{2} e^x + \dfrac{1}{2} e^{-x} = x - 1 + \cosh x$.

21. $y' - 3y/x = x$, $x > 0$, so $I(x) = e^{\int -(3/x)dx} = x^{-3}$.

Multiplying the differential equation by $I(x)$ gives
$x^{-3}y' - 3x^{-4}y = x^{-2} \Rightarrow (x^{-3}y)' = x^{-2} \Rightarrow$

$y = x^3 \left[\displaystyle\int x^{-2}dx + C \right] = -x^2 + Cx^3$. But

$0 = y(1) = -1 + C$ so $C = 1$ and the solution to the initial-value problem is $y = -x^2 + x^3$.

22. $I(x) = e^{\int -2x\,dx} = e^{-x^2}$. Multiplying the differential equation by $I\,(x)$ gives

$e^{-x^2}y' - 2xe^{-x^2}y = 2x \Rightarrow \left(e^{-x^2}y\right)' = 2x \Rightarrow$
$y = e^{x^2} \left[\int 2x\,dx + C \right] = x^2 e^{x^2} + Ce^{x^2}$. But

$3 = y(0) = C$, so the solution to the initial-value problem is

$y = (x^2 + 3)e^{x^2}$.

23. $y' + \left(\dfrac{2x}{1 + x^2}\right)y = \dfrac{3\sqrt{x}}{1 + x^2}$, so

$I(x) = e^{\int [2x/(1+x^2)]dx} = e^{\ln(1+x^2)} = 1 + x^2$.

Multiplying the differential equation by $I(x)$ gives
$(1 + x^2)y' + 2xy = 3\sqrt{x} \Rightarrow ((1 + x^2)y)' = 3\sqrt{x}$

$\Rightarrow y = (1 + x^2)^{-1}\left(\int 3\sqrt{x}\,dx + C\right) = \dfrac{2x^{3/2} + C}{1 + x^2}$. But

$2 = y(0) = C$, so the solution to the initial-value problem is

$y = \dfrac{2x^{3/2} + 2}{1 + x^2}$.

24. $y' + 2\dfrac{y}{x} = \dfrac{\cos x}{x^2}$ $(x \neq 0)$, so $I(x) = e^{\int (2/x)dx} = x^2$.

Multiplying the differential equation by $I\,(x)$ gives
$x^2 y' + 2xy = \cos x \Rightarrow (x^2 y)' = \cos x \Rightarrow$
$y = x^{-2}\left[\int \cos x\,dx + C\right] = x^{-2}(\sin x + C)$,
$x \neq 0$, But $0 = y(\pi) = C$, so the solution to the initial-value problem is
$y = (\sin x)/x^2$.

9 PARAMETRIC EQUATIONS AND POLAR COORDINATES

1–10

(a) Sketch the curve by using the parametric equations to plot points. Indicate with an arrow the direction in which the curve is traced as t increases.

(b) Eliminate the parameter to find a Cartesian equation of the curve.

1. $x = 2t + 4$, $y = t - 1$

2. $x = 3 - t$, $y = 2t - 3$, $-1 \le t \le 4$

3. $x = 1 - 2t$, $y = t^2 + 4$, $0 \le t \le 3$

4. $x = t^2$, $y = 6 - 3t$

5. $x = 1 - t$, $y = 2 + 3t$

6. $x = 3\cos\theta$, $y = 2\sin\theta$, $0 \le \theta \le 2\pi$

7. $x = e^t$, $y = \sqrt{t}$, $0 \le t \le 1$

8. $x = e^t$, $y = e^t$

9. $x = \cos^2 t$, $y = \cos^4 t$

10. $x = \dfrac{1 - t}{1 + t}$, $y = t^2$, $0 \le t \le 1$

11–12 ■ Find dy/dx.

11. $x = \sqrt{t} - t$, $y = t^3 - t$

12. $x = t \ln t$, $y = \sin^2 t$

13–16 ■ Find an equation of the tangent to the curve at the point corresponding to the given value of the parameter.

13. $x = t^2 + t$, $y = t^2 - t$; $t = 0$

14. $x = t \sin t$, $y = t \cos t$; $t = \pi$

15. $x = t^2 + t$, $y = \sqrt{t}$; $t = 4$

16. $x = 2 \sin\theta$, $y = 3 \cos\theta$; $\theta = \pi/4$

17–24 ■ Find dy/dx and d^2y/dx^2.

17. $x = t^2 + t$, $y = t^2 + 1$

18. $x = t + 2\cos t$, $y = \sin 2t$

19. $x = t^4 - 1$, $y = t - t^2$

20. $x = t^3 + t^2 + 1$, $y = 1 - t^2$

21. $x = \sin \pi t$, $y = \cos \pi t$

22. $x = 1 + \tan t$, $y = \cos 2t$

23. $x = e^{-t}$, $y = te^{2t}$

24. $x = 1 + t^2$, $y = t \ln t$

25–29 ■ Plot the point whose polar coordinates are given. Then find two other pairs of polar coordinates of this point, one with $r > 0$ and one with $r < 0$.

25. $(-1, \pi/5)$

26. $(2, -\pi/7)$

27. $(-1, \pi)$

28. $(4, -2\pi/3)$

29. $(-2, 3\pi/2)$

30–37 ■ Find the area of the region that is bounded by the given curve and lies in the specified sector.

30. $r = \theta$, $0 \le \theta \le \pi$

31. $r = e^\theta$, $-\pi/2 \le \theta \le \pi/2$

32. $r = 2\cos\theta$, $0 \le \theta \le \pi/6$

33. $r = 1/\theta$, $\pi/6 \le \theta \le 5\pi/6$

34. $r = \sin 2\theta$, $0 \le \theta \le \pi/6$

35. $r = \cos 3\theta$, $-\pi/12 \le \theta \le \pi/12$

36. $r = 3\sin\theta$, $\pi/4 \le \theta \le 3\pi/4$

37. $r = \theta^2$, $\pi/2 \le \theta \le 3\pi/2$

38–43 ■ Sketch the curve and find the area that it encloses.

38. $r = 5\sin\theta$

39. $r = 4 - \sin\theta$

40. $r = \sin 3\theta$

41. $r = 4(1 - \cos\theta)$

42. $r = 2\cos\theta$

43. $r = 1 + \sin\theta$

CHALLENGE

44. Four bugs are placed at the four corners of a square with side length a. The bugs crawl counterclockwise at the same speed and each bug crawls directly toward the next bug at all times. They approach the center of the square along spiral paths.

(a) Find the polar equation of a bug's path assuming the pole is at the center of the square. (Use the fact that the line joining one bug to the next is tangent to the bug's path.)

(b) Find the distance traveled by a bug by the time it meets the other bugs at the center.

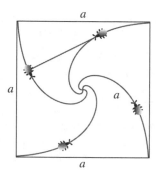

CHALLENGE

45. A curve called the **folium of Descartes** is defined by the parametric equations

$$x = \frac{3t}{1 + t^3} \qquad y = \frac{3t^2}{1 + t^3}$$

(a) Show that if (a, b) lies on the curve, then so does (b, a); that is, the curve is symmetric with respect to the line $y = x$. Where does the curve intersect this line?

(b) Find the points on the curve where the tangent lines are horizontal or vertical.

(c) Show that the line $y = -x - 1$ is a slant asymptote.

(d) Sketch the curve.

(e) Show that a Cartesian equation of this curve is $x^3 + y^3 = 3xy$.

(f) Show that the polar equation can be written in the form

$$r = \frac{3 \sec\theta \tan\theta}{1 + \tan^3\theta}$$

(g) Find the area enclosed by the loop of this curve.

CAS (h) Show that the area of the loop is the same as the area that lies between the asymptote and the infinite branches of the curve. (Use a computer algebra system to evaluate the integral.)

CHALLENGE

46. A circle C of radius $2r$ has its center at the origin. A circle of radius r rolls without slipping in the counterclockwise direction around C. A point P is located on a fixed radius of the rolling circle at a distance b from its center, $0 < b < r$. [See parts (i) and (ii) of the figure.] Let L be the line from the center of C to the center of the rolling circle and let θ be the angle that L makes with the positives x-axis.

(a) Using θ as a parameter, show that parametric equations of the path traced out by P are $x = b \cos 3\theta + 3r \cos\theta$, $y = b \sin 3\theta + 3r \sin\theta$. *Note*: If $b = 0$, the path is a circle of radius $3r$; if $b = r$, the path is an *epicycloid*. The path traced out by P for $0 < b < r$ is called an *epitrochoid*.

(b) Graph the curve for various values of b between 0 and r.

(c) Show that an equilateral triangle can be inscribed in the epitrochoid and that its centroid is on the circle of radius b centered at the origin.

Note: This is the principle of the Wankel rotary engine. When the equilateral triangle rotates with its vertices on the epitrochoid, its centroid sweeps out a circle whose center is at the center of the curve.

(d) In most rotary engines the sides of the equilateral triangles are replaced by arcs of circles centered at the opposite vertices as in part (iii) of the figure. (Then the diameter of the rotor is constant.) Show that the rotor will fit in the epitrochoid if $b \leq 3(2 - \sqrt{3})r/2$.

(i)

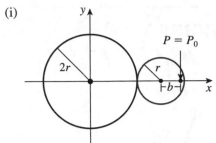

(ii)

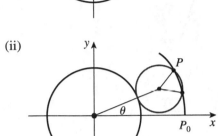

(iii)

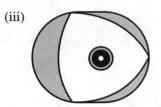

FIGURE FOR PROBLEM 46

9 | ANSWERS TO SELECTED EXERCISES

1. (a)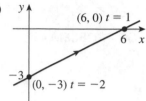

(b) $y = \dfrac{1}{2}x - 3$

2. (a)

(b) $y = 3 - 2x$

3. (a)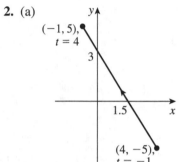

(b) $y = \dfrac{1}{4}(x - 1)^2 + 4$

4. (a)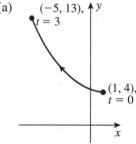

(b) $x = \dfrac{1}{9}(y - 6)^2$

5. (a)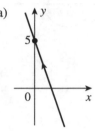

(b) $y = 5 - 3x$

6. (a)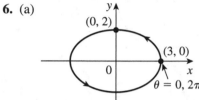

(b) $\dfrac{1}{9}x^2 + \dfrac{1}{4}y^2 = 1$

7. (a)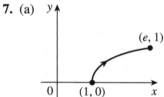

(b) $x = e^{y^2}, 0 \le y \le 1$

Or:

$y = \sqrt{\ln x}, 1 \le x \le e$

8. (a)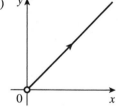

(b) $y = x, x > 0$

9. (a)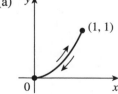

(b) $y = x^2, 0 \le x \le 1$

10. (a)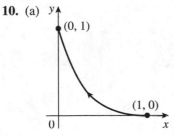

(b) $x = \dfrac{1 - \sqrt{y}}{1 + \sqrt{y}}, 0 \le y \le 1$

Or:

$y = \left(\dfrac{1 - x}{1 + x}\right)^2, 0 \le x \le 1$

11. $\dfrac{(3t^2 - 1)(2\sqrt{t})}{1 - 2\sqrt{t}}$

12. $\dfrac{2 \sin t \cos t}{1 + \ln t}$

13. $y = -x$

14. $y = \dfrac{1}{\pi}x - \pi$

15. $y = \dfrac{1}{36}x + \dfrac{13}{9}$

16. $y = -\dfrac{3}{2}x + 3\sqrt{2}$

17. $1 - \dfrac{1}{2t + 1}, \dfrac{2}{(2t + 1)^3}$

18. $\dfrac{2 \cos 2t}{1 - 2 \sin t}, \dfrac{4(\cos t - \sin 2t + \sin t \sin 2t)}{(1 - 2 \sin t)^3}$

19. $\dfrac{1}{4}t^{-3} - \dfrac{1}{2}t^{-2}, \dfrac{-3 + 4t}{16t^7}$

20. $-\dfrac{2}{3t + 2}, \dfrac{6}{t(3t + 2)^3}$

21. $-\tan \pi t, -\sec^3 \pi t$

22. $-4 \sin t \cos^3 t, 4 \cos^4 t(3 \sin^2 t - \cos^2 t)$

23. $-(2t + 1)e^{3t}, (6t + 5)e^{4t}$

24. $\dfrac{1 + \ln t}{2t}, -\dfrac{\ln t}{4t^3}$

25.

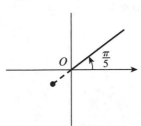

$\left(1, \dfrac{6\pi}{5}\right), \left(-1, \dfrac{11\pi}{5}\right)$

26.

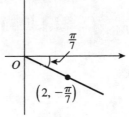

$\left(2, \dfrac{13\pi}{7}\right), \left(-2, \dfrac{6\pi}{7}\right)$

27.

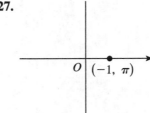

$(-1, 3\pi), (1, 0)$

28.

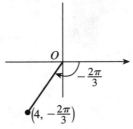

$\left(4, \dfrac{4\pi}{3}\right), \left(-4, \dfrac{\pi}{3}\right)$

29.

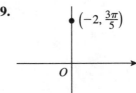

$\left(2, \dfrac{\pi}{2}\right), \left(-2, -\dfrac{\pi}{2}\right)$

30. $\dfrac{1}{6}\pi^3$

31. $\dfrac{1}{4}(e^\pi - e^{-\pi})$

32. $\dfrac{\pi}{6} + \dfrac{\sqrt{3}}{4}$

33. $\dfrac{12}{5\pi}$

34. $\dfrac{4\pi - 3\sqrt{3}}{96}$

35. $\dfrac{1}{24}(\pi + 2)$

36. $\dfrac{9}{8}(\pi + 2)$

37. $\dfrac{121}{160}\pi^5$

38.

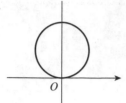

$$\frac{25}{4}\pi$$

39.

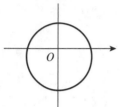

$$\frac{33\pi}{2}$$

40.

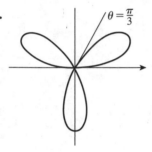

$$\frac{\pi}{4}$$

41.

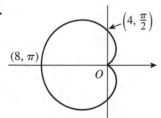

$$24\pi$$

42.

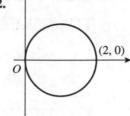

π

43.

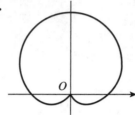

$$\frac{3\pi}{2}$$

45. (a) At $(0,0)$ and $\left(\dfrac{3}{2}, \dfrac{3}{2}\right)$

(b) Horizontal tangents at $(0,0)$ and $\left(\sqrt[3]{2}, \sqrt[3]{4}\right)$;
vertical tangents at $(0,0)$ and $\left(\sqrt[3]{4}, \sqrt[3]{2}\right)$

(d)

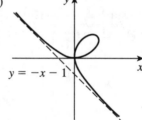

(g) $\dfrac{3}{2}$

9 | SOLUTIONS TO SELECTED EXERCISES

1. (a) $x = 2t + 4$, $y = t - 1$

t	-3	-2	-1	0	1	2
x	-2	0	2	4	6	8
y	-4	-3	-2	-1	0	1

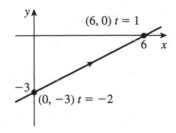

(b) $x = 2t + 4$, $y = t - 1 \Rightarrow$

$x = 2(y + 1) + 4 = 2y + 6$ or $y = \dfrac{1}{2}x - 3$

2. (a) $x = 3 - t$, $y = 2t - 3$, $-1 \le t \le 4$

t	-1	0	1	2	3	4
x	4	3	2	1	0	-1
y	-5	-3	-1	1	3	5

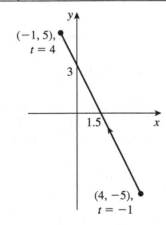

(b) $x = 3 - t \Rightarrow t = 3 - x \Rightarrow$
$y = 2t - 3 = 2(3 - x) - 3 \Rightarrow y = 3 - 2x$

3. (a) $x = 1 - 2t$, $y = t^2 + 4$, $0 \le t \le 3$

t	0	1	2	3
x	1	-1	-3	-5
y	4	5	8	13

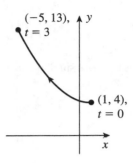

(b) $x = 1 - 2t \Rightarrow 2t = 1 - x \Rightarrow t = \dfrac{1 - x}{2} \Rightarrow$

$y = t^2 + 4 = \left(\dfrac{1 - x}{2}\right)^2 + 4 = \dfrac{1}{4}(x - 1)^2 + 4$ or

$y = \dfrac{1}{4}x^2 - \dfrac{1}{2}x + \dfrac{17}{4}$

4. (a) $x = t^2$, $y = 6 - 3t$

t	-3	-2	-1	0	1	2	3
x	9	4	1	0	1	4	9
y	15	12	9	6	3	0	-3

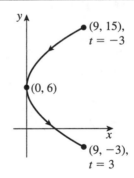

(b) $y = 6 - 3t \Rightarrow 3t = 6 - y \Rightarrow t = \dfrac{6 - y}{3} \Rightarrow$

$x = t^2 = \left(\dfrac{6 - y}{3}\right)^2 = \dfrac{1}{9}(y - 6)^2$

5. (a)

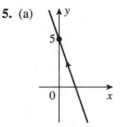

(b) $x = 1 - t$, $y = 2 + 3t \Rightarrow$
$y = 2 + 3(1 - x) = 5 - 3x$, so $3x + y = 5$

6. (a)

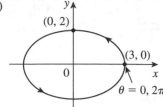

(b) $x = 3 \cos \theta$, $y = 2 \sin \theta$, $0 \le \theta \le 2\pi$ $\Rightarrow$

$$\left(\frac{x}{3}\right)^2 + \left(\frac{y}{2}\right)^2 = \cos^2 \theta + \sin^2 \theta = 1, \text{ or}$$

$$\frac{1}{9}x^2 + \frac{1}{4}y^2 = 1$$

7. (a)

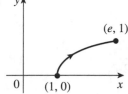

(b) $x = e^t$, $y = \sqrt{t}$ $\Rightarrow$ $x = e^{y^2}$, $0 \le y \le 1$
Or: $y = \sqrt{\ln x}$, $1 \le x \le e$

8. (a)

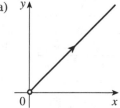

(b) $x = e^t$, $y = e^t$ $\Rightarrow$ $y = x$, $x > 0$

9. (a)

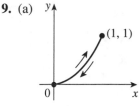

(b) $x = \cos^2 t$, $y = \cos^4 t$ $\Rightarrow$ $y = x^2$, $0 \le x \le 1$

10. (a)

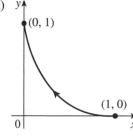

(b) $x = \dfrac{1-t}{1+t}$, $y = t^2$, $0 \le t \le 1$ $\Rightarrow$ $x = \dfrac{1 - \sqrt{y}}{1 + \sqrt{y}}$,

$0 \le y \le 1$

Or: $y = \left(\dfrac{1-x}{1+x}\right)^2$, $0 \le x \le 1$

11. $x = \sqrt{t} - t$, $y = t^3 - t$ $\Rightarrow$ $\dfrac{dy}{dt} = 3t^2 - 1$,

$$\frac{dx}{dt} = \frac{1}{2\sqrt{t}} - 1, \text{ and } \frac{dy}{dx} = \frac{dy/dt}{dx/dt} =$$

$$\frac{3t^2 - 1}{1/(2\sqrt{t}) - 1} = \frac{(3t^2 - 1)(2\sqrt{t})}{1 - 2\sqrt{t}}$$

12. $x = t \ln t$, $y = \sin^2 t$ $\Rightarrow$ $\dfrac{dy}{dt} = 2 \sin t \cos t$,

$$\frac{dx}{dt} = t\left(\frac{1}{t}\right) + (\ln t) \cdot 1 = 1 + \ln t, \text{ and}$$

$$\frac{dy}{dx} = \frac{dy/dt}{dx/dt} = \frac{2 \sin t \cos t}{1 + \ln t}$$

13. $x = t^2 + t$, $y = t^2 - t$; $t = 0$. $\dfrac{dy}{dt} = 2t - 1$, $\dfrac{dx}{dt} = 2t + 1$,

so $\dfrac{dy}{dx} = \dfrac{dy/dt}{dx/dt} = \dfrac{2t - 1}{2t + 1}$. When $t = 0$, $x = y = 0$

and $\dfrac{dy}{dx} = -1$. An equation of the tangent is

$y - 0 = (-1)(x - 0)$ or $y = -x$.

14. $x = t \sin t$, $y = t \cos t$; $t = \pi$. $\dfrac{dy}{dt} = \cos t - t \sin t$,

$$\frac{dx}{dt} = \sin t + t \cos t, \text{ and } \frac{dy}{dx} = \frac{dy/dt}{dx/dt}$$

$$= \frac{\cos t - t \sin t}{\sin t + t \cos t}. \text{ When } t = \pi, (x, y) = (0, -\pi) \text{ and}$$

$\dfrac{dy}{dx} = \dfrac{-1}{-\pi} = \dfrac{1}{\pi}$, so an equation of the tangent is

$$y + \pi = \frac{1}{\pi}(x - 0) \text{ or } y = \frac{1}{\pi}x - \pi.$$

15. $x = t^2 + t$, $y = \sqrt{t}$; $t = 4$. $\dfrac{dy}{dt} = \dfrac{1}{2\sqrt{t}}$, $\dfrac{dx}{dt} = 2t + 1$,

so $\dfrac{dy}{dx} = \dfrac{dy/dt}{dx/dt} = \dfrac{1}{2\sqrt{t}\,(2t + 1)}$. When $t = 4$,

$(x, y) = (20, 2)$ and $\dfrac{dy}{dx} = \dfrac{1}{36}$, so an equation of the

tangent is $y - 2 = \dfrac{1}{36}(x - 20)$ or $y = \dfrac{1}{36}x + \dfrac{13}{9}$.

16. $x = 2 \sin \theta$, $y = 3 \cos \theta$; $\theta = \dfrac{\pi}{4}$. $\dfrac{dx}{d\theta} = 2 \cos \theta$,

$\dfrac{dy}{d\theta} = -3 \sin \theta$, $\dfrac{dy}{dx} = \dfrac{dy/d\theta}{dx/d\theta} = -\dfrac{3}{2} \tan \theta$.

When $\theta = \dfrac{\pi}{4}$, $(x, y) = \left(\sqrt{2}, \dfrac{3\sqrt{2}}{2} \right)$, and

$dy/dx = -\dfrac{3}{2}$, so an equation of the tangent is

$y - \dfrac{3\sqrt{2}}{2} = -\dfrac{3}{2}(x - \sqrt{2})$ or $y = -\dfrac{3}{2}x + 3\sqrt{2}$.

17. $x = t^2 + t$, $y = t^2 + 1$.

$\dfrac{dy}{dx} = \dfrac{dy/dt}{dx/dt} = \dfrac{2t}{2t + 1} = 1 - \dfrac{1}{2t + 1}$;

$\dfrac{d}{dt}\left(\dfrac{dy}{dx} \right) = \dfrac{2}{(2t + 1)^2}$; $\dfrac{d^2y}{dx^2} = \dfrac{d}{dx}\left(\dfrac{dy}{dx} \right) = \dfrac{d(dy/dx)/dt}{dx/dt}$

$= \dfrac{2}{(2t + 1)^3}$

18. $x = t + 2 \cos t$, $y = \sin 2t$. $\dfrac{dy}{dx} = \dfrac{dy/dt}{dx/dt} = \dfrac{2 \cos 2t}{1 - 2 \sin t}$;

$\dfrac{d}{dt}\left(\dfrac{dy}{dx} \right) = \dfrac{(1 - 2 \sin t)(-4 \sin 2t) - 2 \cos 2t(-2 \cos t)}{(1 - 2 \sin t)^2}$

$= \dfrac{4(\cos t - \sin 2t + \sin t \sin 2t)}{(1 - 2 \sin t)^2}$;

$\dfrac{d^2y}{dx^2} = \dfrac{d(dy/dx)/dt}{dx/dt} = \dfrac{4(\cos t - \sin 2t + \sin t \sin 2t)}{(1 - 2 \sin t)^3}$

19. $x = t^4 - 1$, $y = t - t^2 \Rightarrow \dfrac{dy}{dt} = 1 - 2t$, $\dfrac{dx}{dt} = 4t^3$,

$\dfrac{dy}{dx} = \dfrac{dy/dt}{dx/dt} = \dfrac{1 - 2t}{4t^3} = \dfrac{1}{4}t^{-3} - \dfrac{1}{2}t^{-2}$;

$\dfrac{d}{dt}\left(\dfrac{dy}{dx} \right) = -\dfrac{3}{4}t^{-4} + t^{-3}$, $\dfrac{d^2y}{dx^2} = \dfrac{d(dy/dx)/dt}{dx/dt}$

$= \dfrac{-\frac{3}{4}t^{-4} + t^{-3}}{4t^3} \cdot \dfrac{4t^4}{4t^4} = \dfrac{-3 + 4t}{16t^7}$.

20. $x = t^3 + t^2 + 1$, $y = 1 - t^2$. $\dfrac{dy}{dt} = -2t$, $\dfrac{dx}{dt} = 3t^2 + 2t$;

$\dfrac{dy}{dx} = \dfrac{dy/dt}{dx/dt} = \dfrac{-2t}{3t^2 + 2t} = -\dfrac{2}{3t + 2}$; $\dfrac{d}{dt}\left(\dfrac{dy}{dx} \right)$

$= \dfrac{6}{(3t + 2)^2}$; $\dfrac{d^2y}{dx^2} = \dfrac{d(dy/dx)/dt}{dx/dt} = \dfrac{6}{t(3t + 2)^3}$.

21. $x = \sin \pi t$, $y = \cos \pi t$. $\dfrac{dy}{dx} = \dfrac{dy/dt}{dx/dt} = \dfrac{-\pi \sin \pi t}{\pi \cos \pi t}$

$= -\tan \pi t$; $\dfrac{d^2y}{dx^2} = \dfrac{d}{dx}\left(\dfrac{dy}{dx} \right) = \dfrac{d(dy/dx)/dt}{dx/dt}$

$= \dfrac{-\pi \sec^2 \pi t}{\pi \cos \pi t} = -\sec^3 \pi t$.

22. $x = 1 + \tan t$, $y = \cos 2t \Rightarrow \dfrac{dy}{dt} = -2 \sin 2t$,

$\dfrac{dx}{dt} = \sec^2 t$,

$\dfrac{dy}{dx} = \dfrac{dy/dt}{dx/dt} = \dfrac{-2 \sin 2t}{\sec^2 t} = -4 \sin t \cos t \cdot \cos^2 t$

$= -4 \sin t \cos^3 t$;

$\dfrac{d}{dt}\left(\dfrac{dy}{dx} \right) = -4 \sin t \, (3 \cos^2 t)(-\sin t) - 4 \cos^4 t$

$= 12 \sin^2 t \cos^2 t - 4 \cos^4 t$,

$\dfrac{d^2y}{dx^2} = \dfrac{d(dy/dx)/dt}{dx/dt} = \dfrac{4 \cos^2 t(3 \sin^2 t - \cos^2 t)}{\sec^2 t}$

$= 4 \cos^4 t(3 \sin^2 t - \cos^2 t)$.

23. $x = e^{-t}$, $y = te^{2t}$.

$\dfrac{dy}{dx} = \dfrac{dy/dt}{dx/dt} = \dfrac{(2t + 1) e^{2t}}{-e^{-t}} = -(2t + 1)e^{3t}$;

$\dfrac{d}{dt}\left(\dfrac{dy}{dx} \right) = -3(2t + 1) e^{3t} - 2e^{3t} = -(6t + 5)e^{3t}$;

$\dfrac{d^2y}{dx^2} = \dfrac{d}{dx}\left(\dfrac{dy}{dx} \right) = \dfrac{d(dy/dx)/dt}{dx/dt} = \dfrac{-(6t + 5)e^{3t}}{-e^{-t}}$

$= (6t + 5)e^{4t}$.

24. $x = 1 + t^2$, $y = t \ln t$. $\dfrac{dy}{dx} = \dfrac{dy/dt}{dx/dt} = \dfrac{1 + \ln t}{2t}$;

$\dfrac{d}{dt}\left(\dfrac{dy}{dx} \right) = \dfrac{2t(1/t) - (1 + \ln t)2}{(2t)^2} = -\dfrac{\ln t}{2t^2}$;

$\dfrac{d^2y}{dx^2} = \dfrac{d(dy/dx)/dt}{dx/dt} = -\dfrac{\ln t}{4t^3}$.

25. $\left(-1, \dfrac{\pi}{5} \right)$

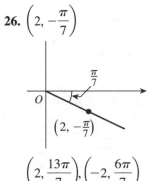

$\left(1, \dfrac{6\pi}{5} \right), \left(-1, \dfrac{11\pi}{5} \right)$

26. $\left(2, -\dfrac{\pi}{7} \right)$

$\left(2, -\dfrac{\pi}{7} \right)$

$\left(2, \dfrac{13\pi}{7} \right), \left(-2, \dfrac{6\pi}{7} \right)$

27. $(-1, \pi)$

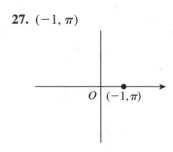

$(-1, 3\pi), (1, 0)$

28. $\left(4, -\dfrac{2\pi}{3}\right)$

$\left(4, \dfrac{4\pi}{3}\right), \left(-4, \dfrac{\pi}{3}\right)$

29. $\left(-2, \dfrac{3\pi}{2}\right)$

$\left(2, \dfrac{\pi}{2}\right), \left(-2, -\dfrac{\pi}{2}\right)$

30. $A = \displaystyle\int_0^\pi \frac{1}{2} r^2 \, d\theta = \int_0^\pi \frac{1}{2} \theta^2 \, d\theta = \left[\frac{1}{6} \theta^3\right]_0^\pi = \frac{1}{6} \pi^3$

31. $A = \displaystyle\int_{-\pi/2}^{\pi/2} \frac{1}{2} e^{2\theta} \, d\theta = \left[\frac{1}{4} e^{2\theta}\right]_{-\pi/2}^{\pi/2} = \frac{1}{4}(e^\pi - e^{-\pi})$

32. $A = \displaystyle\int_0^{\pi/6} \frac{1}{2}(2 \cos\theta)^2 \, d\theta = \int_0^{\pi/6} (1 + \cos 2\theta) \, d\theta$

$= \left[\theta + \frac{1}{2} \sin 2\theta\right]_0^{\pi/6} = \frac{\pi}{6} + \frac{\sqrt{3}}{4}$

33. $A = \displaystyle\int_{\pi/6}^{5\pi/6} \frac{1}{2}(1/\theta)^2 \, d\theta = [-1/(2\theta)]_{\pi/6}^{5\pi/6} = \frac{12}{5\pi}$

34. $A = \displaystyle\int_0^{\pi/6} \frac{1}{2} \sin^2 2\theta \, d\theta = \frac{1}{4} \int_0^{\pi/6} (1 - \cos 4\theta) \, d\theta$

$= \left[\frac{1}{4} \theta - \frac{1}{16} \sin 4\theta\right]_0^{\pi/6} = \frac{4\pi - 3\sqrt{3}}{96}$

35. $A = 2 \displaystyle\int_0^{\pi/12} \frac{1}{2} \cos^2 3\theta \, d\theta = \frac{1}{2} \int_0^{\pi/12} (1 + \cos 6\theta) \, d\theta$

$= \frac{1}{2} \left[\theta + \frac{1}{6} \sin 6\theta\right]_0^{\pi/12} = \frac{1}{24}(\pi + 2)$

36. $A = \displaystyle\int_{\pi/4}^{3\pi/4} \frac{1}{2}(3 \sin\theta)^2 \, d\theta = 2 \int_{\pi/4}^{\pi/2} \frac{9}{4}(1 - \cos 2\theta) \, d\theta$

$= \frac{9}{2} \left[\theta - \frac{1}{2} \sin 2\theta\right]_{\pi/4}^{\pi/2} = \frac{9}{8}(\pi + 2)$

37. $A = \displaystyle\int_{\pi/2}^{3\pi/2} \frac{1}{2}(\theta^2)^2 \, d\theta = \left[\frac{1}{10} \theta^5\right]_{\pi/2}^{3\pi/2} = \frac{121}{160} \pi^5$

38.

$A = \displaystyle\int_0^\pi \frac{1}{2}(5 \sin\theta)^2 \, d\theta = \frac{25}{4} \int_0^\pi (1 - \cos 2\theta) \, d\theta$

$= \frac{25}{4} \left[\theta - \frac{1}{2} \sin 2\theta\right]_0^\pi = \frac{25}{4} \pi$

39.

$A = 2 \displaystyle\int_{-\pi/2}^{\pi/2} \frac{1}{2}(4 - \sin\theta)^2 \, d\theta$

$= \displaystyle\int_{-\pi/2}^{\pi/2} (16 - 8 \sin\theta + \sin^2\theta) \, d\theta$

$= \displaystyle\int_{-\pi/2}^{\pi/2} (16 + \sin^2\theta) \, d\theta$

$= 2 \displaystyle\int_0^{\pi/2} (16 + \sin^2\theta) \, d\theta$

$= 2 \displaystyle\int_0^{\pi/2} \left[16 + \frac{1}{2}(1 - \cos 2\theta)\right] d\theta$

$= 2 \left[\frac{33}{2} \theta - \frac{1}{4} \sin 2\theta\right]_0^{\pi/2} = \frac{33\pi}{2}$

40.

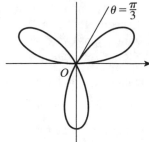

$$A = 6 \int_0^{\pi/6} \frac{1}{2} \sin^2 3\theta \, d\theta = 3 \int_0^{\pi/6} \frac{1}{2} (1 - \cos 6\theta) \, d\theta$$

$$= \frac{3}{2} \left[\theta - \frac{1}{6} \sin 6\theta \right]_0^{\pi/6} = \frac{\pi}{4}$$

41.

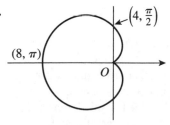

$$A = 2 \int_0^\pi \frac{1}{2} [4(1 - \cos\theta)]^2 \, d\theta$$

$$= 16 \int_0^\pi (1 - 2\cos\theta + \cos^2\theta) \, d\theta$$

$$= 8 \int_0^\pi (3 - 4\cos\theta + \cos 2\theta) \, d\theta$$

$$= 4[6\theta - 8\sin\theta + \sin 2\theta]_0^\pi = 24\pi$$

42.

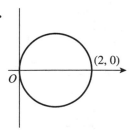

$$A = 2 \int_0^{\pi/2} \frac{1}{2} (2\cos\theta)^2 \, d\theta = 2 \int_0^{\pi/2} (1 + \cos 2\theta) \, d\theta$$

$$= 2 \left[\theta + \frac{1}{2} \sin 2\theta \right]_0^{\pi/2} = \pi$$

43.

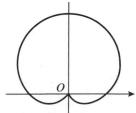

$$A = 2 \int_{-\pi/2}^{\pi/2} \frac{1}{2} (1 + \sin\theta)^2 \, d\theta$$

$$= \int_{-\pi/2}^{\pi/2} (1 + 2\sin\theta + \sin^2 2\theta) \, d\theta$$

$$= [\theta - 2\cos\theta]_{-\pi/2}^{\pi/2} + \int_{-\pi/2}^{\pi/2} \frac{1}{2} (1 - \cos 2\theta) \, d\theta$$

$$= \pi + \frac{1}{2} \left[\theta - \frac{1}{2} \sin 2\theta \right]_{-\pi/2}^{\pi/2} = \pi + \frac{\pi}{2} = \frac{3\pi}{2}$$

45. (a) If (a, b) lies on the curve, then there is some parameter value t_1 such that $\dfrac{3t_1}{1 + t_1^3} = a$ and $\dfrac{3t_1^2}{1 + t_1^3} = b$. If $t_1 = 0$, the point is $(0, 0)$, which lies on the line $y = x$. If $t_1 \neq 0$, then the point corresponding to $t = \dfrac{1}{t_1}$ is given by $x = \dfrac{3(1/t_1)}{1 + (1/t_1)^3} = \dfrac{3t_1^2}{t_1^3 + 1} = b$, $y = \dfrac{3(1/t_1)^2}{1 + (1/t_1)^3} = \dfrac{3t_1}{t_1^3 + 1} = a$. So (b, a) also lies on the curve. [Another way to see this is to do part (e) first; the result is immediate.] The curve intersects the line $y = x$ when $\dfrac{3t}{1 + t^3} = \dfrac{3t^2}{1 + t^3} \Rightarrow t = t^2 \Rightarrow t = 0$ or 1, so the points are $(0, 0)$ and $\left(\dfrac{3}{2}, \dfrac{3}{2} \right)$.

(b) $\dfrac{dy}{dt} = \dfrac{(1 + t^3)(6t) - 3t^2(3t^2)}{(1 + t^3)^2} = \dfrac{6t - 3t^4}{(1 + t^3)^2} = 0$ when $6t - 3t^4 = 3t(2 - t^3) = 0 \Rightarrow t = 0$ or $t = \sqrt[3]{2}$, so there are horizontal tangents at $(0, 0)$ and $(\sqrt[3]{2}, \sqrt[3]{4})$. Using the symmetry from part (a), we see that there are vertical tangents at $(0, 0)$ and $(\sqrt[3]{4}, \sqrt[3]{2})$.

(c) Notice that as $t \to -1^+$, we have $x \to -\infty$ and $y \to \infty$. As $t \to -1^-$, we have $x \to \infty$ and $y \to -\infty$.

Also $y - (-x - 1) = y + x + 1 = $

$$\dfrac{3t + 3t^2 + (1 + t^3)}{1 + t^3} = \dfrac{(t + 1)^3}{1 + t^3} = \dfrac{(t + 1)^2}{t^2 - t + 1} \to 0$$

as $t \to -1$. So $y = -x - 1$ is a slant asymptote.

(d) $\dfrac{dx}{dt} = \dfrac{(1 + t^3)(3) - 3t(3t^2)}{(1 + t^3)^2} = \dfrac{3 - 6t^3}{(1 + t^3)^2}$ and from part (b) we have $\dfrac{dy}{dt} = \dfrac{6t - 3t^4}{(1 + t^3)^2}$. So $\dfrac{dy}{dx} = \dfrac{dy/dt}{dx/dt}$

$= \dfrac{t(2 - t^3)}{1 - 2t^3}$. Also $\dfrac{d^2y}{dx^2} = \dfrac{\dfrac{d}{dt}\left(\dfrac{dy}{dx}\right)}{dx/dt}$

$= \dfrac{2(1 + t^3)^4}{3(1 - 2t^3)^3} > 0 \Leftrightarrow t < \dfrac{1}{\sqrt[3]{2}}$. So the curve is concave upward there and has a minimum point at $(0, 0)$ and a maximum point at $\left(\sqrt[3]{2}, \sqrt[3]{4}\right)$. Using this together with the information from parts (a), (b), and (c), we sketch the curve.

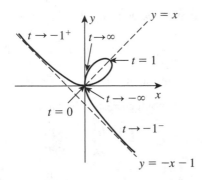

(e) $x^3 + y^3 = \left(\dfrac{3t}{1 + t^3}\right)^3 + \left(\dfrac{3t^2}{1 + t^3}\right)^3 = \dfrac{27t^3 + 27t^6}{(1 + t^3)^3}$

$= \dfrac{27t^3(1 + t^3)}{(1 + t^3)^3} = \dfrac{27t^3}{(1 + t^3)^2}$ and $3xy =$

$3\left(\dfrac{3t}{1 + t^3}\right)\left(\dfrac{3t^2}{1 + t^3}\right) = \dfrac{27t^3}{(1 + t^3)^2}$, so $x^3 + y^3 = 3xy$.

(f) We start with the equation from part (e) and substitute $x = r\cos\theta$, $y = r\sin\theta$. Then $x^3 + y^3 = 3xy \Rightarrow r^3\cos^3\theta + r^3\sin^3\theta = 3r^2\cos\theta\sin\theta$. For $r \neq 0$, this gives $r = \dfrac{3\cos\theta\sin\theta}{\cos^3\theta + \sin^3\theta}$.

Dividing numerator and denominator by $\cos^3\theta$, we obtain $r = \dfrac{3\left(\dfrac{1}{\cos\theta}\right)\dfrac{\sin\theta}{\cos\theta}}{1 + \dfrac{\sin^3\theta}{\cos^3\theta}} = \dfrac{3\sec\theta\tan\theta}{1 + \tan^3\theta}$.

(g) The loop corresponds to $\theta \in \left(0, \dfrac{\pi}{2}\right)$, so its area is

$A = \displaystyle\int_0^{\pi/2} \dfrac{r^2}{2}\,d\theta = \dfrac{1}{2}\int_0^{\pi/2}\left(\dfrac{3\sec\theta\tan\theta}{1 + \tan^3\theta}\right)^2 d\theta$

$= \dfrac{9}{2}\displaystyle\int_0^{\pi/2} \dfrac{\sec^2\theta\tan^2\theta}{(1 + \tan^3\theta)^2}\,d\theta$

$= \dfrac{9}{2}\displaystyle\int_0^{\infty} \dfrac{u^2\,du}{(1 + u^3)^2}$ [let $u = \tan\theta$]

$= \displaystyle\lim_{b\to\infty} \dfrac{9}{2}\left[-\dfrac{1}{3}(1 + u^3)^{-1}\right]_0^b = \dfrac{3}{2}$

(h) By symmetry, the area between the folium and the line $y = -x - 1$ is equal to the enclosed area in the third quadrant, plus twice the enclosed area in the fourth quadrant. The area in the third quadrant is $\dfrac{1}{2}$, and since $y = -x - 1 \Rightarrow r\sin\theta = -r\cos\theta - 1 \Rightarrow r = -\dfrac{1}{\sin\theta + \cos\theta}$, the area in the fourth quadrant is $\dfrac{1}{2}\displaystyle\int_{-\pi/2}^{-\pi/4}\left[\left(-\dfrac{1}{\sin\theta + \cos\theta}\right)^2 - \left(\dfrac{3\sec\theta\tan\theta}{1 + \tan^3\theta}\right)^2\right] d\theta \overset{\text{CAS}}{=} \dfrac{1}{2}$. Therefore, the total area is $\dfrac{1}{3} + 2\left(\dfrac{1}{2}\right) = \dfrac{3}{2}$.

46. (a) Since the smaller circle rolls without slipping around C, the amount of arc traversed on C ($2r\theta$ in the figure) must equal the amount of arc of the smaller circle that has been in contact with C. Since the smaller circle has radius r, it must have turned through an angle of $2r\theta/r = 2\theta$. In addition to turning through an angle 2θ, the little circle has rolled through an angle θ against C. Thus, P has turned through an angle of 3θ as shown in the figure. (If the little circle had turned through an angle of 2θ with its center pinned to the x-axis, then P would have turned only 2θ instead of 3θ. The movement of the little circle around C adds θ to the angle.) From the figure, we see that the center of the small circle has coordinates $(3r\cos\theta, 3r\sin\theta)$. Thus, P has coordinates (x, y), where $x = 3r\cos\theta + b\cos 3\theta$ and $y = 3r\sin\theta + b\sin 3\theta$.

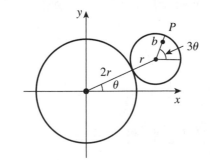

(b)

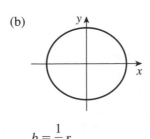

$b = \dfrac{1}{5}r$

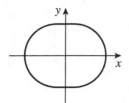

$$b = \frac{2}{5}r$$

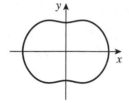

$$b = \frac{3}{5}r$$

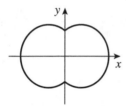

$$b = \frac{4}{5}r$$

(c) The diagram gives an alternate description of point P on the epitrochoid. Q moves around a circle of radius b, and P rotates one-third as fast with respect to Q at a distance of $3r$. Place an equilateral triangle with sides of length $3\sqrt{3}r$ so that its centroid is at Q and one vertex is at P. (The distance from the centroid to a vertex is $\frac{1}{\sqrt{3}}$ times the length of a side of the equilateral triangle.)

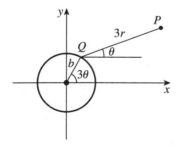

As θ increases by $\frac{2\pi}{3}$, the point Q travels once around the circle of radius b, returning to its original position. At the same time, P (and the rest of the triangle) rotate through an angle of $\frac{2\pi}{3}$ about Q, so P's position is occupied by another vertex. In this way, we see that the epitrochoid traced out by P is simultaneously traced out by the other two vertices as well.

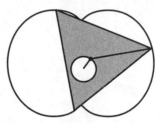

The whole equilateral triangle sits inside the epitrochoid (touching it only with its vertices) and each vertex traces out the curve once while the centroid moves around the circle three times.

(d) We view the epitrochoid as being traced out in the same way as in part (c), by a rotor for which the distance from its center to each vertex is $3r$, so it has radius $6r$. To show that the rotor fits inside the epitrochoid, it suffices to show that for any position of the tracing point P, there are no points on the opposite side of the rotor which are outside the epitrochoid. But the most likely case of intersection is when P is on the y-axis, so as long as the diameter of the rotor (which is $3\sqrt{3}r$) is less than the distance between the y-intercepts, the rotor will fit. The y-intercepts occur when $\theta = \frac{\pi}{2}$ or $\theta = \frac{3\pi}{2} \Rightarrow y = \pm(3r - b)$, so the distance between the intercepts is $6r - 2b$, and the rotor will fit if $3\sqrt{3}r \le 6r - 2b \Leftrightarrow b \le \frac{3(2 - \sqrt{3})}{2}r$.

10 INFINITE SEQUENCES AND SERIES

1. (a) Show that $\tan \frac{1}{2}x = \cot \frac{1}{2}x - 2\cot x$.

(b) Find the sum of the series

$$\sum_{n=1}^{\infty} \frac{1}{2^n} \tan \frac{x}{2^n}$$

2. (a) Show that, for $n = 1, 2, 3, \ldots$,

$$\sin\theta = 2^n \sin\frac{\theta}{2^n}\cos\frac{\theta}{2}\cos\frac{\theta}{4}\cos\frac{\theta}{8}\cdots\cos\frac{\theta}{2^n}$$

(b) Deduce that

$$\frac{\sin\theta}{\theta} = \cos\frac{\theta}{2}\cos\frac{\theta}{4}\cos\frac{\theta}{8}\cdots$$

The meaning of this infinite product is that we take the product of the first n factors and then we take the limit of these partial products as $n \to \infty$.

(c) Show that

$$\frac{2}{\pi} = \frac{\sqrt{2}}{2}\frac{\sqrt{2+\sqrt{2}}}{2}\frac{\sqrt{2+\sqrt{2+\sqrt{2}}}}{2}\cdots$$

This infinite product is due to the French mathematician Francois Viète (1540–1603). Notice that it expresses π in terms of just the number 2 and repeated square roots.

3–7 ■ Find at least 10 partial sums of the series. Graph both the sequence of terms and the sequence of partial sums on the same screen. Does it appear that the series is convergent or divergent? If it is convergent, find the sum. If it is divergent, explain why.

3. $\sum_{n=1}^{\infty} \frac{10}{3^n}$

4. $\sum_{n=1}^{\infty} \sin n$

5. $\sum_{n=1}^{\infty} \frac{n}{n+1}$

6. $\sum_{n=4}^{\infty} \frac{3}{n(n-1)}$

7. $\sum_{n=1}^{\infty} \left(-\frac{2}{7}\right)^{n-1}$

8–21 ■ Determine whether the series is convergent or divergent.

8. $\sum_{n=5}^{\infty} \frac{1}{n^{1.0001}}$

9. $\sum_{n=1}^{\infty} n^{-0.99}$

10. $\sum_{n=1}^{\infty} \frac{2}{\sqrt[3]{n}}$

11. $\sum_{n=1}^{\infty} \left(\frac{2}{n\sqrt{n}} + \frac{3}{n^3}\right)$

12. $\sum_{n=5}^{\infty} \frac{1}{(n-4)^2}$

13. $\sum_{n=1}^{\infty} \frac{1}{2n+3}$

14. $\sum_{n=1}^{\infty} \frac{1}{\sqrt{n}+1}$

15. $\sum_{n=2}^{\infty} \frac{1}{n^2-1}$

16. $\sum_{n=1}^{\infty} ne^{-n^2}$

17. $\sum_{n=1}^{\infty} \frac{n}{2^n}$

18. $\sum_{n=1}^{\infty} \frac{1}{4n^2+1}$

19. $\sum_{n=1}^{\infty} \frac{\arctan n}{1+n^2}$

20. $\sum_{n=1}^{\infty} \frac{\ln n}{n^2}$

21. $\sum_{n=1}^{\infty} \frac{1}{n^2+2n+2}$

22–28 ■ Test the series for convergence or divergence.

22. $\frac{3}{5} - \frac{3}{6} + \frac{3}{7} - \frac{3}{8} + \frac{3}{9} - \cdots$

23. $-5 - \frac{5}{2} + \frac{5}{5} - \frac{5}{8} + \frac{5}{11} - \frac{5}{14} + \cdots$

24. $-\frac{1}{2} + \frac{2}{3} - \frac{3}{4} + \frac{4}{5} - \frac{5}{6} + \frac{6}{7} - \cdots$

25. $\sum_{n=1}^{\infty} \frac{(-1)^{n-1}}{n^2}$

26. $\sum_{n=1}^{\infty} \frac{(-1)^n}{\sqrt{n+3}}$

27. $\sum_{n=1}^{\infty} (-1)^{n+1} \frac{n}{5n+1}$

28. $\sum_{n=2}^{\infty} \frac{(-1)^{n-1}}{n\ln n}$

29–39 ■ Find the radius of convergence and interval of convergence of the series.

29. $\sum_{n=0}^{\infty} nx^n$

30. $\sum_{n=1}^{\infty} \frac{x^n}{n^2}$

31. $\displaystyle\sum_{n=0}^{\infty} \frac{3^n x^n}{(n+1)^2}$

32. $\displaystyle\sum_{n=0}^{\infty} \frac{n^2 x^n}{10^n}$

33. $\displaystyle\sum_{n=2}^{\infty} \frac{x^n}{\ln n}$

34. $\displaystyle\sum_{n=1}^{\infty} \frac{(-1)^n x^{2n-1}}{(2n-1)!}$

35. $\displaystyle\sum_{n=0}^{\infty} \frac{2^n (x-3)^n}{n+3}$

36. $\displaystyle\sum_{n=1}^{\infty} \frac{(x+1)^n}{n(n+1)}$

37. $\displaystyle\sum_{n=0}^{\infty} \sqrt{n}\,(3x+2)^n$

38. $\displaystyle\sum_{n=0}^{\infty} \frac{n}{4^n}(2x-1)^n$

39. $\displaystyle\sum_{n=1}^{\infty} (-1)^n \frac{(x-1)^n}{\sqrt{n}}$

40–46 ■ Find a power series representation for the function and determine the interval of convergence.

40. $f(x) = \dfrac{x}{1-x}$

41. $f(x) = \dfrac{1}{4+x^2}$

42. $f(x) = \dfrac{1+x^2}{1-x^2}$

43. $f(x) = \dfrac{1}{1+4x^2}$

44. $f(x) = \dfrac{1}{x^4+16}$

45. $f(x) = \dfrac{x}{x-3}$

46. $f(x) = \dfrac{2}{3x+4}$

47–48 ■ Use a power series to approximate the definite integral to six decimal places.

47. $\displaystyle\int_0^{0.2} \frac{1}{1+x^4}\,dx$

48. $\displaystyle\int_0^{1/2} \tan^{-1}(x^2)\,dx$

CHALLENGE

49. To construct the **snowflake curve**, start with an equilateral triangle with sides of length 1. Step 1 in the construction is to divide each side into three equal parts, construct an equilateral triangle on the middle part, and then delete the middle part (see the figure). Step 2 is to repeat Step 1 for each side of the resulting polygon. This process is repeated at each succeeding step. The snowflake curve is the curve that results from repeating this process indefinitely.

(a) Let s_n, l_n, and p_n represent the number of sides, the length of a side, and the total length of the nth approximating curve (the curve obtained after Step n of the construction), respectively. Find formulas for s_n, l_n, and p_n.

(b) Show that $p_n \rightarrow \infty$ as $n \rightarrow \infty$.

(c) Sum an infinite series to find the area enclosed by the snowflake curve.

Parts (b) and (c) show that the snowflake curve is infinitely long but encloses only a finite area.

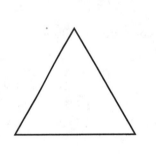

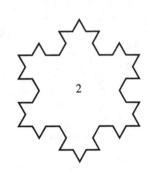
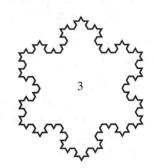

10 | ANSWERS TO SELECTED EXERCISES

1. (b) 0 if $x = 0$, $(1/x) - \cot x$ if $x \neq k\pi$, k an integer

3. 3.33333, 4.44444, 4.81481, 4.93827, 4.97942, 4.99314, 4.99771, 4.99924, 4.99975, 4,99992

Convergent, sum = 5

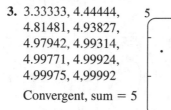

4. 0.8415, 1.7508, 1.8919, 1.1351, 0.1762, -0.1033, 0.5537, 1.5431, 1.9552, 1.4112

Divergent (terms do not approach 0)

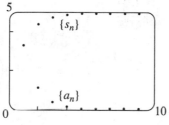

5. 0.50000, 1.16667, 1.91667, 2.71667, 3.55000, 4.40714, 5.28214, 6.17103, 7.07103, 7.98012

Divergent (terms do not approach 0)

6. 0.25000, 0.40000, 0.50000, 0.57143, 0.62500, 0.66667, 0.70000, 0.72727, 0.75000, 0.76923

Convergent, sum = 1

7. 1.000000, 0.714286, 0.795918, 0.772595, 0.779259, 0.777355, 0.777899, 0.777743, 0.777788, 0,777775

Convergent, sum $= \dfrac{7}{9}$

8. Convergent

9. Divergent

10. Divergent

11. Convergent

12. Convergent

13. Divergent

14. Divergent

15. Convergent

16. Convergent

17. Convergent

18. Convergent

19. Convergent

20. Convergent

21. Convergent

22. Convergent

23. Convergent

24. Divergent

25. Convergent

26. Convergent

27. Divergent

28. Convergent

29. $1, (-1, 1)$

30. $1, [-1, 1]$

31. $\dfrac{1}{3}, \left[-\dfrac{1}{3}, \dfrac{1}{3}\right]$

32. $10, (-10, 10)$

33. $1, (-1, 1)$

34. $\infty, (-\infty, \infty)$

35. $\dfrac{1}{2}, \left(\dfrac{5}{2}, \dfrac{7}{2}\right)$

36. $1, [-2, 0]$

37. $\dfrac{1}{3}, \left(-1, -\dfrac{1}{3}\right)$

38. $2, \left(-\dfrac{3}{2}, \dfrac{5}{2}\right)$

39. $1, (0, 2]$

40. $\displaystyle\sum_{n=1}^{\infty} x^n, (-1, 1)$

41. $\displaystyle\sum_{n=0}^{\infty} \dfrac{(-1)^n x^{2n}}{4^{n+1}}, (-2, 2)$

42. $1 + \displaystyle\sum_{n=1}^{\infty} 2x^{2n}, (-1, 1)$

43. $\displaystyle\sum_{n=0}^{\infty} (-1)^n 4^n x^{2n}, \left(-\dfrac{1}{2}, \dfrac{1}{2}\right)$

44. $\displaystyle\sum_{n=0}^{\infty} \dfrac{(-1)^n x^{4n}}{2^{4n+4}}, (-2, 2)$

45. $-\displaystyle\sum_{n=1}^{\infty} \left(\dfrac{x}{3}\right)^n, (-3, 3)$

46. $\displaystyle\sum_{n=0}^{\infty} \dfrac{(-1)^n 3^n x^n}{2^{2n+1}}, \left(-\dfrac{4}{3}, \dfrac{4}{3}\right)$

47. 0.199936

48. 0.041303

49. (a) $s_n = 3 \cdot 4^n$, $l_n = 1/3^n$, $p_n = 4^n/3^{n-1}$

(c) $2\sqrt{3}/5$

10 | SOLUTIONS TO SELECTED EXERCISES

1. (a) Assuming

$x = y = \theta$, we get $\tan 2\theta = \dfrac{2 \tan \theta}{1 - \tan^2 \theta}$, so

$\cot 2\theta = \dfrac{1 - \tan^2 \theta}{2 \tan \theta} \Rightarrow 2 \cot 2\theta = \dfrac{1 - \tan^2 \theta}{\tan \theta}$

$= \cot \theta - \tan \theta$. Replacing θ by $\dfrac{1}{2}x$, we get

$2 \cot x = \cot \dfrac{1}{2}x - \tan \dfrac{1}{2}x$, or $\tan \dfrac{1}{2}x$

$= \cot \dfrac{1}{2}x - 2 \cot x$.

(b) From part (a) with $\dfrac{x}{2^{n-1}}$ in place of x,

$\tan \dfrac{x}{2^n} = \cot \dfrac{x}{2^n} - 2 \cot \dfrac{x}{2^{n-1}}$, so the nth partial

sum of $\displaystyle\sum_{n=1}^{\infty} \dfrac{1}{2^n} \tan \dfrac{x}{2^n}$ is

$s_n = \dfrac{\tan(x/2)}{2} + \dfrac{\tan(x/4)}{4} + \dfrac{\tan(x/8)}{8} + \cdots$

$\quad + \dfrac{\tan(x/2^n)}{2^n}$

$= \left[\dfrac{\cot(x/2)}{2} - \cot x \right] + \left[\dfrac{\cot(x/4)}{4} - \dfrac{\cot(x/2)}{2} \right]$

$\quad + \left[\dfrac{\cot(x/8)}{8} - \dfrac{\cot(x/4)}{4} \right] + \cdots$

$\quad + \left[\dfrac{\cot(x/2^n)}{2^n} - \dfrac{\cot(x/2^{n-1})}{2^{n-1}} \right]$

$= -\cot x + \dfrac{\cot(x/2^n)}{2^n}$ [telescoping sum]

Now $\dfrac{\cot(x/2^n)}{2^n} = \dfrac{\cos(x/2^n)}{2^n \sin(x/2^n)}$

$= \dfrac{\cos(x/2^n)}{x} \cdot \dfrac{x/2^n}{\sin(x/2^n)} \to \dfrac{1}{x} \cdot 1 = \dfrac{1}{x}$ as $n \to \infty$

since $x/2^n \to 0$ for $x \neq 0$. Therefore, if $x \neq 0$ and $x \neq k\pi$ where k is any integer, then

$\displaystyle\sum_{n=1}^{\infty} \dfrac{1}{2^n} \tan \dfrac{x}{2^n} = \lim_{n\to\infty} s_n = \lim_{n\to\infty}\left(-\cot x + \dfrac{1}{2^n} \cot \dfrac{x}{2^n} \right)$

$= -\cot x + \dfrac{1}{x}$

If $x = 0$, then all terms in the series are 0, so the sum is 0.

2. (a) $\sin \theta = 2 \sin \dfrac{\theta}{2} \cos \dfrac{\theta}{2} = 2 \left(2 \sin \dfrac{\theta}{4} \cos \dfrac{\theta}{4} \right) \cos \dfrac{\theta}{2}$

$= 2 \left(2 \left(2 \sin \dfrac{\theta}{8} \cos \dfrac{\theta}{8} \right) \cos \dfrac{\theta}{4} \right) \cos \dfrac{\theta}{2}$

$= \cdots = 2 \left(2 \left(2 \left(\cdots \left(2 \sin \dfrac{\theta}{2^n} \cos \dfrac{\theta}{2^n} \right) \right.\right.\right.$

$\left.\left.\left. \cos \dfrac{\theta}{2^{n-1}} \right) \cdots \right) \cos \dfrac{\theta}{8} \right) \cos \dfrac{\theta}{4} \right) \cos \dfrac{\theta}{2}$

$= 2^n \sin \dfrac{\theta}{2^n} \cos \dfrac{\theta}{2} \cos \dfrac{\theta}{4} \cos \dfrac{\theta}{8} \cdots \cos \dfrac{\theta}{2^n}$

(b) $\sin \theta = 2^n \sin \dfrac{\theta}{2^n} \cos \dfrac{\theta}{2} \cos \dfrac{\theta}{4} \cos \dfrac{\theta}{8} \cdots \cos \dfrac{\theta}{2^n} \Leftrightarrow$

$\dfrac{\sin \theta}{\theta} \cdot \dfrac{\theta/2^n}{\sin(\theta/2^n)}$

$= \cos \dfrac{\theta}{2} \cos \dfrac{\theta}{4} \cos \dfrac{\theta}{8} \cdots \cos \dfrac{\theta}{2^n}.$

Now we let $n \to \infty$, using $\displaystyle\lim_{x\to 0} \dfrac{\sin x}{x} = 1$ with

$x = \dfrac{\theta}{2^n}$: $\displaystyle\lim_{n\to\infty} \left[\dfrac{\sin \theta}{\theta} \cdot \dfrac{\theta/2^n}{\sin(\theta/2^n)} \right]$

$= \displaystyle\lim_{n\to\infty} \left[\cos \dfrac{\theta}{2} \cos \dfrac{\theta}{4} \cos \dfrac{\theta}{8} \cdots \cos \dfrac{\theta}{2^n} \right] \Leftrightarrow \dfrac{\sin \theta}{\theta}$

$= \cos \dfrac{\theta}{2} \cos \dfrac{\theta}{4} \cos \dfrac{\theta}{8} \cdots .$

(c) If we take $\theta = \dfrac{\pi}{2}$ in the result from part (b) and use the half-angle formula

$\cos x = \sqrt{\dfrac{1}{2}(1 + \cos 2x)}$, we get

$\dfrac{\sin \pi/2}{\pi/2} = \cos \dfrac{\pi}{4} \sqrt{\dfrac{\cos \frac{\pi}{4} + 1}{2}}$

$\sqrt{\dfrac{\sqrt{\dfrac{\cos \frac{\pi}{4} + 1}{2}} + 1}{2}}$

$\sqrt{\dfrac{\sqrt{\dfrac{\sqrt{\dfrac{\cos \frac{\pi}{4} + 1}{2}} + 1}{2}} + 1}{2}} \cdots \Rightarrow$

$$\frac{2}{\pi} = \frac{\sqrt{2}}{2}\sqrt{\frac{\frac{\sqrt{2}}{2}+1}{2}}\sqrt{\frac{\sqrt{\frac{\frac{\sqrt{2}}{2}+1}{2}}+1}{2}} \cdots$$

$$= \frac{\sqrt{2}}{2}\frac{\sqrt{2+\sqrt{2}}}{2}\sqrt{\frac{\frac{\sqrt{2+\sqrt{2}}}{2}+1}{2}} \cdots$$

$$= \frac{\sqrt{2}}{2}\frac{\sqrt{2+\sqrt{2}}}{2}\frac{\sqrt{2+\sqrt{2+\sqrt{2}}}}{2} \cdots$$

5.

n	s_n
1	0.50000
2	1.16667
3	1.91667
4	2.71667
5	3.55000
6	4.40714
7	5.28214
8	6.17103
9	7.07103
10	7.98012

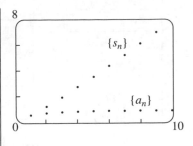

The series diverges, since its terms do not approach 0.

3.

n	s_n
1	3.33333
2	4.44444
3	4.81481
4	4.93827
5	4.97942
6	4.99314
7	4.99771
8	4.99924
9	4.99975
10	4.99992
11	4.99997
12	4.99999

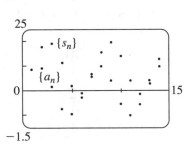

From the graph, it seems that the series converges. In fact, it is a geometric series with $a = \dfrac{10}{3}$ and $r = \dfrac{1}{3}$, so its sum is

$$\sum_{n=1}^{\infty}\frac{10}{3^n} = \frac{10/3}{1-1/3} = 5.$$ Note

that the dot corresponding to $n = 1$ is part of both $\{a_n\}$ and $\{s_n\}$.

6.

n	s_n
4	0.25000
5	0.40000
6	0.50000
7	0.57143
8	0.62500
9	0.66667
10	0.70000
11	0.72727
12	0.75000
13	0.76923
...	...
99	0.96970
100	0.97000

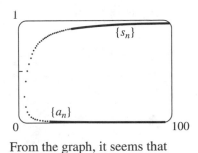

From the graph, it seems that the series converges to about 1. To find the sum, since

$$\frac{3}{i(i-1)} = \frac{3}{i-1} - \frac{3}{i},$$ the

partial sums are

$$s_n = \sum_{i=4}^{n}\left(\frac{3}{i-1} - \frac{3}{i}\right)$$

$$= \left(\frac{3}{3} - \frac{3}{4}\right) + \left(\frac{3}{4} - \frac{3}{5}\right) + \cdots$$

$$+ \left(\frac{3}{n-2} - \frac{3}{n-1}\right) + \left(\frac{3}{n-1} - \frac{3}{n}\right)$$

$$= 1 - \frac{3}{n}$$

and so the sum is $\lim_{n\to\infty} s_n = 1$.

4.

n	s_n
1	0.8415
2	1.7508
3	1.8919
4	1.1351
5	0.1762
6	−0.1033
7	0.5537
8	1.5431
9	1.9552
10	1.4112
11	0.4112
12	−0.1254

The series diverges, since its terms do not approach 0.

7.

n	s_n
1	1.000000
2	0.714286
3	0.795918
4	0.772595
5	0.779259
6	0.777355
7	0.777899
8	0.777743
9	0.777788
10	0.777775
11	0.777779
12	0.777778

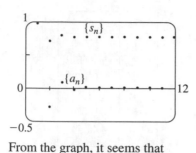

From the graph, it seems that the series converges to about 0.8. In fact, it is a geometric series with $a = 1$ and $r = -\dfrac{2}{7}$, so its sum is

$$\sum_{n=1}^{\infty} \left(-\frac{2}{7}\right)^{n-1} = \frac{1}{1-(-2/7)} = \frac{7}{9}.$$

8. $\sum_{n=5}^{\infty} (1/n^{1.0001})$ is a p-series, $p = 1.0001 > 1$, so it converges.

9. $\sum_{n=1}^{\infty} n^{-0.99} = \sum_{n=1}^{\infty} (1/n^{0.99})$ which diverges since $p = 0.99 < 1$.

10. $\sum_{n=1}^{\infty} \dfrac{2}{\sqrt[3]{n}} = 2 \sum_{n=1}^{\infty} \dfrac{1}{n^{1/3}}$, which is a p-series, $p = \dfrac{1}{3} < 1$, so it diverges.

11. $\sum_{n=1}^{\infty} \left(\dfrac{2}{n\sqrt{n}} + \dfrac{3}{n^3}\right) = 2\sum_{n=1}^{\infty} \dfrac{1}{n^{3/2}} + 3\sum_{n=1}^{\infty} \dfrac{1}{n^3}$, both of which are convergent p-series because $\dfrac{3}{2} > 1$ and $3 > 1$, so $\sum_{n=1}^{\infty} \left(\dfrac{2}{n\sqrt{n}} + \dfrac{3}{n^3}\right)$ converges.

12. $\sum_{n=5}^{\infty} \dfrac{1}{(n-4)^2} = \sum_{n=1}^{\infty} \dfrac{1}{n^2}$ is a p-series, $p = 2 > 1$, so it converges.

13. $f(x) = \dfrac{1}{2x+3}$ is positive, continuous, and decreasing on $[1, \infty)$, so applying the Integral Test,

$$\int_1^{\infty} \frac{dx}{2x+3} = \lim_{t\to\infty}\left[\frac{1}{2}\ln(2x+3)\right]_1^t = \infty \Rightarrow \sum_{n=1}^{\infty}\frac{1}{2n+3}$$

is divergent.

14. Since $\dfrac{1}{\sqrt{x}+1}$ is continuous, positive, and decreasing on $[0, \infty)$ we can apply the Integral Test.

$$\int_1^{\infty} \frac{1}{\sqrt{x}+1} dx = \lim_{t\to\infty}\left[2\sqrt{x} - 2\ln(\sqrt{x}+1)\right]_1^t$$

[using the substitution $u = \sqrt{x} + 1$, so $dx = 2(u-1)du$]

$$= \lim_{t\to\infty}\left([2\sqrt{t} - 2\ln(\sqrt{t}+1)] - (2 - 2\ln 2)\right)$$

Now $2\sqrt{t} - 2\ln(\sqrt{t}+1) = 2\ln\left(\dfrac{e^{\sqrt{t}}}{\sqrt{t}+1}\right)$ and so $\lim_{t\to\infty}[2\sqrt{t} - 2\ln(\sqrt{t}+1)] = \infty$ (using l'Hospital's Rule) so both the integral and the original series diverge.

15. $f(x) = \dfrac{1}{x^2-1}$ is positive, continuous, and decreasing on $[2, \infty)$, so applying the Integral Test,

$$\int_2^{\infty} \frac{dx}{x^2-1} = \int_2^{\infty}\left(\frac{-1/2}{x+1} + \frac{1/2}{x-1}\right) dx$$

$$= \lim_{t\to\infty}\left[\ln\left(\frac{x-1}{x+1}\right)^{1/2}\right]_2^t = \ln\sqrt{3} \Rightarrow \sum_{n=2}^{\infty}\frac{1}{n^2-1}$$

converges.

16. $f(x) = xe^{-x^2}$ is continuous and positive on $[1, \infty)$, and since $f'(x) = e^{-x^2}(1 - 2x^2) < 0$ for $x > 1$, f is decreasing as well. Thus, we can use the Integral Test:

$$\int_1^{\infty} xe^{-x^2}dx = \lim_{t\to\infty}\left[-\frac{1}{2}e^{-x^2}\right]_1^t = 0 - \left(-\frac{1}{2}e^{-1}\right) = \frac{1}{2e}.$$

Since the integral converges, the series converges.

17. $f(x) = \dfrac{x}{2^x}$ is positive and continuous on $[1, \infty)$, and since $f'(x) = \dfrac{1 - x\ln 2}{2^x} < 0$ when $x > \dfrac{1}{\ln 2} \approx 1.44$, f is eventually decreasing, so we can apply the Integral Test. Integrating by parts, we get

$$\int_1^{\infty} \frac{x}{2^x} dx = \lim_{t\to\infty}\left(-\frac{1}{\ln 2}\left[\frac{x}{2^x} + \frac{1}{2^x\ln 2}\right]_1^t\right)$$

$$= \frac{1}{2\ln 2} + \frac{1}{2(\ln 2)^2}$$

since $\lim_{t\to\infty}\dfrac{t}{2^t} = 0$ by l'Hospital's Rule, and so $\sum_{n=1}^{\infty}\dfrac{n}{2^n}$ converges.

18. $f(x) = \dfrac{1}{4x^2+1}$ is continuous, positive and decreasing on $[1, \infty)$, so applying the Integral Test,

$$\int_1^{\infty} \frac{dx}{4x^2+1} = \lim_{t\to\infty}\left[\frac{\arctan 2x}{2}\right]_1^t = \frac{\pi}{4} - \frac{\arctan 2}{2} < \infty,$$

so the series converges.

19. $f(x) = \dfrac{\arctan x}{1 + x^2}$ is continuous and positive on $[1, \infty)$.

$f'(x) = \dfrac{1 - 2x \arctan x}{(1 + x^2)^2} < 0$ for $x > 1$, since

$2x \arctan x \geq \dfrac{\pi}{2} > 1$ for $x \geq 1$. So f is decreasing

and we can use the Integral Test.

$\displaystyle\int_1^\infty \dfrac{\arctan x}{1 + x^2}\, dx = \lim_{t\to\infty}\left[\dfrac{1}{2}(\arctan x)^2\right]_1^t$

$= \dfrac{(\pi/2)^2}{2} - \dfrac{(\pi/4)^2}{2} = \dfrac{3\pi^2}{32}$

so the series converges.

20. $f(x) = \dfrac{\ln x}{x^2}$ is continuous and positive for $x \geq 2$, and

$f'(x) = \dfrac{1 - 2\ln x}{x^3} < 0$ for $x \geq 2$, so f is decreasing.

$\displaystyle\int_2^\infty \dfrac{\ln x}{x^2}\, dx = \lim_{t\to\infty}\left[-\dfrac{\ln x}{x} - \dfrac{1}{x}\right]_2^t$ (by parts) $\overset{\text{H}}{=} 1$.

Thus, $\displaystyle\sum_{n=1}^\infty \dfrac{\ln n}{n^2} = \sum_{n=2}^\infty \dfrac{\ln n}{n^2}$ converges by the

Integral Test.

21. $f(x) = \dfrac{1}{x^2 + 2x + 2}$ is continuous and positive on

$[1, \infty)$, and $f'(x) = -\dfrac{2x + 2}{(x^2 + 2x + 2)^2} < 0$ for $x \geq 1$,

so f is decreasing and we can use the Integral Test.

$\displaystyle\int_1^\infty \dfrac{1}{x^2 + 2x + 2}\, dx = \int_1^\infty \dfrac{1}{(x + 1)^2 + 1}\, dx$

$= \lim_{t\to\infty}\left[\arctan(x + 1)\right]_1^t$

$= \dfrac{\pi}{2} - \arctan 2$

so the series converges as well.

22. $\displaystyle\sum_{n=1}^\infty (-1)^{n-1}\dfrac{3}{n + 4} \cdot b_n = \dfrac{3}{n + 4} > 0$ and $b_{n+1} < b_n$

for all n; $\lim_{n\to\infty} b_n = 0$ so the series converges by the

Alternating Series Test.

23. $-5 + \displaystyle\sum_{n=0}^\infty (-1)^{n-1}\dfrac{5}{3n + 2} \cdot b_n = \dfrac{5}{3n + 2}$ is

decreasing and positive for all n, and

$\lim_{n\to\infty}\dfrac{5}{3n + 2} = 0$ so the series converges by the

Alternating Series Test.

24. $\displaystyle\sum_{n=1}^\infty (-1)^n \dfrac{n}{n + 1}$, $\lim_{n\to\infty}\dfrac{n}{n + 1} = 1$ so $\lim_{n\to\infty}(-1)^n \dfrac{n}{n + 1}$

does not exist and the series diverges by the Test for

Divergence.

25. $\displaystyle\sum_{n=1}^\infty (-1)^{n-1}\dfrac{1}{n^2} \cdot b_n = \dfrac{1}{n^2} > 0$ and $b_{n+1} < b_n$ for all n,

and $\lim_{n\to\infty}\dfrac{1}{n^2} = 0$, so the series converges by the

Alternating Series Test.

26. $\displaystyle\sum_{n=1}^\infty \dfrac{(-1)^n}{\sqrt{n + 3}} \cdot b_n = \dfrac{1}{\sqrt{n + 3}}$ is positive and

decreasing, and $\lim_{n\to\infty}\dfrac{1}{\sqrt{n + 3}} = 0$, so the series

converges by the Alternating Series Test.

27. $\displaystyle\sum_{n=1}^\infty (-1)^{n+1}\dfrac{n}{5n + 1} \cdot \lim_{n\to\infty}\dfrac{n}{5n + 1} = \dfrac{1}{5}$ so

$\lim_{n\to\infty}(-1)^{n+1}\dfrac{n}{5n + 1}$ does not exist and the series

diverges by the Test for Divergence.

28. $\displaystyle\sum_{n=2}^\infty \dfrac{(-1)^{n-1}}{n \ln n} \cdot b_n = \dfrac{1}{n \ln n}$ is positive and decreasing

for $n \geq 2$, and $\lim_{n\to\infty}\dfrac{1}{n \ln n} = 0$ so the series

converges by the Alternating Series Test.

29. If $a_n = nx^n$, then

$\lim_{n\to\infty}\left|\dfrac{a_{n+1}}{a_n}\right| = \lim_{n\to\infty}\left|\dfrac{(n + 1)x^{n+1}}{nx^n}\right|$

$= |x|\lim_{n\to\infty}\dfrac{n + 1}{n} = |x| < 1$

for convergence (by the Ratio Test). So $R = 1$.

When $x = 1$ or -1, $\lim_{n\to\infty} nx^n$ does not exist, so

$\displaystyle\sum_{n=0}^\infty nx^n$ diverges for $x = \pm 1$. So $I = (-1, 1)$.

30. If $a_n = \dfrac{x^n}{n^2}$ then $\lim_{n\to\infty}\left|\dfrac{a_{n+1}}{a_n}\right| = |x|\lim_{n\to\infty}\left(\dfrac{n}{n + 1}\right)^2 = |x| < 1$

for convergence (by the Ratio Test), so $R = 1$. If

$x = \pm 1$, $\displaystyle\sum_{n=1}^\infty |a_n| = \sum_{n=1}^\infty \dfrac{1}{n^2}$, which converges

($p = 2 > 1$), so $I = [-1, 1]$.

31. If $a_n = \dfrac{3^n x^n}{(n+1)^2}$, then

$$\lim_{n\to\infty}\left|\frac{a_{n+1}}{a_n}\right| = \lim_{n\to\infty}\left|\frac{3^{n+1}x^{n+1}}{(n+2)^2}\cdot\frac{(n+1)^2}{3^n x^n}\right|$$

$$= 3|x|\lim_{n\to\infty}\left(\frac{n+1}{n+2}\right)^2 = 3|x| < 1$$

for convergence, so $|x| < \dfrac{1}{3}$ and $R = \dfrac{1}{3}$. When

$x = \dfrac{1}{3}$, $\displaystyle\sum_{n=0}^{\infty}\frac{3^n x^n}{(n+1)^2} = \sum_{n=0}^{\infty}\frac{1}{(n+1)^2} = \sum_{n=1}^{\infty}\frac{1}{n^2}$, which

is a convergent p-series ($p = 2 > 1$). When $x = -\dfrac{1}{3}$,

$$\sum_{n=0}^{\infty}\frac{3^n x^n}{(n+1)^2} = \sum_{n=0}^{\infty}\frac{(-1)^n}{(n+1)^2}, \text{ which converges by the}$$

Alternating Series Test, so $I = \left[-\dfrac{1}{3}, \dfrac{1}{3}\right]$.

32. If $a_n = \dfrac{n^2 x^n}{10^n}$, then

$$\lim_{n\to\infty}\left|\frac{a_{n+1}}{a_n}\right| = \frac{|x|}{10}\lim_{n\to\infty}\left(\frac{n+1}{n}\right)^2 = \frac{|x|}{10} < 1 \text{ for}$$

convergence (by the Ratio Test), so $R = 10$. If

$x = \pm 10$, $|a_n| = n^2 \to \infty$ as $n \to \infty$, so $\displaystyle\sum_{n=0}^{\infty} a_n$

diverges (Test for Divergence) and $I = (-10, 10)$.

33. If $a_n = \dfrac{x^n}{\ln n}$, then

$$\lim_{n\to\infty}\left|\frac{a_{n+1}}{a_n}\right| = \lim_{n\to\infty}\left|\frac{x^{n+1}}{\ln(n+1)}\cdot\frac{\ln n}{x^n}\right|$$

$$= |x|\lim_{n\to\infty}\frac{\ln n}{\ln(n+1)} \overset{H}{=} |x|$$

so $R = 1$. When $x = 1$, $\displaystyle\sum_{n=2}^{\infty}\frac{x^n}{\ln n} = \sum_{n=2}^{\infty}\frac{1}{\ln n}$, which

diverges because $\dfrac{1}{\ln n} > \dfrac{1}{n}$ and $\displaystyle\sum_{n=2}^{\infty}\frac{1}{n}$ is the

divergent harmonic series. When $x = -1$,

$\displaystyle\sum_{n=2}^{\infty}\frac{x^n}{\ln n} = \sum_{n=2}^{\infty}\frac{(-1)^n}{\ln n}$, which converges by the

Alternating Series Test. So $I = [-1, 1)$.

34. If $a_n = \dfrac{(-1)^n x^{2n-1}}{(2n-1)!}$, then

$$\lim_{n\to\infty}\left|\frac{a_{n+1}}{a_n}\right| = \lim_{n\to\infty}\frac{x^2}{(2n+1)\,2n} = 0 < 1 \text{ for all } x.$$

By the Ratio Test the series converges for all x, so $R = \infty$ and $I = (-\infty, \infty)$.

35. If $a_n = \dfrac{2^n(x-3)^n}{n+3}$, then

$$\lim_{n\to\infty}\left|\frac{a_{n+1}}{a_n}\right| = \lim_{n\to\infty}\left|\frac{2^{n+1}(x-3)^{n+1}}{n+4}\cdot\frac{n+3}{2^n(x-3)^n}\right|$$

$$= 2|x-3|\lim_{n\to\infty}\frac{n+3}{n+4} = 2|x-3| < 1$$

for convergence, or $|x-3| < \dfrac{1}{2} \Leftrightarrow \dfrac{5}{2} < x < \dfrac{7}{2}$,

and $R = \dfrac{1}{2}$. When $x = \dfrac{5}{2}$, $\displaystyle\sum_{n=0}^{\infty}\frac{2^n(x-3)^n}{n+3} = \sum_{n=0}^{\infty}\frac{(-1)^n}{n+3}$,

which converges by the Alternating Series Test.

When $x = \dfrac{7}{2}$, $\displaystyle\sum_{n=0}^{\infty}\frac{2^n(x-3)^n}{n+3} = \sum_{n=0}^{\infty}\frac{1}{n+3}$, similar

to the harmonic series, which diverges. So

$I = \left[\dfrac{5}{2}, \dfrac{7}{2}\right]$.

36. If $a_n = \dfrac{(x+1)^n}{n(n+1)}$, then

$$\lim_{n\to\infty}\left|\frac{a_{n+1}}{a_n}\right| = |x+1|\lim_{n\to\infty}\frac{n}{n+2} = |x+1| < 1$$

for convergence, or $-2 < x < 0$ and $R = 1$.

If $x = -2$ or 0, then $|a_n| = \dfrac{1}{n^2+n} < \dfrac{1}{n^2}$, so $\displaystyle\sum_{n=1}^{\infty}|a_n|$

converges since $\displaystyle\sum_{n=1}^{\infty}\frac{1}{n^2}$ does ($p = 2 > 1$), and

$I = [-2, 0]$.

37. If $a_n = \sqrt{n}\,(3x+2)^n$, then

$$\left|\frac{a_{n+1}}{a_n}\right| = \left|\frac{\sqrt{n+1}\,(3x+2)^{n+1}}{\sqrt{n}\,(3x+2)^n}\right|$$

$$= \left|\sqrt{1+\frac{1}{n}}\cdot(3x+2)\right| \to |3x+2| \text{ as}$$

$n \to \infty$ so for convergence, $|3x+2| < 1 \Rightarrow$

$\left|x + \dfrac{2}{3}\right| < \dfrac{1}{3}$ so $R = \dfrac{1}{3}$ and $-1 < x < -\dfrac{1}{3}$.

If $x = -1$, the series becomes $\displaystyle\sum_{n=0}^{\infty}(-1)^n\sqrt{n}$ which

is divergent by the Test for Divergence. If $x = -\dfrac{1}{3}$,

the series is $\displaystyle\sum_{n=0}^{\infty}\sqrt{n}$ which is also divergent by the

Test for Divergence. So $I = \left(-1, -\dfrac{1}{3}\right)$.

38. If $a_n = \dfrac{n}{4^n}(2x-1)^n$, then

$$\left|\frac{a_{n+1}}{a_n}\right| = \left|\frac{(n+1)(2x-1)^{n+1}}{4^{n+1}} \cdot \frac{4^n}{n(2x-1)^n}\right|$$

$$= \left|\frac{2x-1}{4}\left(1+\frac{1}{n}\right)\right| \to \frac{1}{2}\left|x-\frac{1}{2}\right|$$

as $n \to \infty$. For convergence, $\dfrac{1}{2}\left|x-\dfrac{1}{2}\right| < 1 \Rightarrow$

$\left|x-\dfrac{1}{2}\right| < 2 \Rightarrow R = 2$ and $-2 < x - \dfrac{1}{2} < 2 \Rightarrow$

$-\dfrac{3}{2} < x < \dfrac{5}{2}$. If $x = -\dfrac{3}{2}$, the series becomes

$$\sum_{n=0}^{\infty}\frac{n}{4^n}(-4)^n = \sum_{n=0}^{\infty}(-1)^n n \text{ which is divergent by}$$

the Test for Divergence. If $x = \dfrac{5}{2}$, the series is

$$\sum_{n=0}^{\infty}\frac{n}{4^n}4^n = \sum_{n=0}^{\infty}n, \text{ also divergent by the Test for}$$

Divergence. So $I = \left(-\dfrac{3}{2}, \dfrac{5}{2}\right)$.

39. If $a_n = \dfrac{(-1)^n(x-1)^n}{\sqrt{n}}$, then

$$\lim_{n\to\infty}\left|\frac{a_{n+1}}{a_n}\right| = \lim_{n\to\infty}\left|\frac{(x-1)^{n+1}}{\sqrt{n+1}} \cdot \frac{\sqrt{n}}{(x-1)^n}\right|$$

$$= |x-1|\lim_{n\to\infty}\sqrt{\frac{n}{n+1}} = |x-1| < 1$$

for convergence, or $0 < x < 2$, and $R = 1$. When

$x = 0$, $\displaystyle\sum_{n=1}^{\infty}\frac{(-1)^n(x-1)^n}{\sqrt{n}} = \sum_{n=1}^{\infty}\frac{1}{\sqrt{n}}$ which is a

divergent p-series $\left(p = \dfrac{1}{2} < 1\right)$. When $x = 2$, the

series is $\displaystyle\sum_{n=1}^{\infty}\frac{(-1)^n}{\sqrt{n}}$ which converges by the

Alternating Series Test. So $I = (0, 2]$.

"R" stands for "radius of convergence" and "I" stands for "interval of convergence" in this section.

40. $f(x) = \dfrac{x}{1-x} = x\left(\dfrac{1}{1-x}\right) = x\displaystyle\sum_{n=0}^{\infty}x^n = \sum_{n=0}^{\infty}x^{n+1}$

$$= \sum_{n=1}^{\infty}x^n$$

with $R = 1$ and $I = (-1, 1)$.

41. $f(x) = \dfrac{1}{4+x^2} = \dfrac{1}{4}\left(\dfrac{1}{1+x^2/4}\right)$

$$= \frac{1}{4}\sum_{n=0}^{\infty}(-1)^n\left(\frac{x^2}{4}\right)^n$$

$$= \sum_{n=0}^{\infty}\frac{(-1)^n x^{2n}}{4^{n+1}}$$

with $\left|\dfrac{x^2}{4}\right| < 1 \Leftrightarrow x^2 < 4 \Leftrightarrow |x| < 2$, so $R = 2$ and

$I = (-2, 2)$.

42. $f(x) = \dfrac{1+x^2}{1-x^2} = 1 + \dfrac{2x^2}{1-x^2} = 1 + 2x^2\displaystyle\sum_{n=0}^{\infty}(x^2)^n$

$$= 1 + \sum_{n=0}^{\infty}2x^{2n+2} = 1 + \sum_{n=1}^{\infty}2x^{2n}$$

with $|x^2| < 1 \Leftrightarrow |x| < 1$, so $R = 1$ and $I = (-1, 1)$.

43. $f(x) = \dfrac{1}{1+4x^2} = \displaystyle\sum_{n=0}^{\infty}(-1)^n(4x^2)^n$

$$= \sum_{n=0}^{\infty}(-1)^n 4^n x^{2n} \text{ with } |4x^2| < 1$$

so $x^2 < \dfrac{1}{4} \Leftrightarrow |x| < \dfrac{1}{2}$, and so $R = \dfrac{1}{2}$ and $I = \left(-\dfrac{1}{2}, \dfrac{1}{2}\right)$.

44. $f(x) = \dfrac{1}{x^4+16} = \dfrac{1}{16}\left[\dfrac{1}{1+(x/2)^4}\right]$

$$= \frac{1}{16}\sum_{n=0}^{\infty}(-1)^n\left(\frac{x}{2}\right)^{4n} = \sum_{n=0}^{\infty}\frac{(-1)^n x^{4n}}{2^{4n+4}}$$

for $\left|\dfrac{x}{2}\right| < 1 \Leftrightarrow |x| < 2$ so, $R = 2$ and $I = (-2, 2)$.

45. $f(x) = \dfrac{x}{x-3} = 1 + \dfrac{3}{x-3} = 1 - \dfrac{1}{1-x/3}$

$$= 1 - \sum_{n=0}^{\infty}\left(\frac{x}{3}\right)^n = -\sum_{n=1}^{\infty}\left(\frac{x}{3}\right)^n$$

For convergence, $\dfrac{|x|}{3} < 1 \Leftrightarrow |x| < 3$, so $R = 3$ and

$I = (-3, 3)$.

Another Method:

$$f(x) = \frac{x}{x-3} = -\frac{x}{3(1-x/3)} = -\frac{x}{3}\sum_{n=0}^{\infty}\left(\frac{x}{3}\right)^n$$

$$= -\sum_{n=0}^{\infty}\frac{x^{n+1}}{3^{n+1}} = -\sum_{n=1}^{\infty}\frac{x^n}{3^n}$$

46. $f(x) = \dfrac{2}{3x+4} = \dfrac{1}{2}\left(\dfrac{1}{1+3x/4}\right)$

$= \dfrac{1}{2}\displaystyle\sum_{n=0}^{\infty}(-1)^n\left(\dfrac{3x}{4}\right)^n = \displaystyle\sum_{n=0}^{\infty}\dfrac{(-1)^n 3^n x^n}{2^{2n+1}}$

$\left|\dfrac{3x}{4}\right| < 1$ so $R = \dfrac{4}{3}$ and $I = \left(-\dfrac{4}{3}, \dfrac{4}{3}\right)$.

47. We use the representation

$$\int \dfrac{dx}{1+x^4} = C + \sum_{n=0}^{\infty}\dfrac{(-1)^n x^{4n+1}}{4n+1}$$

with $C = 0$. So

$$\int_0^{0.2}\dfrac{dx}{1+x^4} = \left[x - \dfrac{x^5}{5} + \dfrac{x^9}{9} - \dfrac{x^{13}}{13} + \cdots\right]_0^{0.2}$$

$$= 0.2 - \dfrac{0.2^5}{5} + \dfrac{0.2^9}{9} - \dfrac{0.2^{13}}{13} + \cdots$$

Since the series is alternating, the error in the nth-order approximation is less than the first neglected term, by The Alternating Series Estimation Theorem. If we use only the first two terms of the series, then the error is at most $0.2^9/9 \approx 5.7 \times 10^{-8}$. So, to six decimal places, $\displaystyle\int_0^{0.2}\dfrac{dx}{1+x^4} \approx 0.2 - \dfrac{0.2^5}{5} = 0.199936$.

48. We use the representation

$$\int \tan^{-1}(x^2)\, dx = C + \sum_{n=0}^{\infty}(-1)^n\dfrac{x^{4n+3}}{(2n+1)(4n+3)}$$

with $C = 0$:

$$\int_0^{1/2}\tan^{-1}(x^2)\, dx$$

$$= \left[\dfrac{x^3}{3} - \dfrac{x^7}{21} + \dfrac{x^{11}}{55} - \dfrac{x^{15}}{105} + \dfrac{x^{19}}{171} - \cdots\right]_0^{1/2}$$

$$= \dfrac{0.5^3}{3} - \dfrac{0.5^7}{21} + \dfrac{0.5^{11}}{55} - \dfrac{0.5^{15}}{105} + \dfrac{0.5^{19}}{171} - \cdots$$

The series is alternating, so if we use only the first four terms of the series, then the error is at most $0.5^{19}/171 \approx 1.1 \times 10^{-8}$. So, to six decimal places,

$$\int_0^{1/2}\tan^{-1}(x^2)\, dx$$

$$\approx \dfrac{1}{3}(0.5)^3 - \dfrac{1}{21}(0.5)^7 + \dfrac{1}{55}(0.5)^{11} - \dfrac{1}{105}(0.5)^{15}$$

$$\approx 0.041303$$

49. (a) At each stage, each side is replaced by four shorter sides, each of length $\dfrac{1}{3}$ of the side length at the preceding stage.

$s_0 = 3$	$\ell_0 = 1$
$s_1 = 3 \bullet 4$	$\ell_1 = 1/3$
$s_2 = 3 \bullet 4^2$	$\ell_2 = 1/3^2$
$s_3 = 3 \bullet 4^3$	$\ell_3 = 1/3^3$
$\cdots$	$\cdots$

Writing s_0 and ℓ_0 for the number of sides and the length of the side of the initial triangle, we generate the table above. In general, we have $s_n = 3 \cdot 4^n$ and $\ell_n = \left(\dfrac{1}{3}\right)^n$, so the length of the perimeter at the nth stage of construction is $p_n = s_n\ell_n = 3 \cdot 4^n \cdot \left(\dfrac{1}{3}\right)^n = 3 \cdot \left(\dfrac{4}{3}\right)^n$.

(b) $p_n = \dfrac{4^n}{3^{n-1}} = 4\left(\dfrac{4}{3}\right)^{n-1}$. Since $\dfrac{4}{3} > 1$, $p_n \to \infty$ as $n \to \infty$.

(c) The area of each of the small triangles added at a given stage is one-ninth of the area of the triangle added at the preceding stage. Let a be the area of the original triangle. Then the area a_n of each of the small triangles added at stage n is $a_n = a \cdot \dfrac{1}{9^n} = \dfrac{a}{9^n}$. Since a small triangle is added to each side at every stage, it follows that the total area A_n added to the figure at the nth stage is $A_n = s_{n-1} \cdot a_n = 3 \cdot 4^{n-1} \cdot \dfrac{a}{9^n} = a \cdot \dfrac{4^{n-1}}{3^{2n-1}}$. Then the total area enclosed by the snowflake curve is $A = a + A_1 + A_2 + A_3 + \cdots = a + a \cdot \dfrac{1}{3} + a \cdot \dfrac{4}{3^3} + a \cdot \dfrac{4^2}{3^5} + a \cdot \dfrac{4^3}{3^7} + \cdots$.

After the first term, this is a geometric series with common ratio $\dfrac{4}{9}$, so $A = a + \dfrac{a/3}{1 - \frac{4}{9}}$

$= a + \dfrac{a}{3} \cdot \dfrac{9}{5} = \dfrac{8a}{5}$. But the area of the original equilateral triangle with side 1 is $a = \dfrac{1}{2} \cdot 1 \cdot \sin\dfrac{\pi}{3} = \dfrac{\sqrt{3}}{4}$. So the area enclosed by the snowflake curve is $\dfrac{8}{5} \cdot \dfrac{\sqrt{3}}{4} = \dfrac{2\sqrt{3}}{5}$.

11 | PARTIAL DERIVATIVES

1–14 ■ Find the indicated partial derivatives.

1. $f(x, y) = x^3y^5$; $f_x(3, -1)$

2. $f(x, y) = \sqrt{2x + 3y}$; $f_y(2, 4)$

3. $f(x, y) = xe^{-y} + 3y$; $\dfrac{\partial f}{\partial y}(1, 0)$

4. $f(x, y) = \sin(y - x)$; $\dfrac{\partial f}{\partial y}(3, 3)$

5. $z = \dfrac{x^3 + y^3}{x^2 + y^2}$; $\dfrac{\partial z}{\partial x}, \dfrac{\partial z}{\partial y}$

6. $z = x\sqrt{y} - \dfrac{y}{\sqrt{x}}$; $\dfrac{\partial z}{\partial x}, \dfrac{\partial z}{\partial y}$

7. $z = \dfrac{x}{y} + \dfrac{y}{x}$; $\dfrac{\partial z}{\partial x}$

8. $z = (3xy^2 - x^4 + 1)^4$; $\dfrac{\partial z}{\partial x}, \dfrac{\partial z}{\partial y}$

9. $u = xy \sec(xy)$; $\dfrac{\partial u}{\partial x}$

10. $u = \dfrac{x}{x + t}$; $\dfrac{\partial u}{\partial x}, \dfrac{\partial u}{\partial t}$

11. $f(x, y, z) = xyz$; $f_y(0, 1, 2)$

12. $f(x, y, z) = \sqrt{x^2 + y^2 + z^2}$; $f_z(0, 3, 4)$

13. $u = xy + yz + zx$; u_x, u_y, u_z

14. $u = x^2y^3t^4$; u_x, u_y, u_t

15–20 ■ Find the first partial derivatives of the function.

15. $f(x, y) = x^3y^5 - 2x^2y + x$

16. $f(x, y) = x^2y^2(x^4 + y^4)$

17. $f(x, y) = x^4 + x^2y^2 + y^4$

18. $f(x, y) = \ln(x^2 + y^2)$

19. $f(x, y) = e^x \tan(x - y)$

20. $f(s, t) = s/\sqrt{s^2 + t^2}$

21–26 ■ Find all the second partial derivatives.

21. $f(x, y) = x^2y + x\sqrt{y}$

22. $f(x, y) = \sin(x + y) + \cos(x - y)$

23. $z = (x^2 + y^2)^{3/2}$

24. $z = \cos^2(5x + 2y)$

25. $z = t \sin^{-1}\sqrt{x}$

26. $z = x^{\ln t}$

27–30 ■ Find the indicated partial derivative.

27. $f(x, y) = x^2y^3 - 2x^4y$; f_{xxx}

28. $f(x, y) = e^{xy^2}$; f_{xxy}

29. $f(x, y, z) = x^5 + x^4y^4z^3 + yz^2$; f_{xyz}

30. $f(x, y, z) = e^{xyz}$; f_{yzy}

31–39 ■ Find the local maximum and minimum values and saddle point(s) of the function. If you have three-dimensional graphing software, graph the function with a domain and viewpoint that reveal all the important aspects of the function.

31. $f(x, y) = x^2 + y^2 + 4x - 6y$

32. $f(x, y) = 4x^2 + y^2 - 4x + 2y$

33. $f(x, y) = 2x^2 + y^2 + 2xy + 2x + 2y$

34. $f(x, y) = x^3 - 3xy + y^3$

35. $f(x, y) = x^2 + y^2 + x^2y + 4$

36. $f(x, y) = xy - 2x - y$

37. $f(x, y) = y\sqrt{x} - y^2 - x + 6y$

38. $f(x, y) = \dfrac{x^2y^2 - 8x + y}{xy}$

39. $f(x, y) = \dfrac{(x + y + 1)^2}{x^2 + y^2 + 1}$

CHALLENGE

40. A rectangle with length L and width W is cut into four smaller rectangles by two lines parallel to the sides. Find the maximum and minimum values of the sum of the squares of the areas of the smaller rectangles.

CHALLENGE

41. Marine biologists have determined that when a shark detects the presence of blood in the water, it will swim in the direction in which the concentration of the blood increases most rapidly. Based on certain tests, the concentration of blood (in parts per million) at a point $P(x, y)$ on the surface of seawater is approximated by

$$C(x, y) = e^{-(x^2+2y^2)/10^4}$$

where x and y are measured in meters in a rectangular coordinate system with the blood source at the origin.

(a) Identify the level curves of the concentration function and sketch several members of this family together with a path that a shark will follow to the source.

(b) Suppose a shark is at the point (x_0, y_0) when it first detects the presence of blood in the water. Find an equation of the shark's path by setting up and solving a differential equation.

CHALLENGE

42. A long piece of galvanized sheet metal w inches wide is to be bent into a symmetric form with three straight sides to make a rain gutter. A cross-section is shown in the figure.

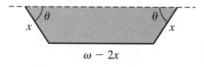

(a) Determine the dimensions that allow the maximum possible flow; that is, find the dimensions that give the maximum possible cross-sectional area.

(b) Would it be better to bend the metal into a gutter with a semicircular cross-section than a three-sided cross-section?

CHALLENGE

43. For what values of the number r is the function

$$f(x, y, z) = \begin{cases} \dfrac{(x + y + z)^r}{x^2 + y^2 + z^2} & \text{if } (x, y, z) \neq 0 \\ 0 & \text{if } (x, y, z) = 0 \end{cases}$$

continuous on $\mathbb{R}^3$?

11 | ANSWERS TO SELECTED EXERCISES

1. -27

2. $\dfrac{3}{8}$

3. 2

4. -1

5. $\dfrac{x^4 + 3x^2y^2 - 2xy^3}{(x^2 + y^2)^2}, \dfrac{3x^2y^2 + y^4 - 2yx^3}{(x^2 + y^2)^2}$

6. $\sqrt{y} + \dfrac{y}{2x^{3/2}}, \dfrac{x}{2\sqrt{y}} - \dfrac{1}{\sqrt{x}}$

7. $\dfrac{1}{y} - \dfrac{y}{x^2}$

8. $4(3xy^2 - x^4 + 1)^3(3y^2 - 4x^3), 24xy(3xy^2 - x^4 + 1)^3$

9. $y \sec(xy)[1 + xy \tan(xy)]$

10. $\dfrac{t}{(x + t)^2}, \dfrac{x}{(x + t)^2}$

11. 0

12. $\dfrac{4}{5}$

13. $y + z, x + z, y + x$

14. $2xy^3t^4, 3x^2y^2t^4, 4x^2y^3t^3$

15. $f_x(x, y) = 3x^2y^5 - 4xy + 1, f_y(x, y) = 5x^3y^4 - 2x^2$

16. $f_x(x, y) = 6x^5y^2 + 2xy^6, f_y(x, y) = 6y^5x^2 + 2yx^6$

17. $f_x(x, y) = 4x^3 + 2xy^2, f_y(x, y) = 2x^2y + 4y^3$

18. $f_x(x, y) = \dfrac{2x}{x^2 + y^2}, f_y(x, y) = \dfrac{2y}{x^2 + y^2}$

19. $f_x(x, y) = e^x[\tan(x - y) + \sec^2(x - y)],$
$f_y(x, y) = -e^x \sec^2(x - y)$

20. $f_x(s, t) = \dfrac{t^2}{(s^2 + t^2)^{3/2}}, f_t(s, t) = -\dfrac{st}{(s^2 + t^2)^{3/2}}$

21. $f_{xx} = 2y, f_{xy} = 2x + \dfrac{1}{2\sqrt{y}}, f_{yx} = 2x + \dfrac{1}{2\sqrt{y}},$
$f_{yy} = -\dfrac{x}{4y^{3/2}}$

22. $f_{xx} = -\sin(x + y) - \cos(x - y),$
$f_{xy} = -\sin(x + y) + \cos(x - y),$
$f_{yx} = -\sin(x + y) + \cos(x - y),$
$f_{yy} = -\sin(x + y) - \cos(x - y)$

23. $z_{xx} = \dfrac{3(2x^2 + y^2)}{\sqrt{x^2 + y^2}}, z_{xy} = \dfrac{3xy}{\sqrt{x^2 + y^2}}, z_{yx} = \dfrac{3xy}{\sqrt{x^2 + y^2}},$
$z_{yy} = \dfrac{3(x^2 + 2y^2)}{\sqrt{x^2 + y^2}}$

24. $z_{xx} = 50[\sin^2(5x + 2y) - \cos^2(5x + 2y)],$
$z_{xy} = 20[\sin^2(5x + 2y) - \cos^2(5x + 2y)],$
$z_{yx} = 20[\sin^2(5x + 2y) - \cos^2(5x + 2y)],$
$z_{yy} = 8[\sin^2(5x + 2y) - \cos^2(5x + 2y)]$

25. $z_{xx} = \dfrac{t(2x - 1)}{4(x - x^2)^{3/2}}, z_{xt} = \dfrac{1}{2\sqrt{x - x^2}}, z_{tx} = \dfrac{1}{2\sqrt{x - x^2}},$
$z_{tt} = 0$

26. $z_{xx} = (\ln t)[(\ln t) - 1] x^{(\ln t)-2},$
$z_{xt} = x^{(\ln t)-1} \dfrac{1 + \ln t \ln x}{t}, z_{tx} = x^{(\ln t)-1} \dfrac{1 + \ln t \ln x}{t},$
$z_{tt} = x^{\ln t} \ln x \dfrac{(\ln x) - 1}{t^2}$

27. $-48xy$

28. $2y^3 e^{xy^2}(2 + xy^2)$

29. $f_{xyz} = 48x^3y^3z^2$

30. $x^2z(2 + xyz)e^{xyz}$

31. Minimum $f(-2, 3) = -13$

32. Minimum $f\left(\dfrac{1}{2}, -1\right) = -2$

33. Minimum $f(0, -1) = -1$

34. Minimum $f(1, 1) = -1$, saddle point $(0, 0)$

35. Minimum $f(0, 0) = 4$, saddle points $(\pm\sqrt{2}, -1)$

36. Saddle point $(1, 2)$

37. Maximum $f(4, 4) = 12$

38. Maximum $f\left(-\dfrac{1}{2}, 4\right) = -6$

39. Minima $f(-(1 + y), y) = 0$, maximum $f(1, 1) = 3$

40. $L^2W^2, \dfrac{1}{4}L^2W^2$

42. (a) $x = w/3$, base $= w/3$

    (b) Yes

11 | SOLUTIONS TO SELECTED EXERCISES

1. $f(x, y) = x^3y^5 \Rightarrow f_x(x, y) = 3x^2y^5$, $f_x(3, -1) = -27$

2. $f(x, y) = \sqrt{2x + 3y} \Rightarrow$

$$f_y(x, y) = \frac{1}{2}(2x + 3y)^{-1/2}(3),$$

$$f_y(2, 4) = \frac{3/2}{\sqrt{4 + 12}} = \frac{3}{8}$$

3. $f(x, y) = xe^{-y} + 3y \Rightarrow \partial f/\partial y = x(-1)e^{-y} + 3$, $(\partial f/\partial y)(1, 0) = -1 + 3 = 2$

4. $f(x, y) = \sin(y - x) \Rightarrow \partial f/\partial x = -\cos(y - x)$, $(\partial f/\partial x)(3, 3) = -\cos(0) = -1$

5. $z = \dfrac{x^3 + y^3}{x^2 + y^2} \Rightarrow$

$$\frac{\partial z}{\partial x} = \frac{3x^2(x^2 + y^2) - (x^3 + y^3)(2x)}{(x^2 + y^2)^2}$$

$$= \frac{x^4 + 3x^2y^2 - 2xy^3}{(x^3 + y^2)^2},$$

$$\frac{\partial z}{\partial y} = \frac{3y^2(x^2 + y^2) - (x^3 + y^3)(2y)}{(x^2 + y^2)^2}$$

$$= \frac{3x^2y^2 + y^4 - 2yx^3}{(x^2 + y^2)^2}$$

6. $z = x\sqrt{y} - \dfrac{y}{\sqrt{x}} \Rightarrow$

$$\frac{\partial z}{\partial x} = \sqrt{y} - y\left(-\frac{1}{2}\right)x^{-3/2} = \sqrt{y} + \frac{y}{2x^{3/2}},$$

$$\frac{\partial z}{\partial y} = x\left(\frac{1}{2}\right)y^{-1/2} - \frac{1}{\sqrt{x}} = \frac{x}{2\sqrt{y}} - \frac{1}{\sqrt{x}}$$

7. $z = \dfrac{x}{y} + \dfrac{y}{x} \Rightarrow \dfrac{\partial z}{\partial x} = \dfrac{1}{y} - \dfrac{y}{x^2}$

8. $z = (3xy^2 - x^4 + 1)^4 \Rightarrow$

$\partial z/\partial x = 4(3xy^2 - x^4 + 1)^3(3y^2 - 4x^3)$,

$\partial z/\partial y = 4(3xy^2 - x^4 + 1)^3(6xy)$

$\quad\quad = 24xy(3xy^2 - x^4 + 1)^3$

9. $u = xy\sec(xy) \Rightarrow$

$\partial u/\partial x = y\sec(xy) + xy[\sec(xy)\tan(xy)](y)$

$\quad\quad = y\sec(xy)[1 + xy\tan(xy)]$

10. $u = \dfrac{u}{x + t} \Rightarrow \dfrac{\partial u}{\partial x} = \dfrac{1(x + t) - x(1)}{(x + t)^2} = \dfrac{t}{(x + t)^2}$,

$$\frac{\partial u}{\partial t} = x(-1)(x + 1)^{-2}(1) = -\frac{x}{(x + t)^2}$$

11. $f(x, y, z) = xyz \Rightarrow f_y(x, y, z) = xz$, so $f_y(0, 1, 2) = 0$.

12. $f(x, y, z) = \sqrt{x^2 + y^2 + z^2} \Rightarrow$

$$f_z(x, y, z) = \frac{1}{2}(x^2 + y^2 + z^2)^{-1/2}(2z), \text{ so}$$

$$f_z(0, 3, 4) = \frac{4}{\sqrt{0 + 9 + 16}} = \frac{4}{5}.$$

13. $u = xy + yz + zx \Rightarrow u_x = y + z$, $u_y = x + z$, $u_z = y + x$

14. $u = x^2y^3t^4 \Rightarrow u_x = 2xy^3t^4$, $u_y = 3x^2y^2t^4$, $u_t = 4x^2y^3t^3$

15. $f(x, y) = x^3y^5 - 2x^2y + x \Rightarrow$

$f_x(x, y) = 3x^2y^5 - 4xy + 1$, $f_y(x, y) = 5x^3y^4 - 2x^2$

16. $f(x, y) = x^2y^2(x^4 + y^4) \Rightarrow$

$f_x(x, y) = 2xy^2(x^4 + y^4) + x^2y^2(4x^3) = 6x^5y^2 + 2xy^6$

and by symmetry $f_y(x, y) = 6y^5x^2 + 2yx^6$.

17. $f(x, y) = x^4 + x^2y^2 + y^4 \Rightarrow f_x(x, y) = 4x^3 + 2xy^2$, $f_y(x, y) = 2x^2y + 4y^3$

18. $f(x, y) = \ln(x^2 + y^2) \Rightarrow$

$$f_x(x, y) = \frac{1}{x^2 + y^2}(2x) = \frac{2x}{x^2 + y^2}, f_y(x, y) = \frac{2y}{x^2 + y^2}$$

19. $f(x, y) = e^x\tan(x - y) \Rightarrow$

$f_x(x, y) = e^x\tan(x - y) + e^x\sec^2(x - y)$

$\quad\quad = e^x[\tan(x - y) + \sec^2(x - y)]$,

$f_y(x, y) = e^x[\sec^2(x - y)](-1) = -e^x\sec^2(x - y)$

20. $f(s, t) = \dfrac{s}{\sqrt{s^2 + t^2}} \Rightarrow$

$$f_s(s, t) = \frac{(1)\sqrt{s^2 + t^2} - s\left(\dfrac{1}{2}\right)(s^2 + t^2)^{-1/2}(2s)}{(\sqrt{s^2 + t^2})^2}$$

$$= \frac{|s^2 + t^2| - s^2}{|s^2 + t^2|\sqrt{s^2 + t^2}} = \frac{t^2}{(s^2 + t^2)^{3/2}},$$

$$f_t(s, t) = s\left(-\frac{1}{2}\right)(s^2 + t^2)^{-3/2}(2t) = -\frac{st}{(s^2 + t^2)^{3/2}}$$

21. $f(x, y) = x^2y + x\sqrt{y} \Rightarrow f_x = 2xy + \sqrt{y}$,

$f_y = x^2 + \dfrac{x}{2\sqrt{y}}$. Thus $f_{xx} = 2y$, $f_{xy} = 2x + \dfrac{1}{2\sqrt{y}}$,

$f_{yx} = 2x + \dfrac{1}{2\sqrt{y}}$ and $f_{yy} = -\dfrac{x}{4y^{3/2}}$.

22. $f(x, y) = \sin(x + y) + \cos(x - y) \Rightarrow$

$f_x = \cos(x + y) - \sin(x, y),$

$f_y = \cos(x + y) + \sin(x - y).$ Thus

$f_{xx} = -\sin(x + y) - \cos(x - y),$

$f_{xy} = -\sin(x + y) + \cos(x - y),$

$f_{yx} = -\sin(x + y) + \cos(x - y)$ and

$f_{yy} = -\sin(x + y) - \cos(x - y).$

23. $z = (x^2 + y^2)^{3/2} \Rightarrow$

$z_x = \dfrac{3}{2}(x^2 + y^2)^{1/2}(2x) = 3x(x^2 + y^2)^{1/2}$ and

$z_y = 3y(x^2 + y^2)^{1/2}.$ Thus

$z_{xx} = 3(x^2 + y^2)^{1/2} + 3x(x^2 + y^2)^{-1/2}\left(\dfrac{1}{2}\right)(2x)$

$= \dfrac{3(x^2 + y^2) + 3x^2}{\sqrt{x^2 + y^2}} = \dfrac{3(2x^2 + y^2)}{\sqrt{x^2 + y^2}}$ and

$z_{xy} = 3x\left(\dfrac{1}{2}\right)(x^2 + y^2)^{-1/2}(2y) = \dfrac{3xy}{\sqrt{x^2 + y^2}}.$ By

symmetry $z_{yx} = \dfrac{3xy}{\sqrt{x^2 + y^2}}$ and $z_{yy} = \dfrac{3(x^2 + 2y^2)}{\sqrt{x^2 + y^2}}.$

24. $z = \cos^2(5x + 2y) \Rightarrow$

$z_x = [2\cos(5x + 2y)][-\sin(5x + 2y)](5)$

$= -10\cos(5x + 2y)\sin(5x + 2y)$ and

$z_y = [2\cos(5x + 2y)][-\sin(5x + 2y)](2)$

$= -4\cos(5x + 2y)\sin(5x + 2y)$

Thus

$z_{xx} = (10)(5)\sin^2(5x + 2y) + (-10)(5)\cos^2(5x + 2y)$

$= 50[\sin^2(5x + 2y) - \cos^2(5x + 2y)],$

$z_{xy} = (10)(2)\sin^2(5x + 2y) + (-10)(2)\cos^2(5x + 2y)$

$= 20[\sin^2(5x + 2y) - \cos^2(5x + 2y)],$

$z_{yx} = -(-4)(5)\sin^2(5x + 2y) + (-4)(5)\cos^2(5x + 2y)$

$= 20[\sin^2(5x + 2y) - \cos^2(5x + 2y)],$

$z_{yy} = -(-4)(2)\sin^2(5x + 2y) + (-4)(2)\cos^2(5x + 2y)$

$= 8[\sin^2(5x + 2y) - \cos^2(5x + 2y)]$

25. $z = t\sin^{-1}\sqrt{x} \Rightarrow$

$z_x = t\dfrac{1}{\sqrt{1 - \left(\sqrt{x}\right)^2}}\left(\dfrac{1}{2}\right)x^{-1/2} = \dfrac{t}{2\sqrt{x - x^2}},$

$z_t = \sin^{-1}\sqrt{x}.$ Thus

$z_{xx} = \dfrac{1}{2}t\left(-\dfrac{1}{2}\right)(x - x^2)^{-3/2}(1 - 2x) = \dfrac{t(2x - 1)}{4(x - x^2)^{3/2}},$

$z_{xt} = \dfrac{1}{2\sqrt{x - x^2}},$

$z_{tx} = \dfrac{1}{\sqrt{1 - \left(\sqrt{x}\right)^2}}\left(\dfrac{1}{2}x^{-1/2}\right) = \dfrac{1}{2\sqrt{x - x^2}},$ and $z_{tt} = 0.$

26. $z = x^{\ln t} \Rightarrow z_x = (\ln t)x^{(\ln t)-1}, \ln z = (\ln t)(\ln x)$ so

$z_t = (x^{\ln t})\left(\dfrac{1}{t}\right)\ln x = x^{\ln t}\dfrac{\ln x}{t}.$ Thus

$z_{xx} = (\ln t)[(\ln t) - 1]x^{(\ln t)-2},$

$\ln z_x = \ln(\ln t) + [(\ln t) - 1]\ln x,$ so

$z_{xt} = z_x\left[\dfrac{1}{\ln t}\left(\dfrac{1}{t}\right) + \dfrac{1}{t}\ln x\right]$

$= (\ln t)x^{(\ln t)-1}\dfrac{1 + (\ln t)(\ln x)}{t\ln t}$

$= x^{(\ln t)-1}\dfrac{1 + \ln t\ln x}{t}$

Also

$z_{tx} = \dfrac{(\ln t)x^{(\ln t)-1}\ln x + (1/x)x^{\ln t}}{t}$

$= x^{(\ln t)-1}\dfrac{1 + \ln t\ln x}{t}$ and

$z_{tt} = \left[\dfrac{\partial}{\partial t}(x^{\ln t})\right]\left(\dfrac{\ln t}{t}\right) + x^{\ln t}[-(\ln x)t^{-2}]$

$= x^{\ln t}\ln x\dfrac{(\ln x) - 1}{t^2}$

27. $f(x, y) = x^2y^3 - 2x^4y \Rightarrow f_x = 2xy^3 - 8x^3y,$

$f_{xx} = 2y^3 - 24x^2y, f_{xxx} = -48xy$

28. $f(x, y) = e^{xy^2} \Rightarrow f_x = y^2e^{xy^2}, f_{xx} = y^4e^{xy^2},$

$f_{xxy} = 4y^3e^{xy^2} + 2xy^5e^{xy^2} = 2y^3e^{xy^2}(2 + xy^2)$

29. $f(x, y, z) = x^5 + x^4y^4z^3 + yz^2 \Rightarrow$

$f_x = 5x^4 + 4x^3y^4z^3, f_{xy} = 16x^3y^3z^3,$ and

$f_{xyz} = 48x^3y^3z^2$

30. $f(x, y, z) = e^{xyz} \Rightarrow f_y = xze^{xyz},$

$f_{yz} = xe^{xyz} + xz(xy)e^{xyz} = xe^{xyz}(1 + yxz),$ and

$f_{yzy} = x(xz)e^{xyz}(1 + xyz) + xe^{xyz}(xz)$

$= x^2z(2 + xyz)e^{xyz}$

31. $f(x, y) = x^2 + y^2 + 4x - 6y \Rightarrow f_x = 2x + 4,$

$f_y = 2y - 6, f_{xx} = f_{yy} = 2, f_{xy} = 0.$ Then $f_x = 0$ and

$f_y = 0$ implies $(x, y) = (-2, 3)$ and $D(-2, 3) = 4 > 0,$

so $f(-2, 3) = -13$ is a local minimum.

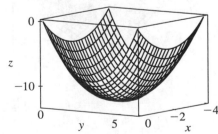

32. $f(x, y) = 4x^2 + y^2 - 4x + 2y \Rightarrow f_x = 8x - 4,$
$f_y = 2y + 2, f_{xx} = 8, f_{yy} = 2, f_{xy} = 0.$ Then $f_x = 0$ and
$f_y = 0$ implies (x, y) is $\left(\frac{1}{2}, -1\right)$ and $D\left(\frac{1}{2}, -1\right) =$
$16 > 0,$ so $f\left(\frac{1}{2}, -1\right) = -2$ is a local minimum.

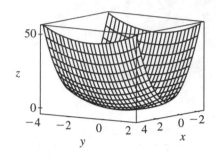

33. $f(x, y) = 2x^2 + y^2 + 2xy + 2x + 2y \Rightarrow$
$f_x = 4x + 2y + 2, f_y = 2y + 2x + 2, f_{xx} = 4, f_{yy} = 2,$
$f_{xy} = 2.$ Then $f_x = 0$ and $f_y = 0$ implies $2x = 0,$ so the
critical point is $(0, -1).$ $D(0, -1) = 8 - 4 > 0,$ so
$f(0, -1) = -1$ is a local minimum.

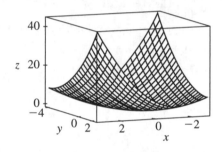

34. $f(x, y) = x^3 - 3xy + y^3 \Rightarrow f_x = 3x^2 - 3y,$
$f_y = 3y^2 - 3x, f_{xx} = 6x, f_{yy} = 6y, f_{xy} = -3.$ Then
$f_x = 0$ implies $x^2 = y$ and substituting into $f_y = 0$
gives $x = 0$ or $x = 1.$ Thus the critical points are
$(0, 0)$ and $(1, 1).$

Now $D(0, 0) = -9 < 0$ so $(0, 0)$ is a saddle point
and $D(1, 1) = 36 - 9 > 0$ while $f_{xx}(1, 1) = 6$ so
$f(1, 1) = -1$ is a local minimum.

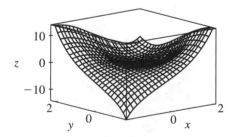

35. $f(x, y) = x^2 + y^2 + x^2y + 4 \Rightarrow f_x = 2x + 2xy,$
$f_y = 2y + x^2, f_{xx} = 2 + 2y, f_{yy} = 2, f_{xy} = 2x.$

Then $f_y = 0$ implies $y = -\frac{1}{2}x^2,$ substituting into

$f_x = 0$ gives $2x - x^3 = 0$ so $x = 0$ or $x = \pm\sqrt{2}.$
Thus the critical points are $(0, 0), (\sqrt{2}, -1)$ and
$(-\sqrt{2}, -1).$ Now $D(0, 0) = 4, D(\sqrt{2}, -1) = -8 =$
$D(-\sqrt{2}, -1), f_{xx}(0, 0) = 2, f_{xx}(\pm\sqrt{2}, -1) = 0.$
Thus $f(0, 0) = 4$ is a local minimum and
$(\pm\sqrt{2}, -1)$ are saddle points.

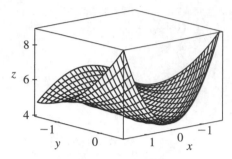

36. $f(x, y) = xy - 2x - y \Rightarrow f_x = y - 2, f_y = x - 1,$
$f_{xx} = f_{yy} = 0, f_{xy} = 1$ and the only critical point is
$(1, 2).$ Now $D(1, 2) = -1,$ so $(1, 2)$ is a saddle point
and f has no local maximum or minimum.

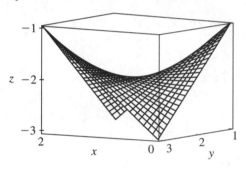

37. $f(x, y) = y\sqrt{x} - y^2 - x + 6y \Rightarrow f_x = y/(2\sqrt{x}) - 1,$
$f_y = \sqrt{x} - 2y + 6, f_{yy} = -2, f_{xx} = -\frac{1}{4}yx^{-3/2},$
$f_{xy} = 1/(2\sqrt{x}).$ Then $f_x = 0$ implies $y = 2\sqrt{x}$ and
substituting into $f_y = 0$ gives $-3\sqrt{x} + 6 = 0$ or
$x = 4.$ Thus the only critical point is $(4, 4).$
$D(4, 4) = -\frac{1}{8}(-2) - \left(\frac{1}{4}\right)^2 > 0$ and $f_{xx}(4, 4) = -\frac{1}{8},$
so $f(4, 4) = 12$ is a local maximum.

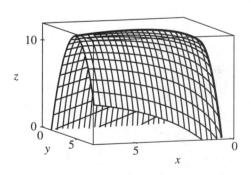

38. $f(x, y) = \dfrac{x^2y^2 - 8x + y}{xy} \Rightarrow f_x = y - x^{-2}$,

$f_y = x + 8y^{-2}$, $f_{xx} = 2x^{-3}$, $f_{yy} = -16y^{-3}$ and $f_{xy} = 1$.
Then $f_x = 0$ implies $y = x^{-2}$, substituting into $f_y = 0$

gives $x + 8x^4 = 0$ so $x = 0$ or $x = -\dfrac{1}{2}$ but $(0, y)$

is not in the domain of f. Thus the only critical

point is $\left(-\dfrac{1}{2}, 4\right)$. Then $f_{xx}\left(-\dfrac{1}{2}, 4\right) = -16$ and

$D\left(-\dfrac{1}{2}, 4\right) = 4 - 1 > 0$ so $f\left(-\dfrac{1}{2}, 4\right) = -6$ is a

local maximum.

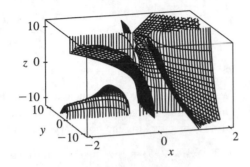

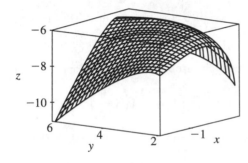

39. $f(x, y) = \dfrac{(x + y + 1)^2}{x^2 + y^2 + 1} \Rightarrow$

$f_x = \dfrac{2(x + y + 1)(x^2 + y^2 + 1) - (x + y + 1)^2(2x)}{(x^2 + y^2 + 1)^2}$

and $f_x = 0$ implies
$2(x + y + 1)[(x^2 + y^2 + 1) - (x + y + 1)x] = 0$
or $(x + y + 1)(y^2 + 1 - xy - x) = 0$, so

$x = -(1 + y)$ or $x = \dfrac{y^2 + 1}{y + 1}$ (Note: In the latter

$y \neq -1$; otherwise we get $0 = 2$.) Similarly

$f_y = \dfrac{2(x + y + 1)(x^2 + y^2 + 1) - (x + y + 1)^2(2y)}{(x^2 + y^2 + 1)^2}$

and $f_y = 0$ implies $(x + y + 1)(x^2 + 1 - xy - y) = 0$.
Thus $x = -(1 + y)$ also satisfies $f_y = 0$ and all
points of the form $(-(1 + y), y)$ are critical points.

Substituting $x = \dfrac{y^2 + 1}{y + 1}$ into $x^2 + 1 - xy - y = 0$

and simplifying gives $-2y^3 + 2 = 0$ or $y = 1$ and

$x = 1$. Note that $x = \dfrac{y^2 + 1}{y + 1}$ is not a zero of

$x + y + 1$. So $(1, 1)$ is the only other critical point.
Now for each y, $f(-(1 + y), y) = 0$ but $f(x, y) \geq 0$.
Thus the points $(-(1 + y), y)$ are local minima
with value 0.

Also

$(x + y + 1)^2 = (x + y)^2 + 2(x + y) + 1$

$\qquad \leq 2x^2 + 2y^2 + 1 + 2(x + y)$

$\qquad \leq 2x^2 + 2y^2 + 1 + (x^2 + y^2 + 2)$

$\qquad = 3(x^2 + y^2 + 1)$

The last inequality is true because $0 \leq (x - 1)^2 + (y - 1)^2$.

Thus, $f(x, y) = \dfrac{(x + y + 1)^2}{x^2 + y^2 + 1} \leq 3$. But $f(1, 1) = 3$ so

$f(1, 1) = 3$ is a local maximum.

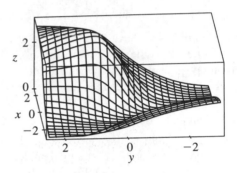

40. The areas of the smaller rectangles are $A_1 = xy$,
$A_2 = (L - x)y$, $A_3 = (L - x)(W - y)$, $A_4 = x(W - y)$.
For $0 \leq x \leq L$, $0 \leq y \leq W$, let

$f(x, y) = A_1^2 + A_2^2 + A_3^2 + A_4^2$

$\qquad = x^2y^2 + (L - x)^2y^2 + (L - x)^2(W - y)^2 + x^2(W - y)^2$

$\qquad = [x^2 + (L - x)^2][y^2 + (W - y)^2]$

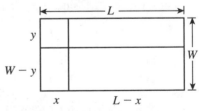

Then we need to find the maximum and minimum
values of $f(x, y)$. Here $f_x(x, y) = [2x - 2(L - x)]$

$[y^2 + (W - y)^2] = 0 \Rightarrow 4x - 2L = 0$ or $x = \dfrac{1}{2}L$, and

$f_y(x, y) = [x^2 + (L - x)^2][2y - 2(W - y)] = 0 \Rightarrow$
$4y - 2W = 0$ or $y = W/2$. Also $f_{xx} = 4[y^2 + (W - y)^2]$,
$f_{yy} = 4[x^2 + (L - x)^2]$, and $f_{xy} = (4x - 2L)(4y - 2W)$.
Then $D = 16[y^2 + (W - y)^2][x^2 + (L - x)^2] -$

$(4x - 2L)^2(4y - 2W)^2$. Thus when $x = \dfrac{1}{2}L$ and

$y = \dfrac{1}{2}W$, $D > 0$ and $f_{xx} = 2W^2 > 0$. Thus a minimum of f occurs at $\left(\dfrac{1}{2}L, \dfrac{1}{2}W\right)$ and this minimum value is $f\left(\dfrac{1}{2}L, \dfrac{1}{2}W\right) = \dfrac{1}{4}L^2W^2$. There are no other critical points, so the maximum must occur on the boundary. Now along the width of the rectangle let $g(y) = f(0, y) = f(L, y) = L^2[y^2 + (W - y)^2]$, $0 \le y \le W$. Then $g'(y) = L^2[2y - 2(W - y)] = 0 \Leftrightarrow y = \dfrac{1}{2}W$.

And $g\left(\dfrac{1}{2}\right) = \dfrac{1}{2}L^2W^2$. Checking the endpoints, we get $g(0) = g(W) = L^2W^2$. Along the length of the rectangle let $h(x) = f(x, 0) = f(x, W) = W^2[x^2 + (L - x)^2]$, $0 \le x \le L$. By symmetry $h'(x) = 0 \Leftrightarrow x = \dfrac{1}{2}L$ and $h\left(\dfrac{1}{2}L\right) = \dfrac{1}{2}L^2W^2$. At the endpoints we have $h(0) = h(L) = L^2W^2$. Therefore L^2W^2 is the maximum value of f. This maximum value of f occurs when the "cutting" lines correspond to sides of the rectangle.

42. (a) The area of a trapezoid is $\dfrac{1}{2}h(b_1 + b_2)$, where h is the height (the distance between the two parallel sides) and b_1, b_2 are the lengths of the bases (the parallel sides). From the figure in the text, we see that $h = x \sin \theta$, $b_1 = w - 2x$, and $b_2 = w - 2x + 2x \cos \theta$. Therefore the cross-sectional area of the rain gutter is

$$A(x, 0) = \dfrac{1}{2}x \sin \theta \, [(w - 2x) + (w - 2x + 2x \cos \theta)]$$

$$= (x \sin \theta)(w - 2x + x \cos \theta)$$

$$= wx \sin \theta - 2x^2 \sin \theta + x^2 \sin \theta \cos \theta,$$

$$0 < x \le \dfrac{1}{2}w, \ 0 < \theta \le \dfrac{\pi}{2}$$

We look for the critical points of A: $\partial A/\partial x = w \sin \theta - 4x \sin \theta + 2x \sin \theta \cos \theta$ and $\partial A/\partial \theta = wx \cos \theta - 2x^2 \cos \theta + x^2(\cos^2 \theta - \sin^2 \theta)$, so $\partial A/\partial x = 0 \Leftrightarrow \sin \theta(w - 4x + 2x \cos \theta) = 0 \Leftrightarrow \cos \theta = \dfrac{4x - w}{2x} = 2 - \dfrac{w}{2x} \ \left(0 < \theta \le \dfrac{\pi}{2} \Rightarrow \sin \theta > 0\right)$. If, in addition, $\partial A/\partial \theta = 0$, then

$$0 = wx \cos \theta - 2x^2 \cos \theta + x^2(2\cos^2\theta - 1)$$

$$= wx\left(2 - \dfrac{w}{2x}\right) - 2x^2\left(2 - \dfrac{w}{2x}\right) +$$

$$\quad x^2\left[2\left(2 - \dfrac{w}{2x}\right)^2 - 1\right]$$

$$= 2wx - \dfrac{1}{2}w^2 - 4x^2 + wx +$$

$$\quad x^2\left[8 - \dfrac{4w}{x} + \dfrac{w^2}{2x^2} - 1\right]$$

$$= -wx + 3x^2 = x(3x - w)$$

Since $x > 0$, we must have $x = \dfrac{1}{3}w$, in which case $\cos \theta = \dfrac{1}{2}$, so $\theta = \dfrac{\pi}{3}$, $\sin \theta = \dfrac{\sqrt{3}}{2}$, $k = \dfrac{\sqrt{3}}{6}w$, $b_1 = \dfrac{1}{3}w$, $b_2 = \dfrac{2}{3}w$, and $A = \dfrac{\sqrt{3}}{12}w^2$.

We can argue from the physical nature of this problem that we have found a local maximum of A. Now checking the boundary of A, let

$$g(\theta) = A(w/2, \theta) = \dfrac{1}{2}w^2 \sin \theta - \dfrac{1}{2}w^2 \sin \theta + \dfrac{1}{4}w^2 \sin \theta \cos \theta = \dfrac{1}{8}w^2 \sin 2\theta, \ 0 < \theta \le \dfrac{\pi}{2}.$$

Clearly g is maximized when $\sin 2\theta = 1$ in which case $A = \dfrac{1}{8}w^2$. Also along the line $\theta = \dfrac{\pi}{2}$, let $h(x) = A\left(x, \dfrac{\pi}{2}\right) = wx - 2x^2$, $0 < x < \dfrac{1}{2}w \Rightarrow h'(x) = w - 4x = 0 \Leftrightarrow x = \dfrac{1}{4}w$, and $h\left(\dfrac{1}{4}w\right) = w\left(\dfrac{1}{4}w\right) - 2\left(\dfrac{1}{4}w\right)^2 = \dfrac{1}{8}w^2$.

Since $\dfrac{1}{8}w^2 < \dfrac{\sqrt{3}}{12}w^2$, we conclude that the local maximum found earlier was an absolute maximum.

(b) If the metal were bent into a semi-circular gutter of radius r, we would have $w = \pi r$ and $A = \dfrac{1}{2}\pi r^2 = \dfrac{1}{2}\pi\left(\dfrac{w}{\pi}\right)^2 = \dfrac{w^2}{2\pi}$. Since $\dfrac{w^2}{2\pi} > \dfrac{\sqrt{3}w^2}{12}$, it *would* be better to bend the metal into a gutter with a semicircular cross-section.

12 MULTIPLE INTEGRALS

1–6 ■ Find the gradient vector field of f.

1. $f(x, y) = x^5 - 4x^2y^3$

2. $f(x, y) = \sin(2x + 3y)$

3. $f(x, y) = e^{3x} \cos 4y$

4. $f(x, y, z) = xyz$

5. $f(x, y, z) = xy^2 - yz^3$

6. $f(x, y, z) = x \ln(y - z)$

7–12 ■ Evaluate the surface integral.

7. $\iint_S y \, dS$, S is the part of the plane $3x + 2y + z = 6$ that lies in the first octant

8. $\iint_S xz \, dS$, S is the triangular with vertices $(1, 0, 0)$, $(0, 1, 0)$, and $(0, 0, 1)$

9. $\iint_S x \, dS$, S is the surface $y = x^2 + 4z$, $0 \le x \le 2$, $0 \le z \le 2$

10. $\iint_S (y^2 + z^2) \, dS$, S is the part of the paraboloid $x = 4 - y^2 - z^2$ that lies in front of the plane $x = 0$

11. $\iint_S yz \, dS$, S is the part of the plane $z = y + 3$ that lies inside the cylinder $x^2 + y^2 = 1$

12. $\iint_S yz \, dS$, S is the surface with parametric equations $x = uv$, $y = u + v$, $z = u - v$, $u^2 + v^2 \le 1$

13. If $[\![x]\!]$ denotes the greatest integer in x, evaluate the integral

$$\iint_R [\![x + y]\!] \, dA$$

where $R = \{(x, y) \mid 1 \le x \le 3, 2 \le y \le 5\}$.

14. Evaluate the integral

$$\int_0^1 \int_0^1 e^{\max\{x^2, y^2\}} \, dy \, dx$$

where $\max\{x^2, y^2\}$ means the larger of the numbers x^2 and y^2.

15. Find the average value of the function

$$f(x) = \int_x^1 \cos(t^2) \, dt \text{ on the interval } [0, 1].$$

16. If $\mathbf{a}$, $\mathbf{b}$, and $\mathbf{c}$ are constant vectors, $\mathbf{r}$ is the position vector $x\mathbf{i} + y\mathbf{j} + z\mathbf{k}$, and E is given by the inequalities $0 \le \mathbf{a} \cdot \mathbf{r} \le \alpha$, $0 \le \mathbf{b} \cdot \mathbf{r} \le \beta$, $0 \le \mathbf{c} \cdot \mathbf{r} \le \gamma$, show that

$$\iiint_E (\mathbf{a} \cdot \mathbf{r})(\mathbf{b} \cdot \mathbf{r})(\mathbf{c} \cdot \mathbf{r}) \, dV = \frac{(\alpha\beta\gamma)^2}{8|\mathbf{a} \cdot (\mathbf{b} \times \mathbf{c})|}$$

17. The double integral $\int_0^1 \int_0^1 \dfrac{1}{1 - xy} \, dx \, dy$ is an improper integral and could be defined as the limit of double integrals over the rectangle $[0, t] \times [0, t]$ as $t \to 1^-$. But if we expand the integrand as a geometric series, we can express the integral as the sum of an infinite series. Show that

$$\int_0^1 \int_0^1 \frac{1}{1 - xy} \, dx \, dy = \sum_{n=1}^{\infty} \frac{1}{n^2}$$

18. Find approximations to $\iint_R (x - 3y^2)\, dA$ by choosing the sample point to be the (a) upper left corner, (b) upper right corner, (c) lower left corner, (d) lower right corner of each subrectangle.

19. (a) Estimate the volume of the solid that lies below the surface $z = x^2 + 4y$ and above the rectangle $R = \{(x, y)\,|\,0 \le x \le 2, 0 \le y \le 3\}$. Use a Riemann sum with $m = 2$, $n = 3$, and take the sample point to be the upper right corner of each subrectangle.

(b) Use the Midpoint Rule to estimate the volume of the solid in part (a).

20. If $R = [-2, 2] \times [-1, 1]$, use a Riemann sum with $m = n = 4$ to estimate the value of $\iint_R (2x + x^2 y)\, dA$. Take the sample points to be the lower left corners of the subrectangles.

12 | ANSWERS TO SELECTED EXERCISES

1. $(5x^4 - 8xy^3)\mathbf{i} - (12x^2y^2)\mathbf{j}$

2. $2\cos(2x + 3y)\mathbf{i} + 3\cos(2x + 3y)\mathbf{j}$

3. $\langle 3e^{3x}\cos 4y, -4e^{3x}\sin 4y \rangle$

4. $\langle yz, xz, xy \rangle$

5. $\langle y^2, 2xy - z^3, -3yz^2 \rangle$

6. $\left\langle \ln(y - z), \dfrac{x}{y - z}, -\dfrac{x}{y - z} \right\rangle$

7. $3\sqrt{14}$

8. $\dfrac{\sqrt{3}}{24}$

9. $\dfrac{33\sqrt{33} - 17\sqrt{17}}{6}$

10. $\dfrac{\pi}{60}(391\sqrt{17} + 1)$

11. $\dfrac{\sqrt{2}\pi}{4}$

12. 0

13. 30

15. $\dfrac{1}{2}\sin 1$

18. (a) -17.75

     (b) -15.75

     (c) -8.75

     (d) -6.75

19. (a) 63

     (b) 43.5

20. -11

12 | SOLUTIONS TO SELECTED EXERCISES

1. $\nabla f(x, y) = f_x(x, y)\mathbf{i} + f_y(x, y)\mathbf{j}$
$$= (5x^4 - 8xy^3)\mathbf{i} - (12x^2y^2)\mathbf{j}$$

2. $\nabla f(x, y) = f_x(x, y)\mathbf{i} + f_y(x, y)\mathbf{j}$
$$= 2\cos(2x + 3y)\mathbf{i} + 3\cos(2x + 3y)\mathbf{j}$$

3. $\nabla f(x, y) = \langle f_x, f_y \rangle = \langle 3e^{3x}\cos 4y, -4e^{3x}\sin 4y \rangle$

4. $\nabla f(x, y, z) = \langle f_x, f_y, f_z \rangle = \langle yz, xz, xy \rangle$

5. $\nabla f(x, y, z) = \langle f_x, f_y, f_z \rangle = \langle y^2, 2xy - z^3, -3yz^2 \rangle$

6. $\nabla f(x, y, z) = \langle f_x, f_y, f_z \rangle$
$$= \left\langle \ln(y - z), \frac{x}{y - z}, -\frac{x}{y - z} \right\rangle$$

7. $\mathbf{r}(x, y) = x\mathbf{i} + y\mathbf{j} + (6 - 3x - 2y)\mathbf{k}$, $\mathbf{r}_x \times \mathbf{r}_y = 3\mathbf{i} + 2\mathbf{j} + \mathbf{k}$ (the normal to the plane) and $|\mathbf{r}_x \times \mathbf{r}_y| = \sqrt{14}$. The given plane meets the first octant in the line $3x + 2y = 6$, $z = 0, x \geq 0, y \geq 0$, so $D = \{(x, y) \mid 0 \leq x \leq \frac{1}{3}(6 - 2y), 0 \leq y \leq 3\}$. Then
$$\iint_S y\, dS = \int_0^3 \int_0^{(6-2y)/3} y\sqrt{14}\, dx\, dy$$
$$= \sqrt{14} \int_0^3 \left(2y - \frac{2}{3}y^2\right) dy = 3\sqrt{14}$$

8. $\mathbf{r}(x, y) = x\mathbf{i} + y\mathbf{j} + (1 - x - y)\mathbf{k}$, $0 \leq x \leq 1 - y$, $0 \leq y \leq 1$, $|\mathbf{r}_x \times \mathbf{r}_y| = \sqrt{3}$. Then
$$\iint_S xz\, dS = \int_0^1 \int_0^{1-y} (x(1 - y) - x^2)\sqrt{3}\, dx\, dy$$
$$= \sqrt{3} \int_0^1 \left[\frac{1}{2}(1 - y)^3 - \frac{1}{3}(1 - y)^3\right] dy = \frac{\sqrt{3}}{24}$$

9. Using x and z as parameters, we have $\mathbf{r}(x, z) = x\mathbf{i} + (x^2 + 4z)\mathbf{j} + z\mathbf{k}$, $0 \leq x \leq 2$, $0 \leq z \leq 2$. Then $\mathbf{r}_x \times \mathbf{r}_z = (\mathbf{i} + 2x\mathbf{j}) \times (4\mathbf{j} + \mathbf{k}) = 2x\mathbf{i} - \mathbf{j} + 4\mathbf{k}$ and $|\mathbf{r}_x \times \mathbf{r}_z| = \sqrt{4x^2 + 17}$. Thus
$$\iint_S x\, dS = \int_0^2 \int_0^2 x\sqrt{4x^2 + 17}\, dx\, dz$$
$$= \int_0^2 dz \int_0^2 x\sqrt{4x^2 + 17}\, dx$$
$$= 2\left[\frac{1}{12}(4x^2 + 17)^{3/2}\right]_0^2 = \frac{33\sqrt{33} - 17\sqrt{17}}{6}$$

10. $\mathbf{r}(y, z) = (4 - y^2 - z^2)\mathbf{i} + y\mathbf{j} + z\mathbf{k}$, $0 \leq y^2 + z^2 \leq 4$, so $\mathbf{r}_y \times \mathbf{r}_z = (-2y\mathbf{i} + \mathbf{j}) \times (-2z\mathbf{i} + \mathbf{k}) = \mathbf{i} + 2y\mathbf{j} + 2z\mathbf{k}$ and $|\mathbf{r}_y \times \mathbf{r}_z| = \sqrt{4y^2 + 4z^2 + 1}$. Then

$$\iint_S (y^2 + z^2)\, dS$$
$$= \iint_{y^2 + z^2 \leq 4} (y^2 + z^2)\sqrt{4y^2 + 4z^2 + 1}\, dA$$
$$= \int_0^{2\pi} \int_0^2 r^2\sqrt{4r^2 + 1}\, r\, dr\, d\theta$$
$$= \int_0^{2\pi} d\theta \int_0^2 r^3\sqrt{4r^2 + 1}\, dr$$

Substituting $u = 4r^2 + 1$, so $du = 8r\, dr$ and $r^2 = \frac{1}{4}(u - 1)$, gives

$$\iint_S (y^2 + z^2)\, dS = 2\pi \int_1^{17} \frac{1}{8}\frac{1}{4}(u - 1)\sqrt{u}\, du$$
$$= \frac{\pi}{16}\left[\frac{2}{5}u^{5/2} - \frac{2}{3}u^{3/2}\right]_1^{17}$$
$$= \frac{\pi}{16}\left[\frac{2}{5}(289\sqrt{17} - 1) - \frac{2}{3}(17\sqrt{17} - 1)\right]$$
$$= \frac{\pi}{16}\left(\frac{1564}{15}\sqrt{17} + \frac{4}{15}\right) = \frac{\pi}{60}(391\sqrt{17} + 1)$$

11. S is the part of the plane $z = y + 3$ over the disk $D = \{(x, y) \mid x^2 + y^2 \leq 1\}$. Thus
$$\iint_S yz\, dS = \iint_D y(y + 3)\sqrt{(0)^2 + (1)^2 + 1}\, dA$$
$$= \sqrt{2} \int_0^{2\pi} \int_0^1 r\sin\theta\,(r\sin\theta + 3)r\, dr\, d\theta$$
$$= \sqrt{2} \int_0^{2\pi} \left[\frac{1}{4}r^4\sin^2\theta + r^3\sin\theta\right]_{r=0}^{r=1} d\theta$$
$$= \sqrt{2} \int_0^{2\pi} \left(\frac{1}{4}\sin^2\theta + \sin\theta\right) d\theta$$
$$= \sqrt{2}\left[\frac{1}{4}\left(\frac{1}{2}\theta - \frac{1}{4}\sin 2\theta\right) - \cos\theta\right]_0^{2\pi}$$
$$= \frac{\sqrt{2}\pi}{4}$$

12. $\mathbf{r}(u, v) = uv\mathbf{i} + (u + v)\mathbf{j} + (u - v)\mathbf{k}$, $u^2 + v^2 \leq 1$ and $|\mathbf{r}_u \times \mathbf{r}_v| = \sqrt{4 + 2u^2 + 2v^2}$. Then
$$\iint_S yx\, dS = \iint_{u^2 + v^2 \leq 1} (u^2 - v^2)\sqrt{4 + 2u^2 + 2v^2}\, dA$$
$$= \int_0^{2\pi} \int_0^1 r^2(\cos^2\theta - \sin^2\theta)\sqrt{4 + 2r^2}\, r\, dr\, d\theta$$
$$= \left[\int_0^{2\pi} (\cos^2\theta - \sin^2\theta)\, d\theta\right]\left[\int_0^1 r^3\sqrt{4 + 2r^2}\, dr\right]$$
$$= 0 \text{ since the first integral is } 0.$$

13.

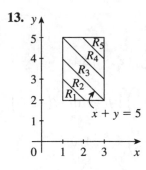

Let $R = \bigcup_{i=1}^{5} R_i$, where
$R_i = \{(x, y) \,|\, x + y \geq i + 2, x + y < i + 3, 1 \leq x \leq 3, 2 \leq y \leq 5\}$.

$$\iint_R [x + y] \, dA = \sum_{i=1}^{5} \iint_{R_i} [x + y] \, dA =$$

$\sum_{i=1}^{5} [x + y] \iint_{R_i} dA$, since $[x + y] = \text{constant} =$

$i + 2$ for $(x, y) \in R_i$. Therefore

$$\iint_R [x + y] \, dA = \sum_{i=1}^{5} (i + 2) [A(R_i)]$$
$$= 3A(R_1) + 4A(R_2) + 5A(R_3) + 6A(R_4) + 7A(R_5)$$
$$= 3\left(\frac{1}{2}\right) + 4\left(\frac{3}{2}\right) + 5(2) + 6\left(\frac{3}{2}\right) + 7\left(\frac{1}{2}\right) = 30$$

15. $f_{ave} = \dfrac{1}{b-a} \displaystyle\int_a^b f(x) \, dx = \dfrac{1}{1-0} \int_0^1 \left[\int_x^1 \cos(t^2) \, dt \right] dx$

$$= \int_0^1 \int_x^1 \cos(t^2) \, dt \, dx$$
$$= \int_0^1 \int_0^t \cos(t^2) \, dx \, dt \quad \text{[changing the order of integration]}$$
$$= \int_0^1 t \cos(t^2) \, dt = \frac{1}{2} \sin(t^2) \Big]_0^1 = \frac{1}{2} \sin 1$$

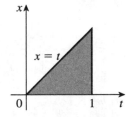

17. Since $|xy| < 1$, except at $(1, 1)$, the formula for the sum of a geometric series gives $\dfrac{1}{1 - xy} = \displaystyle\sum_{n=0}^{\infty} (xy)^n$, so

$$\int_0^1 \int_0^1 \frac{1}{1 - xy} \, dx \, dy = \int_0^1 \int_0^1 \sum_{n=0}^{\infty} (xy)^n \, dx \, dy$$
$$= \sum_{n=0}^{\infty} \int_0^1 \int_0^1 (xy)^n \, dx \, dy$$

$$= \sum_{n=0}^{\infty} \left[\int_0^1 x^n \, dx \right]\left[\int_0^1 y^n \, dy \right] = \sum_{n=0}^{\infty} \frac{1}{n+1} \cdot \frac{1}{n+1}$$
$$= \sum_{n=0}^{\infty} \frac{1}{(n+1)^2} = \frac{1}{1^2} + \frac{1}{2^2} + \frac{1}{3^2} + \cdots = \sum_{n=0}^{\infty} \frac{1}{n^2}$$

18. (a) $\displaystyle\sum_{i=1}^{2} \sum_{j=1}^{2} f(x_{ij}^*, y_{ij}^*) \, \Delta A$

$$= f\left(0, \frac{3}{2}\right) \Delta A + f(0, 2)\Delta A + f\left(1, \frac{3}{2}\right)\Delta A$$
$$\quad + f(1, 2)\Delta A$$
$$= \left(-\frac{27}{4}\right)\frac{1}{2} + (-12)\frac{1}{2} + \left(1 - \frac{27}{4}\right)\frac{1}{2}$$
$$\quad + (1 - 12)\frac{1}{2}$$
$$= -17.75$$

(b) $\dfrac{1}{2}\left[f\left(1, \frac{3}{2}\right) + f(1, 2) + f\left(2, \frac{3}{2}\right) + f(2, 2) \right]$

$$= \frac{1}{2}\left[-\frac{23}{4} + (-11) + \left(-\frac{19}{4}\right) + (-10) \right]$$
$$= \frac{1}{2}\left(-\frac{63}{2}\right) = -15.75$$

(c) $\dfrac{1}{2}\left[f(0, 1) + f\left(0, \frac{3}{2}\right) + f(1, 1) + f\left(1, \frac{3}{2}\right) \right]$

$$= \frac{1}{2}\left[-3 - \frac{27}{4} - 2 - \frac{23}{4} \right] = -8.75$$

(d) $\dfrac{1}{2}\left[f(1, 1) + f\left(1, \frac{3}{2}\right) + f(2,1) + f\left(2, \frac{3}{2}\right) \right]$

$$= \frac{1}{2}\left[-2 - \frac{23}{4} - 1 - \frac{19}{4} \right] = -6.75$$

19. (a) The subrectangles are shown in the figure. The surface is the graph of $f(x, y) = x^2 + 4y$ and $\Delta A = 1$, so we estimate

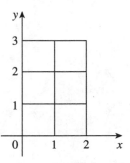

$$V \approx \sum_{i=1}^{2} \sum_{j=1}^{3} f(x_i, y_j) \, \Delta A$$
$$= f(1, 1)\Delta A + f(1, 2)\Delta A + f(1, 3)\Delta A$$
$$\quad + f(2, 1)\Delta A + f(2, 2)\Delta A + f(2, 3)\Delta A$$
$$= 5(1) + 9(1) + 13(1) + 8(1) + 12(1) + 16(1)$$
$$= 63$$

(b) $V \approx \sum_{i=1}^{2} \sum_{j=1}^{3} f(\bar{x}_i, \bar{y}_j) \Delta A$

$= f\left(\frac{1}{2}, \frac{1}{2}\right) \Delta A + f\left(\frac{1}{2}, \frac{3}{2}\right) \Delta A + f\left(\frac{1}{2}, \frac{5}{2}\right) \Delta A$

$\quad + f\left(\frac{3}{2}, \frac{1}{2}\right) \Delta A + f\left(\frac{3}{2}, \frac{3}{2}\right) \Delta A + f\left(\frac{3}{2}, \frac{5}{2}\right) \Delta A$

$= \frac{9}{4}(1) + \frac{25}{4}(1) + \frac{41}{4}(1) + \frac{17}{4}(1) + \frac{33}{4}(1) + \frac{49}{4}(1)$

$= \frac{87}{2} = 43.5$

20. The subrectangles are shown in the figure.

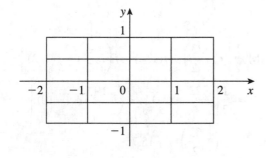

Since $\Delta A = \frac{1}{2}$, we estimate

$\iint_R (2x + x^2 y)\, dA \approx \sum_{i=1}^{4} \sum_{j=1}^{4} f(x_{ij}^*, y_{ij}^*)\, \Delta A$

$= \frac{1}{2}\Big[f(-2, -1) + f\left(-2, -\frac{1}{2}\right) + f(-2, 0) + f\left(-2, \frac{1}{2}\right)$

$\quad + f(-1, -1) + f\left(-1, -\frac{1}{2}\right) + f(-1, 0)$

$\quad + f\left(-1, \frac{1}{2}\right) + f(0, -1) + f\left(0, -\frac{1}{2}\right)$

$\quad + f(0, 0) + f\left(0, \frac{1}{2}\right) + f(1, -1)$

$\quad + f\left(1, -\frac{1}{2}\right) + f(1, 0) + f\left(1, \frac{1}{2}\right) \Big]$

$= \frac{1}{2}(-22) = -11$

13 VECTOR CALCULUS

1–17 ■ Solve the differential equation.

1. $y'' - 3y' + 2y = 0$ **2.** $y'' - y' = 0$

3. $3y'' - 8y' - 3y = 0$ **4.** $y'' + 9y' + 20y = 0$

5. $y'' + 2y' + 10y = 0$ **6.** $y'' + 10y' + 41y = 0$

7. $y'' = y$ **8.** $9y'' - 30y' + 25y = 0$

9. $y'' + 25y = 0$ **10.** $y'' - 4y' + 13y = 0$

11. $2y'' + y' = 0$ **12.** $y'' - 2y' - 4y = 0$

13. $y'' - y' + 2y = 0$ **14.** $y'' = -5y$

15. $\dfrac{d^2y}{dx^2} + 2\dfrac{dy}{dx} - y = 0$ **16.** $2\dfrac{d^2y}{dx^2} + 5\dfrac{dy}{dx} + y = 0$

17. $2\dfrac{d^2y}{dx^2} + \dfrac{dy}{dx} + 3y = 0$

18–24 ■ Solve the differential equation or initial-value problem using the method of undetermined coefficients.

18. $y'' - y' - 6y = \cos 3x$ **19.** $y'' + 2y' + 2y = x^3 - 1$

20. $y'' - 4y' + 4y = e^{-x}$

21. $y'' - 7y' + 12y = \sin x - \cos x$

22. $y'' + 36y = 2x^2 - x$

23. $y'' - 2y' + 5y = x + \sin 3x, \ y(0) = 1, \ y'(0) = 2$

24. $y'' + 2y = e^x \sin x, \ y(0) = 1, \ y'(0) = 1$

25. Let S be a smooth parametric surface and let P be a point such that each line that starts at P intersects S at most once. The solid angle $\Omega(S)$ subtended by S at P is the set of lines starting at P and passing through S. Let $S(a)$ be the intersection of $\Omega(S)$ with the surface of the sphere with center P and radius a. Then the measure of the solid angle (in *steradians*) is defined to be

$$|\Omega(S)| = \frac{\text{area of } S(a)}{a^2}$$

Apply the Divergence Theorem to the part of $\Omega(S)$ between $S(a)$ and S to show that

$$|\Omega(S)| = \iint\limits_S \frac{\mathbf{r} \cdot \mathbf{n}}{r^3} \, ds$$

where $\mathbf{r}$ is the radius vector from P to any point on S, $r = |\mathbf{r}|$, and the unit normal vector $\mathbf{n}$ is directed away from P.

This shows that the definition of the measure of a solid angle is independent of the radius a of the sphere. Thus, the measure of the solid angle is equal to the area subtended on a *unit* sphere. (Note the analogy with the definition of radian measure.) The total solid angle subtended by a sphere at its center is thus 4π steradians.

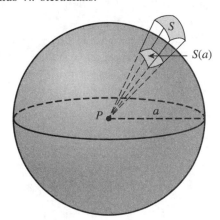

26. Verify that the Divergence Theorem is true for the vector field $\mathbf{F}(x, y, z) = xz \, \mathbf{i} + yz \, \mathbf{j} + 3z^2 \mathbf{k}$ on the solid bounded by the paraboloid $z = x^2 + y^2$ and the plane $z = 1$.

13 | ANSWERS TO SELECTED EXERCISES

1. $y = c_1 e^x + c_2 e^{2x}$

2. $y = c_1 + c_2 e^x$

3. $y = c_1 e^{-x/3} + c_2 e^{3x}$

4. $y = c_1 e^{-4x} + c_2 e^{-5x}$

5. $y = e^{-x}(c_1 \cos 3x + c_2 \sin 3x)$

6. $y = e^{-5x}(c_1 \cos 4x + c_2 \sin 4x)$

7. $y = c_1 e^x = c_2 e^{-x}$

8. $y = c_1 e^{5x/3} + c_2 x e^{5x/3}$

9. $y = c_1 \cos 5x + c_2 \sin 5x$

10. $y = e^{2x}(c_1 \cos 3x + c_2 \sin 3x)$

11. $y = c_1 + c_2 e^{-x/2}$

12. $y = c_1 e^{(1-\sqrt{5})x} + c_2 e^{(1+\sqrt{5})x}$

13. $y = e^{x/2}\left[c_1 \cos\left(\frac{\sqrt{7}}{2}x\right) + c_2 \sin\left(\frac{\sqrt{7}}{2}x\right) \right]$

14. $y = c_1 \cos \sqrt{5}x + c_2 \sin \sqrt{5}x$

15. $y = c_1 e^{(-1+\sqrt{2})x} + c_2 e^{(-1-\sqrt{2})x}$

16. $y = c_1 e^{(-5+\sqrt{17})x/4} + c_2 e^{(-5-\sqrt{17})x/4}$

17. $y = e^{-x/4}\left[c_1 \cos\left(\frac{\sqrt{23}}{4}x\right) + c_2 \sin\left(\frac{\sqrt{23}}{4}x\right) \right]$

18. $y(x) = c_1 e^{3x} + c_2 e^{-2x} - \frac{5}{78}\cos 3x - \frac{1}{78}\sin 3x$

19. $y(x) = e^{-x}(c_1 \cos x + c_2 \sin x) + \frac{1}{2}x^3 - \frac{3}{2}x^2 + \frac{3}{2}x - \frac{1}{2}$

20. $y(x) = e^{2x}(c_1 x + c_2) + \frac{1}{9}e^{-x}$

21. $y(x) = c_1 e^{3x} + c_2 e^{4x} - \frac{2}{85}\cos x + \frac{9}{85}\sin x$

22. $y(x) = c_1 \cos 6x + c_2 \sin 6x + \frac{1}{18}x^2 - \frac{1}{36}x - \frac{1}{324}$

23. $y(x) = e^x \left[\frac{523}{650}\cos 2x + \frac{797}{1300}\sin 2x \right]$
$+ \frac{1}{5}x + \frac{2}{25} + \frac{3}{26}\cos 3x - \frac{1}{13}\sin 3x$

24. $y(x) = \frac{5}{4}\cos \sqrt{2}x + \frac{1}{\sqrt{2}}\sin \sqrt{2}x$
$+ \frac{1}{4}e^x(-\cos x + \sin x)$

13 | SOLUTIONS TO SELECTED EXERCISES

1. The auxiliary equation is $r^2 - 3r + 2 = (r-2)(r-1) = 0$, so $y = c_1 e^x + c_2 e^{2x}$.

2. The auxiliary equation is $r^2 - r = r(r-1) = 0$, so $y = c_1 + c_2 e^x$.

3. The auxiliary equation is $3r^2 - 8r - 3 = (3r + 1)(r - 3) = 0$, so $y = c_1 e^{-x/3} + c_2 e^{3x}$.

4. The auxiliary equation is $r^2 + 9r + 20 = (r + 4)(r + 5) = 0$, so $y = c_1 e^{-4x} + c_2 e^{-5x}$.

5. The auxiliary equation is $r^2 + 2r + 10 = 0 \Rightarrow r = -1 \pm 3i$, so $y = e^{-x}(c_1 \cos 3x + c_2 \sin 3x)$.

6. The auxiliary equation is $r^2 + 10r + 41 = 0 \Rightarrow r = -5 \pm 4i$, so $y = e^{-5x}(c_1 \cos 4x + c_2 \sin 4x)$.

7. The auxiliary equation is $r^2 - 1 = (r - 1)(r + 1) = 0$, so $y = c_1 e^x + c_2 e^{-x}$.

8. The auxiliary equation is $9r^2 - 30r + 25 = (3r - 5)^2 = 0$, so $y = c_1 e^{5x/3} + c_2 x e^{5x/3}$.

9. The auxiliary equation is $r^2 + 25 = 0 \Rightarrow r = \pm 5i$, so $y = c_1 \cos 5x + c_2 \sin 5x$.

10. The auxiliary equation is $r^2 - 4r + 13 = 0 \Rightarrow r = 2 \pm 3i$, so $y = e^{2x}(c_1 \cos 3x + c_2 \sin 3x)$.

11. The auxiliary equation is $2r^2 + r = r(2r + 1) = 0$, so $y = c_1 + c_2 e^{-x/2}$.

12. The auxiliary equation is $r^2 - 2r - 4 = 0 \Rightarrow r = 1 \pm \sqrt{5}$, so $y = c_1 e^{(1-\sqrt{5})x} + c_2 e^{(1+\sqrt{5})x}$.

13. The auxiliary equation is
$$r^2 - r + 2 = 0 \Rightarrow r = \frac{1}{2}(1 \pm \sqrt{7}i), \text{ so}$$
$$y = e^{x/2}\left[c_1 \cos\left(\frac{\sqrt{7}}{2}x\right) + c_2 \sin\left(\frac{\sqrt{7}}{2}x\right)\right].$$

14. The auxiliary equation is $r^2 + 5 = 0 \Rightarrow r = \pm\sqrt{5}i$, so $y = c_1 \cos \sqrt{5}x + c_2 \sin \sqrt{5}x$.

15. The auxiliary equation is $r^2 + 2r - 1 = 0 \Rightarrow r = -1 \pm \sqrt{2}$, so $y = c_1 e^{(-1+\sqrt{2})x} + c_2 e^{(-1-\sqrt{2})x}$.

16. The auxiliary equation is $2r^2 + 5r + 1 = 0 \Rightarrow r = \frac{1}{4}(-5 + \sqrt{17})$, so $y = c_1 e^{(-5+\sqrt{17})x/4} + c_2 e^{(-5-\sqrt{17})x/4}$.

17. The auxiliary equation is $2r^2 + r + 3 = 0 \Rightarrow r = \frac{1}{4}(-1 \pm \sqrt{23}i)$, so
$$y = e^{-x/4}\left[c_1 \cos\left(\frac{\sqrt{23}}{4}x\right) + c_2 \sin\left(\frac{\sqrt{23}}{4}x\right)\right].$$

18. The auxiliary equation is $r^2 - r - 6 = (r - 3)(r + 2) = 0$, so the complementary solution is $y_c(x) = c_1 e^{3x} + c_2 e^{-2x}$. Try the particular solution $y_p(x) = A \cos 3x + B \sin 3x$, so $y_p' = 3B \cos 3x - 3A \sin 3x$ and $y_p'' = -9A \cos 3x - 9B \sin 3x$. Substitution gives
$(-9A \cos 3x - 9B \sin 3x) - (3B \cos 3x - 3A \sin 3x) - 6(A \cos 3x + B \sin 3x) = \cos 3x \Rightarrow$
$\cos 3x = (-15A - 3B) \cos 3x + (3A - 15B) \sin 3x$.
Hence $-15A - 3B = 1$ and $3A - 15B = 0 \Rightarrow$
$A = -\dfrac{5}{78}$, $B = -\dfrac{1}{78}$ and the general solution is
$$y(x) = y_c + y_p = c_1 e^{3x} + c_2 e^{-2x} - \frac{5}{78}\cos 3x$$
$$-\frac{1}{78}\sin 3x.$$

19. The auxiliary equation is $r^2 + 2r + 2 = 0$ with roots $-1 \pm i$, so the complementary solution is $y_c(x) = e^{-x}(c_1 \cos x + c_2 \sin x)$. For the particular solution try $y_p(x) = Ax^3 + Bx^2 + Cx + D$. So $y_p' = 3Ax^2 + 2Bx + C$ and $y_p'' = 6Ax + 2B$. Substitution into the differential equation gives
$(6Ax + 2B) + 2(3Ax^2 + 2Bx + C)$
$\qquad + 2(Ax^3 + Bx^2 + Cx + D) = x^3 - 1 \Rightarrow$
$x^3 - 1 = 2Ax^3 + (6A + 2B)x^2 + (6A + 4B + 2C)x$
$\qquad + (2B + 2C + 2D)$

Comparing coefficients gives $A = \dfrac{1}{2}$, $B = -\dfrac{3}{2}$, $C = \dfrac{3}{2}$, $D = -\dfrac{1}{2}$. Hence the general solution is
$y(x) = y_c + y_p$
$\qquad = e^{-x}(c_1 \cos x + c_2 \sin x) + \dfrac{1}{2}x^3 - \dfrac{3}{2}x^2 + \dfrac{3}{2}x - \dfrac{1}{2}$

20. The complementary solution is $y_c(x) = e^{2x}(c_1 x + c_2)$, so try a particular solution $y_p(x) = Ae^{-x}$. Then $y_p'' = y_p' = y_p = Ae^{-x}$ and substitution into the differential equation gives $Ae^{-x} + 4Ae^{-x} + 4Ae^{-x} = e^{-x}$ $\Rightarrow A = \dfrac{1}{9}$. Hence the general solution is
$y(x) = e^{2x}(c_1 x + c_2) + \dfrac{1}{9}e^{-x}$.

21. The complementary solution is $y_c(x) = c_1 e^{3x} + c_2 e^{4x}$. Since the arguments of the sine and cosine on the right side of the differential equation are the same (both x), try $y_p(x) = C \cos x + D \sin x$. Then $y_p' = -C \sin x + D \cos x$ and $y_p'' = -C \cos x - D \sin x$. Substitution into the differential equation gives $-C \cos x - D \sin x - 7(-C \sin x + D \cos x) + 12(C \cos x + D \sin x) = \sin x - \cos x \Rightarrow (11C - 7D) \cos x + (7C + 11D) \sin x = \sin x - \cos x \Rightarrow 11C - 7D = -1$ and $7C + 11D = 1$. Hence

$$y_p(x) = -\frac{2}{85} \cos x + \frac{9}{85} \sin x$$ and the general solution is $y(x) = c_1 e^{3x} + c_2 e^{4x} - \frac{2}{85} \cos x + \frac{9}{85} \sin x$.

22. The complementary solution is $y_c(x) = c_1 \cos 6x + c_2 \sin 6x$. Try $y_p(x) = Ax^2 + Bx + C$. Then $y_p' = 2Ax + B$ and $y_p'' = 2A$; substitution gives

$$2A + 36(Ax^2 + Bx + C) = 2x^2 - x. \quad A = \frac{1}{18},$$
$$B = -\frac{1}{36}, \quad C = -\frac{1}{324}.$$ The general solution is
$$y(x) = c_1 \cos 6x + c_2 \sin 6x + \frac{1}{18}x^2 - \frac{1}{36}x - \frac{1}{324}.$$

23. Since the roots of $r^2 - 2r + 5 = 0$ are $1 \pm 2i$, $y_c(x) = e^x(c_1 \cos 2x + c_2 \sin 2x)$. For $y'' - 2y' + 5y = x$ try $y_{P1}(x) = Ax + B$. Then $0 - 2A + 5(Ax + B) = x$, so $y_{P1}(x) = \frac{1}{5}x + \frac{2}{25}$. For $y'' - 2y' + 5y = \sin 3x$ try $y_{P2}(x) = A \cos 3x + B \sin 3x$. Then $y_{P2}' = -3A \sin 3x + 3B \cos 3x$ and $y_{P2}'' = -9A \cos 3x - 9B \sin 3x$. Substituting into the differential equation gives $-9A \cos 3x - 9B \sin 3x + 6A \sin 3x - 6B \cos 3x + 5A \cos 3x + 5B \sin 3x = \sin 3x$. Thus $(-9A - 6B + 5A) = 0$ and $(-9B + 6A + 5B) = 1$, so $A = \frac{3}{26}$ and $B = -\frac{1}{13}$. Hence the general solution is $y(x) = e^x(c_1 \cos 2x + c_2 \sin 2x)$

$$+ \frac{1}{5}x + \frac{2}{25} + \frac{3}{26} \cos 3x - \frac{1}{13} \sin 3x$$

But $1 = y(0) = c_1 + \frac{2}{25} + \frac{3}{26} \Rightarrow c_1 = \frac{523}{650}$,

$2 = y'(0) = c_1 + 2c_2 + \frac{1}{5} - \frac{3}{13} \Rightarrow c_2 = \frac{797}{1300}$. Thus

the solution to the initial-value problem is

$$y(x) = e^x \left[\frac{523}{650} \cos 2x + \frac{797}{1300} \sin 2x \right]$$
$$+ \frac{1}{5}x + \frac{2}{25} + \frac{3}{26} \cos 3x - \frac{1}{13} \sin 3x$$

24. $y_c(x) = c_1 \cos \sqrt{2}x + c_2 \sin \sqrt{2}x$.
Try $y_p(x) = e^x(A \cos x + B \sin x)$, then $y_p' = e^x(A \cos x + B \sin x - A \sin x + B \cos x)$ and $y_p'' = e^x(2B \cos x - 2A \sin x)$. Substitution into the differential equation gives

$$e^x(2B \cos x - 2A \sin x) + 2e^x(A \cos x + B \sin x) = e^x \sin x$$

so $A = -\frac{1}{4}, B = \frac{1}{4}$. Hence the general solution is

$$y(x) = c_1 \cos \sqrt{2}x + c_2 \sin \sqrt{2}x + \frac{1}{4}e^x(-\cos x + \sin x).$$

But $1 = y(0) = c_1 - \frac{1}{4} \Rightarrow c_1 = \frac{5}{4}$ and

$1 = y'(0) = \sqrt{2}c_2 + 0 \Rightarrow c_2 = \frac{1}{\sqrt{2}}$. Thus the
solution to the initial-value problem is

$$y(x) = \frac{5}{4} \cos \sqrt{2}x + \frac{1}{\sqrt{2}} \sin \sqrt{2}x$$
$$+ \frac{1}{4}e^x(-\cos x + \sin x).$$

25. Let S_1 be the portion of $\Omega(S)$ between $S(a)$ and S, and let ∂S_1 be its boundary. Also let S_L be the lateral surface of S_1 [that is, the surface of S_1 except S and $S(a)$]. Applying the Divergence Theorem

we have $\iint_{\partial S_1} \frac{\mathbf{r} \cdot \mathbf{n}}{r^3} dS = \iiint_{S_1} \nabla \cdot \frac{\mathbf{r}}{r^3} dV$. But

$$\nabla \cdot \frac{\mathbf{r}}{r^3} = \left\langle \frac{\partial}{\partial x}, \frac{\partial}{\partial y}, \frac{\partial}{\partial z} \right\rangle \cdot \left\langle \frac{x}{(x^2 + y^2 + z^2)^{3/2}}, \right.$$
$$\left. \frac{y}{(x^2 + y^2 + z^2)^{3/2}}, \frac{z}{(x^2 + y^2 + z^2)^{3/2}} \right\rangle$$

$$= \frac{(x^2 + y^2 + z^2 - 3x^2) + (x^2 + y^2 + z^2 - 3y^2) + (x^2 + y^2 + z^2 - 3z^2)}{(x^2 + y^2 + z^2)^{5/2}} = 0$$

$$\Rightarrow \iint_{\partial S_1} \frac{\mathbf{r} \cdot \mathbf{n}}{r^3} dS = \iiint_{S_1} 0 \, dV = 0.$$ On the other

hand, notice that for the surfaces of ∂S_1 other than $S(a)$ and S, $\mathbf{r} \cdot \mathbf{n} = 0 \Rightarrow$

$$0 = \iint_{\partial S_1} \frac{\mathbf{r} \cdot \mathbf{n}}{r^3} dS = \iint_S \frac{\mathbf{r} \cdot \mathbf{n}}{r^3} dS + \iint_{S(a)} \frac{\mathbf{r} \cdot \mathbf{n}}{r^3} dS$$

$$+ \iint_{SL} \frac{\mathbf{r} \cdot \mathbf{n}}{r^3} dS = \iint_S \frac{\mathbf{r} \cdot \mathbf{n}}{r^3} dS + \iint_{S(a)} \frac{\mathbf{r} \cdot \mathbf{n}}{r^3} dS$$

$$\Rightarrow \iint_S \frac{\mathbf{r} \cdot \mathbf{n}}{r^3} dS = -\iint_{S(a)} \frac{\mathbf{r} \cdot \mathbf{n}}{r^3} dS.$$

Notice that on $S(a)$, $r = a \Rightarrow \mathbf{n} = -\dfrac{\mathbf{r}}{r} = -\dfrac{\mathbf{r}}{a}$ and $\mathbf{r} \cdot \mathbf{r} = r^2 = a^2$, so that

$$-\iint_{S(a)} \frac{\mathbf{r} \cdot \mathbf{n}}{r^3}\, dS = \iint_{S(a)} \frac{\mathbf{r} \cdot \mathbf{r}}{a^4}\, dS = \iint_{S(a)} \frac{a^2}{a^4}\, dS$$

$$= \frac{1}{a^2} \iint_{S(a)} dS = \frac{\text{area of } S(a)}{a^2} = |\Omega(S)|.$$

Therefore $|\Omega(S)| = \displaystyle\iint_S \frac{\mathbf{r} \cdot \mathbf{n}}{r^3}\, dS.$

26. div $\mathbf{F} = 8z$, so

$$\iiint_E \text{div } \mathbf{F}\, dV = \int_0^{2\pi} \int_0^1 \int_{r^2}^1 8zr\, dz\, dr\, d\theta$$

$$= 2\pi \int_0^1 (4r - 4r^5)\, dr = \frac{8}{3}\pi$$

On S_1: $\mathbf{F} = x\mathbf{i} + y\mathbf{j} + 3\mathbf{k}$, $\mathbf{n} = \mathbf{k}$ and

$$\iint_{S_1} \mathbf{F} \cdot d\mathbf{S} = \iint_{S_1} 3\, dS = 3\pi.$$

On S_2: $\mathbf{F} = (x^3 + xy^2)\mathbf{i} + (y^3 + yx^2)\mathbf{j} + 3(x^2 + y^2)^2\mathbf{k}$, $-(\mathbf{r}_x \times \mathbf{r}_y) = 2x\mathbf{i} + 2y\mathbf{j} - \mathbf{k}$ and

$$\iint_{S_2} \mathbf{F} \cdot d\mathbf{S} = \iint_{x^2 + y^2 \le 1} (-x^4 - y^4 - 2x^2 y^2)\, dA$$

$$= -\int_0^{2\pi} \int_0^1 r^5\, dr\, d\theta = -\frac{\pi}{3}$$

Hence $\displaystyle\iint_S \mathbf{F} \cdot d\mathbf{S} = 3\pi - \frac{\pi}{3} = \frac{8}{3}\pi.$

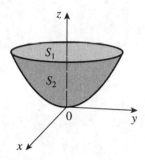